A DICTIONARY OF
ENGLISH WEIGHTS AND MEASURES

A Dictionary of
ENGLISH WEIGHTS
AND MEASURES
From Anglo-Saxon Times
to the Nineteenth Century

Ronald Edward Zupko

THE UNIVERSITY OF WISCONSIN PRESS

Madison, Milwaukee, and London, 1968

To my parents
MICHAEL EDWARD ZUPKO
FRANCES BARTEK ZUPKO

And my wife
JANET KWIATKOWSKA ZUPKO

Published by
The University of Wisconsin Press
Box 1379, Madison, Wisconsin 53701
The University of Wisconsin Press, Ltd.
27–29 Whitfield Street, London, W.1

Printed in the United States of America by
Kingsport Press, Inc., Kingsport, Tennessee

Library of Congress Catalog Card Number 68–14038

ACKNOWLEDGMENTS

To single out for recognition everyone who, directly or indirectly, made this dictionary possible would be difficult indeed. However, I wish to give special recognition to the contributions of four people who were very much responsible for the book's development and final form.

First, a deep debt of gratitude must be paid to the late Professor Robert L. Reynolds of the University of Wisconsin, whose continuous inspiration and scholarly advice were of great value throughout the long period of research. Even during his illness, Professor Reynolds worked untiringly for me, then his doctoral student of Medieval Economic History, and he was always ready to aid in the investigation of new sources and in the re-evaluation and reinterpretation of old concepts and notions concerning English weights and measures.

Secondly, Professor Frederic G. Cassidy of the University of Wisconsin made many valuable suggestions concerning the proper organization of the etymologies and variant spellings within the entries. He also advised me as to the best possible method for organizing the bibliography.

Thirdly, the University of Wisconsin Press and, in particular, Miss Joan Krager (Editor) have put considerable effort into constructing the best possible format and organization for the dictionary, appendixes, and tables.

Lastly, I wish to express my warmest appreciation to my wife, Janet Kwiatkowska Zupko, who held the position of Chemistry Librarian at the University of Wisconsin while I completed the research and writing of this book. She listened patiently and critically to revision after revision and made many substantive comments which have improved the overall presentation.

v

Final thanks must be given to Marquette University for awarding me a Non-Government Research Grant and to the following colleagues who provided both moral and intellectual support: Professors David E. Gardinier, Thomas E. Hachey, Frank L. Klement, Alfred D. Low, William D. Miller, F. Paul Prucha, S.J., G. Michael Riley, and Ralph E. Weber.

R. E. Z.

Milwaukee, Wisconsin
July, 1967

CONTENTS

INTRODUCTION

The complexity of medieval and early modern English weights and measures has long presented an obstacle to scholarly research on western European economic history. The problem is really twofold: first, the approximate dimensions of many nonstandardized measuring units, used by both the Crown and the regional and local markets, varied from time to time and from place to place; second, the specific dimensions even of standard weights and measures used in any given period are often poorly understood. Too many times the researcher, investigating certain facets of economic and social development, has not taken these ambiguities into consideration, or has not even been aware of them, and has automatically assumed that a particular measuring unit contained or equaled a fixed amount. Such assumptions have led to inaccuracies in many textbooks and monographs. Hence, this book is directed toward clarifying some of the confusion and bringing a new focus to the field of metrology in general and a new understanding of the units in particular.

The tables which follow will aid the reader in using the dictionary. Since it would be impractical to give the year and reign for every citation (e.g., 25 Edward III), I have, in most instances, provided only the year in which a manuscript or law was written. Table I has been compiled for rapid identification of the ruling sovereign for any given year cited in the dictionary. Table II contains all of the abbreviations used throughout the dictionary; they are alphabetically arranged for quick reference. Table III lists the metric prefixes that form smaller and larger multiples of the liter, gram, meter, and are, and Table IV contains the basic English and American equivalents for these four metric units. The latter two tables will enable the reader to make further correlations between metric and nonmetric units that are beyond the scope of this book.

The dictionary uses a number of textual devices to help the reader gain rapid and accurate access to the material. All entry headings are printed in boldface, and a dash separates them from their variant spellings (e.g., **acre** — 1 æcer (OED), æcyr (OED); 1–2 acr . . .). The variants are arranged according to the centuries in which they were most commonly used; the numbers preceding them identify the centuries:

1 = pre-12th century	6 = 16th century
2 = 12th century	7 = 17th century
3 = 13th century	8 = 18th century
4 = 14th century	9 = 19th century
5 = 15th century	? = no century given in source

If there is no citation for a certain variant spelling within an entry, its source reference is indicated in parentheses (e.g., 1 æcer (OED) . . . 1–2 acr). The abbreviation L preceding a variant indicates that that variant was a Latin form used in scholarly treatises in England.

The etymologies, always in square brackets, immediately follow the variant spellings. Generally when an etymology is well known and can be easily found in the *Oxford English Dictionary* (OED) or *Webster's New International Dictionary*, 3rd edition (WNID3), only a shortened form is given in the entry, and the reader should refer to one of these standard etymological dictionaries for further information (e.g., **acre** — 1 æcer (OED) . . . 6 acer (McCaw) [ME *aker* < OE *æcer; see* WNID3]). If no etymology is given, an asterisk (*) indicates that the derivation of the word is unknown.

Following the etymological comments either a general explanation for the unit is given or, if there are variations within the unit, each major variation or group of variations is discussed in a separate paragraph. In addition, wherever possible, metric equivalents are included in parentheses; the equivalents have been carried out to two decimal places for the approximate units and usually to three decimal places for the exact. But, if the unit's measurement or description is identical to that of another more commonly known unit, the words "equivalent to" follow the etymological comments.

After each major metrological variation or group of variations there are citations from medieval and early modern sources:

The date in boldface type at the beginning of these citations always
represents the year in which the manuscript or book was written
and never the publication date.

The code name and numbers after the date identify the source (e.g.,
1198 Feet 3.8: De vij . . . Ridon').

The code name always refers to a corresponding title in the bibliography.

A Roman numeral following the code name, but preceding the period
before the page number, supplies the volume (e.g., **1443** Brokage
II.7).

An Arabic number in such a position refers to one of several books
listed under that particular code name in the bibliography (e.g.,
Feet 3.8 refers to the third book under the code name Feet).

The number after the period is always the page number. If there is
no volume number and the bibliographical code name has only
one title listed under it, the page number immediately follows the
source reference (e.g., Caernarvon 242).

Whenever a measuring unit has several variations which do not
fit into any of the other major sections, or for which there is no
explanation in the documents as to their relative value, they are
placed at the end of the entry in a separate paragraph.

It should be noted that in the illustrative quotations all manuscript
abbreviations have been expanded in italic type (e.g., "Et xl ptice"
is changed to "Et xl p*er*tice"). Also, letters superscripted in the source
have been placed on the same line as the rest of the word, with
brackets indicating the change (e.g., gr^{a}na is amended to gr[a]na).
Similarly, whenever Roman numerals in manuscripts were written
above another numeral (e.g., $\overset{xx}{V}$) or elevated to the right of some
number (e.g., V^{xx}), they have been placed on the text line, with
brackets again indicating the change. If multiplication or addition is
involved, the appropriate arithmetical sign has been placed between
the numbers (e.g., V^{xx}XII = 112 is changed to V [$\times$] xx [+] XII =
112). Other abbreviations, such as l., li., and lib. for *liber*, *libra*
(pound) and the apothecary symbols $\ni$ for scruple, $\mathfrak{Z}$ for dram,
$\mathfrak{Z}$ for ounce, and ℔ for apothecary pound, have been retained as in
the original source.

In Appendix I are definitions of the terms used to describe the
weights and measures in the entries. Appendix II contains a list of

the principal laws which regulated and standardized the units. Only the salient features of these laws are outlined, since a thorough analysis is available elsewhere.*

The bibliography includes only those sources which provide information on individual weights and measures and which discuss some of the problems characteristic of metrology in general. No fictional sources were used in the data compilation and illustrative quotations. Works on the metric system are omitted since that phase of metrology is not an integral part of medieval and early modern English measuring units. However, the bibliography does include the names of several reference books on weights and measures in which the interested reader may find leads to metrical literature.

* Ronald Edward Zupko, "A Dictionary of Medieval English Weights and Measures" (Ph.D. dissertation, University of Wisconsin, 1966), pp. 38–83.

TABLE I

ENGLISH MONARCHS FOR YEARS CITED IN TEXT

Edward "The Elder"	899–925	Henry V	1413–22
Athelstan	925–40	Henry VI	1422–61
Edgar "The Peaceable"	959–75	Edward IV	1461–83
Ethelred II	978–1016	Edward V	1483
Edward "The Confessor"	1042–66	Richard III	1483–85
Harold	1066	Henry VII	1485–1509
William I	1066–87	Henry VIII	1509–47
William II	1087–1100	Edward VI	1547–53
Henry I	1100–1135	Mary	1553–58
Stephen	1135–54	Elizabeth I	1558–1603
Henry II	1154–89	James I	1603–25
Richard I	1189–99	Charles I	1625–49
John	1199–1216	Charles II	1660–85
Henry III	1216–72	James II	1685–88
Edward I	1272–1307	William III	1689–1702
Edward II	1307–27	Anne	1702–14
Edward III	1327–77	George I	1714–27
Richard II	1377–99	George II	1727–60
Henry IV	1399–1413	George III	1760–1820

TABLE II

ABBREVIATIONS

AF	= Anglo-French		Gr	= Greek	
AL	= Anglo-Latin		ha	= hektare	
alter	= alteration		hg	= hektogram	
ap	= apothecary		Hind	= Hindustani	
Ar	= Arabic		hl	= hektoliter	
avdp	= avoirdupois		hm	= hektometer	
bbl	= barrel		Icel	= Icelandic	
bu	= bushel		Ir	= Irish	
c	= about, around		It	= Italian	
C	= hundred		kg	= kilogram	
Celt	= Celtic		kl	= kiloliter	
cent	= century		km	= kilometer	
cf	= compare		l	= liter	
cg	= centigram		L	= Latin	
cl	= centiliter		lb	= pound	
cm	= centimeter		LG	= Low German	
coll	= collective		LL	= Late Latin	
cu	= cubic		m	= meter	
Cwt	= hundredweight		M	= thousand or thousandweight	
Dan	= Danish		m-a	= measure of area	
dg	= decigram		m-c	= measure of capacity	
dial	= dialect, dialectal		MDu	= Middle Dutch	
dim	= diminutive		ME	= Middle English	
dkg	= dekagram		MedL	= Medieval Latin	
dkl	= dekaliter		merc	= mercantile	
dkm	= dekameter		MF	= Middle French	
dl	= deciliter		mg	= milligram	
dm	= decimeter		MHG	= Middle High German	
dr	= dram		mi	= mile	
Du	= Dutch		ml	= milliliter	
dwt	= pennyweight		m-l	= measure of length	
E	= English		MLG	= Middle Low German	
F	= French		mm	= millimeter	
fem	= feminine		modif	= modification	
ft	= foot		m-q	= measure of quantity	
g	= gram		n	= noun	
G	= German		neut	= neuter	
Gael	= Gaelic		Nor	= Norwegian	
gal	= gallon		OE	= Old English	
Gmc	= Germanic		OF	= Old French	
Goth	= Gothic		OHG	= Old High German	
gr	= grain		OIt	= Old Italian	

TABLE II (*continued*)

OLG	= Old Low German		Scand	= Scandinavian
ON	= Old Norse		Sem	= Semitic
ONF	= Old North French		Skr	= Sanskrit
OPr	= Old Provençal		Sp	= Spanish
OS	= Old Saxon		sq	= square
OSp	= Old Spanish		sv	= sub verbo
oz	= ounce		Sw	= Swedish
perh	= perhaps		t	= troy
pk	= peck		tow	= tower
pl	= plural		trans	= translated, translation
poss	= possessive		ult	= ultimately
Pr	= Provençal		var	= variant(s)
prob	= probably		vb	= verb
pt	= pint		VL	= Vulgar Latin
qt	= quart		W	= Welsh
s	= scruple		wt	= weight
Sc	= Scottish		yd	= yard

TABLE III
BASIC METRIC PREFIXES

PREFIX	SIGNIFICATION
deka-	10
hekto-	100
kilo-	1000
deci-	0.1
centi-	0.01
milli-	0.001

TABLE IV
BASIC METRIC UNITS

METRIC	ENGLISH AND AMERICAN
Length	
Centimeter	0.3937 inch
Meter	$\begin{cases} 39.37 \text{ inches} \\ 3.2808 \text{ ft} \\ 1.0936 \text{ yd} \end{cases}$
Kilometer	0.6214 mi
Area	
Square meter	$\begin{cases} 10.7638 \text{ sq ft} \\ 1.1960 \text{ sq yd} \end{cases}$
Square kilometer	0.3861 sq mi
Are	$\begin{cases} 119.596 \text{ sq yd} \\ 0.025 \text{ acres} \end{cases}$
Hektare	2.471 acres
Weight	
Gram	$\begin{cases} 15.4324 \text{ gr} \\ 0.0353 \text{ oz avdp} \end{cases}$
Kilogram	2.2046 lb avdp
Metric ton	$\begin{cases} 0.9842 \text{ long ton} \\ 1.1023 \text{ short ton} \end{cases}$
Capacity	
Liter	$\begin{cases} 61.0250 \text{ cu inches} \\ 0.0353 \text{ cu ft} \\ 0.8799 \text{ B.I. qt} \\ 1.0567 \text{ U.S. qt} \end{cases}$
Hektoliter	$\begin{cases} 21.9973 \text{ B.I. gal} \\ 26.4178 \text{ U.S. gal} \\ 2.7491 \text{ B.I. bu} \\ 2.8378 \text{ U.S. bu} \end{cases}$

A DICTIONARY OF
ENGLISH WEIGHTS AND MEASURES

A

acer, acr, acra. ACRE

acre — 1 æcer (OED), æcyr (OED); 1–2 acr; 2 æker (OED); 2–5 L
acra; 2–7 aker; 3 akre (Langtoft); 4–9 acre; 5 akere (OED), akyr
(Prior), akyre (OED), hakere (OED); 5–6 akir; 6 acer (McCaw)
[ME *aker* < OE *æcer; see* WNID3]. A m-a for land in England,
Wales, Scotland, and Ireland which, in its earliest usage, probably
referred to the amount of land which one yoke of oxen could plow
in a day.

In England the acre was standardized during the High Middle
Ages at 160 sq PERCHES of 16½ ft each, or 4840 sq yd, or 43,560
sq ft (0.405 ha). This statutory acre was 40 perches in length and
4 in breadth and was equal to 4 ROODS of 40 sq perches each. —
1198 Feet 3.8: De vij acris terre cum pertinentiis in Ridon'; *ibid* 65:
iiij acras terre et iij rodas. *c*1200 Caernarvon 242: Tres pedes
faciunt vlnam quin*que* ulne & d*i*midia faciunt p*er*ticam. Et xl p*er*-
tice in longitudinem & iiij in latitudine faciunt vnam acram ter*re*.
1200 Feet 3.108: Et j acram juxta domum Willelmi filii Wictiue.
1206 Feet 2.46: De dimidia acra terre. *c*1230 Clerkenwell 134: Vna
acra terre in parochia de Sidingeburne. **1283** Battle xliii: Et sunt
ibidem in campis qui vocantur Horscroftes lxxviij acræ separales.
*c*1400 Hall 41: Nota quod lxviii milia lepores possunt sedere in una
acra terre mensurata. *c*1461 *Ibid* 7: Et iiii perches en laeure et xl en
longure font I acre de terre. . . . Et quinque ulne et dimidia faciunt
perticam et xl pertice in longitudine et quatuor in latitudine
faciunt unam acram. **1494** Fabyan 246: An acre conteyneth xl.
perches in length, and iiii. in brede. **1502** Arnold 173: Of what
lengith soo euer they be, clx. perches make an akir. **1603** Henllys
133: For whereas the statute *de terris mensurandis* appointeth the
pole to be xvi foote & di . . . and that 4 of these in bredth, and
40 in length make the acre. **1615** Collect. Stat. 464: And forty
pearches, and 4. in bredth make an acre. **1616** Hopton 165: So

3

that an Acre hath 43560 square Feete, 4840 square Yards, and 160 square Pearches. **1635** Dalton 150: Forty pole in length, and foure in breadth (or 160 pole) doe make an acre. **1647** Digges 1: Five Yards, ½. a Pearch: fortie Pearches in length and foure in breadth, an Acre. **1784** Ency. meth. 139: L'acre de terre d'Angleterre est de 4 fardingdeales. *See* FARTHINGDALE

Since the size of the acre was defined in terms of the linear perch, regional variations arose whenever the length of the perch (16½ ft by statute, or 5.029 m) or the number of sq perches in the acre (160 by statute) differed from the statutory standards. For example, acres larger than the statutory acre were used (*c*1800) in Cheshire, 10,240 sq yd (*c*0.86 ha); Cornwall, 5760 sq yd (*c*0.48 ha); Lincolnshire, 5 roods (*c*0.51 ha); Westmorland, 6760 sq yd (0.565 ha) or 160 perches of 6¼ sq yd each; Ireland, 7840 sq yd (0.655 ha) or 160 sq perches, each perch equal to 7 yd; and Scotland, 6150⁴⁄₁₀ sq yd (*c*0.51 ha) (Second Rep. 5). Acres smaller than the statutory acre were used (*c*1800) in Bedfordshire, 2 roods (*c*0.20 ha); Dorsetshire, generally 134 sq perches (*c*0.34 ha); Leicestershire, 2308¼ sq yd (*c*0.19 ha); Worcestershire, 90 to 141 sq perches (*c*0.23 to *c*0.36 ha); and North Wales, 4320 sq yd (0.361 ha) for the erw or standard acre and 3240 sq yd (0.271 ha) for the STANG or customary acre (Second Rep. 5). Some regions had acres (*c*1800) both larger and smaller than the statutory acre: Hampshire, 107 to 180 sq perches (*c*0.27 to *c*0.45 ha) and Sussex, 107, 110, 120, 130, or 212 sq perches (*c*0.27 to *c*0.54 ha) (Second Rep. 5). Other variations resulting from diverse perch lengths appeared from time to time. — *c*1100 Bello 11: Pertica habet longitudinis sedecim pedes. Acra habet in longitudine quadraginta perticas, et quatuor in latitudine. *c*1400 Henley 68: E pur ceo ke les acres ne sunt mye touz de une mesure kar en acon pays mesurent il par la verge de xviii peez e . . . de xx peez e . . . de xxii peez e . . . de xxiiij peez. *c*1475 Hall 14: And sum of thame [perches] be of xviij fote, sum of xx fote, and sum of xxi fote; but of what lengthe so euer thei be, euermore this is yt serteyn, that viii [×] xx perchys make an aker. **1537** Benese 4: An acre bothe of woodlande, and also of fylde land is always xl. perches in length, and iiii. perches in bredth, although an acre of woodlande be more in quantite . . . because the perche of woodlande is longer. **1665** Assize 6: In many Countries [= districts] this Pole or Perch doth vary, as in

some places it is 18 foot, and in some other places 21 foot. . . . Of
the which Poles . . . 40 in length, and four of them in breadth,
make the Acre of Land or Wood.

acreme [*; *see* OED]. A late medieval and early modern law term
which designated an area of land containing 10 acres or 48,400
sq yd (4.050 ha). It appears to be synonymous with the FARTHING-
DALE. — **1669** Worlidge 321: An Acreme of Land is ten Acres.
1725 Bradley sv: Acreme of Land, ten Acres of Land.

æcer, æcyr, æker. ACRE

aghendole — 6 akendoule; 6–7 aghendole; 7 aighendole [perh OE
aghtand, an eighth part, + *dole*, DOLIUM]. A m-c for grain in the
county of Lancaster equal to ⅛ COOMB or ½ bu (*c*l.76 dkl).
— **1586** Shuttleworths 1095: 2 metts and 3 akendoule . . . 15s. 1d.
1605 *Ibid:* 1 peck, 2s. 6d.; 1 aghendole, 7½ d. **1617** *Ibid:* 4 score
and 15 metts and 3 aighendole . . . £38 3s.

aighendole, akendoule. AGHENDOLE

aker, akere, akir, akre, akyr, akyre. ACRE

alm, alme. AUME

alna. ELL

ambær, ambar. AMBER

amber — 1 ambær (OED), ambar (OED), amber, ambre, L ambrum,
omber (OED), ombor (OED), ombra; 1–3 L ambra [OE *amber*,
vessel, pail, dry measure; akin to OS *ēmbar*, pail, OHG *ambar*,
borrowed in Gmc < L *amphora*, two-handled narrow-necked jar].
A m-c for grain and liquids that varied in size, with 4 bu (*c*1.41 hl)
being the most common. — *c*900 Select Doc. 73: XXX ombra
gades uuelesces. *c*940 Du Cange sv ambra: De duabus meis firmis
dent eis singulis mensibus Ambra plena farinæ. *c*1000 *Ibid:* Et
reddere debet 120. mensuras, quas Angli dicunt Ambres, de sale.
*c*1100 Bello 35: Willelmus . . . dedit et concessit . . . de dominio
suo . . . unam quoque hidam terræ . . . et annuatim centum
ambras. *c*1283 trans in Battle xiii: To carry 2 ambræ, 2 bushels and
a half of salt. **1285** trans in Cal. Char. 2.300: And of twenty am-
bers (ambras) of salt yearly at Leya. **1678** Du Cange sv ambra:
Ambrum, Amber, Anglo-Saxonibus, Vasis vinarii genus, vel
mensura.

ambra, ambre, ambrum. AMBER

ame. AUME

anaphorum. OENOPHORUM

ancel, ancell. AUNCEL

anchor. ANKER

anker — 7 ankor (OED); 7–9 anker; 8 anchor (OED) [Du and G *anker* < MedL *ancheria*, small barrel, prob < OHG *hant-kar*, hand vessel]. Before and after 1800 a m-c for wine which in England contained 10 wine gal (3.785 dkl) and in Scotland, 20 Scots pt (3.41 dkl) (Second Rep. 6).

ankor. ANKER

ansul. AUNCEL

asine [MF *asine* < L *asinus*, an ass]. A m-c (the load or burden of one ass, prob a sack-load) used principally for wine, without standard dimensions. — **1371** York Mem. 1.14: Et que chescun estraunge marchaunt des vins paie, pur chescun asine de vyne Rynois amesne a la citee et mys a la vent, ij s.

auln, aulne, aum. AUME

aume — 5–7 alm (OED), alme (OED); 7 auln, awme (OED); 7–8 ame (OED), aum; 7–9 aume, awm; 8 aulne [prob < MedL *āma*, wine measure]. A m-c for wine containing 40 gal (1.51 hl) or sometimes equal to a wine TIERCE of 42 gal (1.59 hl). — **1696** Phillips sv auln: Aum of Renish Wine, a measure containing 40 Gallons, and as many pints over and above. **1717** Dict. Rus. sv: Aume, (of Rhenish Wine) a Measure containing 160 Paris-Pints, or 40 English Gallons. **1721** Bailey sv aulne: Of Rhenish Wine, a Vessel that contains 40 Gallons. **1820** Second Rep. 6: Aume or Awm . . . A tierce of wine, or 42 gallons.

auncel — 4–5 auncere (OED), aunsell, aunselle (OED), aunser (OED); 5–7 auncel, auncell, auncelle (OED); 6 ancell; 6–7 ancel (OED); 7 L ansul, avuncell, awnsel (OED); 8 auricel (error for auncel) [ME *auncel* < AF *auncelle* < OF *lancelle* < OIt *lancella*, small balance, < *lance*, balance, < L *lanx*, scalepan]. An illegal scale which was similar to a primitive steelyard. It consisted of a rod or beam suspended or supported at a specified point near the end from which the goods to be weighed were hung, while along the graduated longer section of the rod an auncel weight was moved until equilibrium was attained. In the Middle Ages the weigher usually used his forefinger or the edge of his hand as a fulcrum. By the early modern period most auncels were supplied with a handle at the fulcrum for lifting. It was very easy for the weigher to cheat and relatively difficult for the customer to check him, for the

former could tilt the scale very slightly or use defective auncel
weights. — *c*1461 Hall 13: Aunsell weyght is forboden by the
Parlement; and also holy Chyrche hath cursyd all theym that by or
sell by that weyght, for itt is . . . false. **1470** Year Bk. 158: Les
stokks en chescun vil sont ordenew par le statut de anno xxv E. iii
cap. ii pur ceux . . . qe vsent les auncelx weyghts. **1517** Hall 51: The
Ancell Beame, which being altogeather prohibited yet are used by
many; *ibid* 53: Which is the Ancell Waight which yarne choppers
and others doe buie by. **1587** Stat. 20: It is accorded and stablished,
that this weight called Auncell, betwixt buyers and sellers shall be
wholie put out. And that euerie sale and buying be by the balance.
1615 Collect. Stat. 465: That this weight called Auncell . . . shall
be wholly take away. **1657** Tower 79: The print forbidding Auncel
weights . . . agreeth with the Record. **1678** Du Cange sv ansul:
Genus ponderis apud Anglos, idem forte quod etiamnum Avuncell
weight dicunt. **1717** Dict. Rus. sv auricel-weight: Quasi Hand-
Sale-Weight . . . is a kind of Weight with Scales hanging, or Hooks
fasten'd at each end of a Beam or Shaft, which a Man us'd to lift up
from his Fore-finger or Hand.
auncell, auncelle, auncere, aunsell, aunselle, aunser. AUNCEL
auoyxdepois. AVOIRDUPOIS
auricel. AUNCEL
aveirdepeis, averdepays, averdepois, averdepoise, averdepoiz, averde-
   poys, averdupois, avoirdepois, avoirdepoiz, avoirdepoys. AVOIRDU-
   POIS
avoirdupois — 4 avoirdepoys; 4–5 haberdepase (Glazebrook); 4–7
   avoirdepois; 5 averdepays (Shuttleworths), habertypoie, haburdepeyse; 6 auoyxdepois (OED), avoirdepoiz, habardepayce, habardepayse, habardepayx (OED), habardepoix, habardypeyse (Nicholson), haberdepoysse (Hall); 6–7 haberdepois, haverdupois; 7
   averdepoise (OED), averdepoiz, averdepoys (Sheppard), haberde-
   poies, haburdypoyse; 7–8 averdupois; 7–9 averdepois, avoirdupois;
   ? aveirdepeis (Prior), avoirdupoys (Prior), haberdepayes (Prior)
   [ME *avoirdepois, averdepeis,* goods sold by weight, < OF *avoirde-*
   pois, averdepeis < *aver, avoir,* goods, property, + *de,* of, + *peis,*
   pois, weight, < L *pensum; see* WNID3]. A system of wt which
   originally applied to goods sold by wt rather than by capacity, the
   piece, or otherwise. — *c*1350 Swithun 80: Una bala cujuslibet
   avoir de poys. **1353** Report 1.420: Itempur ces que nous avons

entendu que ascuns marchauntz achatent avoir de pois leynz, et autres merchandises per un pois, et vendent per un autre. *c*1461 Hall 12: The weghtes of Ynglond be made by nunbyr; for (there) be iij maner of weyghtes, that is to say; Troy and Aunsell, and also lyeng weyghtes odyrwyse callyd Haburdy Poyse. **1474** Cov. Leet 396: The seid xxxij graynes of whete take out of the myddes of the Ere makith a sterling peny & xx sterling makith a Ounce of haburdepeyse; and xvj Ouncez makith a li. **1496** Seventh Rep. 29: The same tyme ordeined that xvi uncs of Troie maketh the Haberty poie. **1517** Hall 48: So makyth the whete afore namyd the Habar de Payse once . . . . And xvi of that onces the trewe habar de poix lib. *c*1525 *Ibid* 40: Item xvi onces Habar de Payce ys. a lib. . . . Item xviii onces di. of Troy weyghte makys xvi onces Habar de payse. **1532** Seventh Rep. 31: Beef, pork, mutton, and veal shall be sold by weight called haver-du-pois. **1588** Hall 45: Avoir de poiz waight is to bee used for other commodities, ffor Merchandize, and for Grocers. **1603** Henllys 138: And all spice, Iron, Rosen, pitche and other drugges uttered by the mercers are sold by the haberde-poies pound. **1606** Hall 37: There is onely two sortes of waightes used in England the which are allowed by Statute, the one called Troy waight, the other Haberdepois waight; *ibid* 38: This waight of Haberdepois is allowed alsoe by Statute being 16 oz. to the pound waight with the which is wayed all phisick drugges, grocery wares, rozen, wax, pitch, tarr, tallowe, sope, hempe, fflaxe, all metalles and mineralles. **1635** Dalton 143: Averdepois weight is by custome . . . and thereby are weighed all kind of Grocerie wares, Physicall drugs, Butter, Cheese, Flesh, Wax, Pitch, Tarre, Tallow, Wools, Hemp, Flax, Yron, Steele, Lead. **1657** Tower 419: That there may no more be taken for weighing in any place of the Realm for any Aver-depoiz than in London. **1665** Assize 2: There is also another weight named Avoirdupois weight, whereunto there is 16 ounces for the pound. **1682** Hall 29: Aver-du-pois conteynes: every pound, 16 ounces; every ounce, 8 drgmes [*sic*]; every dragme, 3 scruples; every scruple, 20 graines. **1688** Bernardi 137–38: Libra equidem Avoirdupois qua solent populares mei graviores mercium æstimare quam pretiosiores, $\frac{1}{112}$ Hundredi sui sive centenarii crassi, 16 unciæ, $128 = 16 \times 8$ drachmæ; *ibid* 138: Habet et libra Avoirdupois scripulos suos $384 = 128 \times 3$, gravans nobis 1,2169, sed ratione Wybardica $17\frac{7}{14} = 1{,}2413$ libræ de Troy. **1708** Cham-

berlayne 206: But the Avoirdupois Pound is more than the Troy
Pound, for 14 Pound Avoirdupois are = to 17 Pound Troy-
Weight. **1710** Harris 1. sv weight: And the other is called Averdu-
pois, containing 16 Ounces in the Pound. **1717** Dict. Rus. sv dram:
Dram or Drachm, the just Weight of sixty Grains of Wheat; in
Avoir-du-pois Weight, the sixteenth part of an ounce; *ibid* sv
hundred-weight: But ordinarily a Pound is the least Quantity
taken notice of in Aver-du-pois Gross Weight; *ibid* sv pound:
A sort of Weight containing 16 Ounces Avoir-du-pois. **1742** Account 1.553: The single Averdupois Bell Pound, against the flat
Averdupois Pound Weight, was found . . . to be heavier by Two
Troy Grains and a half. **1778** Diderot XXVI.420: L'avoir-du-pois
est de seize onces. **1790** Jefferson 1.986: So that the pound troy
contains 5760 grains, of which 7000 are requisite to make the
pound avoirdupois. **1793** Leake 30–31: This Avoirdupois originally signified no more than Goods in gross, or by wholesale.

avoirdupoys. AVOIRDUPOIS
avuncell. AUNCEL
awm, awme. AUME
awnsel. AUNCEL

B

baele. BALE

bag — 3–7 bagge; 4–9 bag; 5 bague (Southampton 1); 6 bage; 6–7 bagg [ME *bagge* < ON *baggi*]. A m-c varying in size according to its contents (*c*1700–1800): almonds, 3 Cwt (152.406 kg); aniseed, 3 to 4 Cwt (152.406 to 203.208 kg); cotton yarn, 2½ to 4¼ Cwt (113.397 to 192.776 kg); currants, 4 Cwt (203.208 kg); goats-hair, 2 to 4 Cwt (101.604 to 203.208 kg); lime, 1 heaped bu (*c*4.50 dkl); pepper, 1¼ to 3 Cwt (61.235 to 146.964 kg); and Spanish wool, 240 lb (108.862 kg) (Dict. Rus. sv and Second Rep. 6). *See* HUNDRED

The bag also had local variations (*c*1800): Devonshire, wheat, 2 bu totaling 140 lb (63.503 kg); Kent and Surrey, hops, 2½ Cwt (127.005 kg); Shropshire, wheat, 3 bu (*c*1.06 hl); Scotland, flour, 91 English lb (41.277 kg), and barley, 279 or 280 English lb (126.552 or 127.005 kg); and South Wales, oats, 7 heaped MEASURES or 8½ striked or leveled measures, making 170 qt or 5 bu and 10 qt (*c*2.99 hl) (Second Rep. 6).

However, bags of aloes, alum, brush-making materials, fish, ginger, hops, and soap do not appear to have had specific sizes. — *c*1420 Gras 1.461: xii bagges de aloe. **1443** Brokage II.174: 1 parvo bagge saponis. **1509** Gras 1.564: xxv bages aluminis; *ibid* 566: i packe cum ii bages ginger continent iii [×] c libras; *ibid* 567: ii bages spletes; *ibid* 569: i bage cum hethe pro brusshes. **1704** Mer. Adven. 243: Ffor bearing to the Weighouse a bagg of hops and weighing 2 [d.] per C.

bage, bagg, bagge, bague. BAG

bail, bal, bala. BALE

balatt. BALET

bale — 3 boillun, boyllum, boylun, buyllon (Cal. Lib. 2); 3–4 L bala; 4–9 bale; 5 baele (Southampton 1); 5–6 bal; 5–7 bayl (OED); 6 balle; 6–8 ball (OED); 7–8 bail (OED) [ME *bale* < OF *bale*, *balle*, of Gmc origin]. A m-q or m-c, variously defined for different items. Originally it denoted a large bundle of more or less cylindrical shape, but by the late Middle Ages it had come to designate a closely pressed, rectangularly shaped package, wrapped generally in canvas and tightly corded or hooped with copper or iron.

The bale was used most often for buckram, 60 pieces; fustian, generally 40 or 45 half-pieces; and paper, 10 REAMS. — **1502** Arnold 206: A balle bokrom conteyneth lx. pecis . . . a balle fustian conteyneth xlv. half peces. **1507** Gras 1.697: Fustyon' the balle containing xl hallfe peces. *c***1590** Hall 25: The bale of paper is 10 reames of paper. **1616** Hopton 164: A Bale of Paper is 10 Reame, or 200 Quires.

The bale was also used (*c*1700 and 1800) for boultel (bolting cloth), 20 pieces; caraway seeds, 3 Cwt (152.406 kg); cochineal, 1½ Cwt (76.203 kg); cotton yarn, 3 to 4 Cwt (136.077 to 181.436 kg); raw silk, 1 to 4 Cwt (50.802 to 203.208 kg); Spanish wool, 2¼ Cwt (114.304 kg); and thread, 100 bolts (Dict. Rus. sv and Second Rep. 6). *See* HUNDRED

Bales used for the following items did not have standard dimensions. — **1239** trans in Cal. Lib. 1.367: And a bale (*boyllum*) of ginger . . . a bale (*boylun*) of cinnamon . . . four bales (*boilluns*) of dates. **1242** trans in *ibid* 2.154: For a bale (*bala*) of ginger. *c***1300** Swithun 80: Una bala cujuslibet avoir de poys. **1303** Gras 1.161: Bala de bresil. **1304** *Ibid* 168: Pro ii bales basane. **1308** *Ibid* 362: Adduxit ii balas basani. **1323** *Ibid* 209: De quodlibet balo zucre. **1439** Southampton 2.63: 1 bale panni; *ibid* 70: 2 balys de streyt. **1443** Brokage II.1: Cum c allei et 1 bale alym; *ibid* 2: lx bal' amigdalorum . . . 1 bale madr'; *ibid* 3: Cum viii bal' dates; *ibid* 15: 1 parvo bal cere. **1509** Gras 1.698: Lycerus the balle.

balet — 5 balett, balette (OED); 5–6 balet; 6 balatt, ballet, ballett [ME *balet* < OF *balete, ballete*, dim of *bale, balle; see* BALE]. A m-q or m-c for many products and generally equal to ½ bale. — **1439** Southampton 2.12: 4 balett' de wode; *ibid* 55: Pro 2 balett' de wastyng paper; *ibid* 70: 1 balett panni continente 7 pannos sine grano et 18 vergas grany; *ibid* 72: Pro 2 balett' pellium vitulinarum continentibus 30 dosyn'; *ibid* 88: Pro 2 balett' grani pro panno; *ibid* 90: Pro i balet granis paradisi; *ibid* 91: 2 balett' rys. **1443** Brokage II.1: Cum viii balett waid'; *ibid* 81: Cum lx balett'

waid. **1509** Gras 1.562: iii balletts annessede. *c***1550** Welsh 62:
3 balletts canvas; *ibid* 73: 1 ballet crassum; *ibid* 237: 7 balattes . . .
toloss wood.

balett, balette. BALET

ball, balle. BALE

ballet, ballette. BALET

band — 4–5 bande (OED); 6–7 band [ME *bande*, strip, < MF *bande*,
strip, edge, side]. A wt for iron, the equivalent, in 1600, of 24
STONE (*c*152.41 kg) (Shuttleworths 790).

bande. BAND

barayl, barel, barele, barell, barelle, barellus. BARREL

barge-load. KEEL

barill, barillus. BARREL

barleycorn — 4–5 L ordeum [ME *barly corn, barlye corne; see*
WNID3, sv barley; *see ibid*, sv corn]. The artificial standard upon
which medieval linear measures and the ap, avdp, and t lb were
based. The INCH, for example, was defined by statute as the length
of 3 medium-sized barleycorns placed end to end. The ft was then
made equal to 12 of these inches; the CUBIT, 18; the yd, 36; the ELL,
45; and the FATHOM, 72. The ap and t lb contained 5760 barleycorns, while the avdp lb contained 7000. — *c***1300** Hall 7: Nota
quod tria grana ordei de medio spice faciunt pollicem. *c***1400** *Ibid* 9:
Sciendum quod tria grana ordei vel quatuor grana frumenti, in
medio spice sumpta, in longitudine faciunt pollicem Regis. **1537**
Benese 3: The lengthe of an ynche after some mens opinion, is
made by the length of thry barlye cornes, the which rule is not at
all tymes true. For the lengthe of a barlye corne of some tyllage is
lenger, and of some tyllage is shorter, after the fatnes and leanesse
of the lande, where it was sowen upon. Therefore in makynge of an
ynche after thys rule, it shulde be sometymes lenger, and sometymes shorter, after the lengthe and shortenes of the barlye cornes.
See GRAIN; INCH; POUND

barrall. BARREL

barrel — 3 L barillus (Swinfield); 4 barayl (OED), L barrellus; 4–5
barele (OED); 4–6 barell, barelle, L barellus, barrelle; 4–7 barel;
5–6 barylle; 5–7 barrell; 6 barill, barrall, baryll (Remembrance),
beryll (OED); 7–9 barrel [ME *barel, barell* < MF *baril*, barrel,
cask]. A m-c for both wet and dry products. It was a nearly cylin-

drical wooden vessel generally wider in the middle than at the ends, its length exceeding its breadth. It was often formed of curved staves bound together by hoops.

A bbl of ale contained 32 gal (c1.48 hl) and was equal to 4 ale FIRKINS of 8 gal each or 2 ale KILDERKINS of 16 gal each. In 1688 it was changed to 34 gal (c1.57 hl), and in 1803 it was standardized at 36 gal (c1.66 hl). — **1393** Henry Derby 157: Pro iiij barellis ceruisie. **1517** Hall 49: Be alwayes xxxii galons' to the barell, xvi galons' to the ale kylderkyn, and viii galons to the ale ffyrkyn. **1587** Stat. 595: And that euery barrell for ale shall conteine xxxii. gallons, euerie kilderkin . . . xvi. gallons, and euerie ferkin . . . viii gallons of the kings standard gallon. **1635** Dalton 144: 32 gallons maketh the Barrell. **1665** Sheppard 14: Of Ale . . . The Barrell 32 . . . Gallons. **1682** Hall 29: But Ale hath no more than 32 gallons to the barrell: and therefore but 64 pottles, 128 quarts, and 256 pints.

A bbl of beer contained 36 gal (c1.66 hl) and was equal to 4 beer firkins of 9 gal each or 2 beer kilderkins of 18 gal each. In 1688 it was changed to 34 gal (c1.57 hl), and in 1803 it was fixed once again at 36 gal (c1.66 hl). — **1443** Brokage II.191: ii barellis byre. c1475 Gras 1.193: Of a barel of bier. **1502** Arnold 246: The barell of beer, xxxvi galones. **1517** Hall 50: That there shuld' be no lesse assyse for bere than xxxvi galons to the barelle. **1547** trans in Cal. Pat. 23.397: Licence to the king's servant Galter de Loenus to export 300 'tonnes' of beer in 'buttes, pypes, hoggesheddes, pontions or barrelles'. **1587** Stat. 595: And that euerie barrell for beere shall conteine xxxvi. gallons. c1590 Hall 22: The firkin contenyth 9 galons: the barill contenith 36 gallons. **1635** Dalton 148: And so Beere measure containeth in the barrell foure gallons more than Wine, or any other vessel. **1682** Hall 29: 1 Barrell conteynes: 2 Kilderkins, 4 Firkins, 36 Gallons, 72 Pottles, 144 Quarts, 288 Pints.

The capacity of a bbl of butter or soap conformed to the ale bbl capacity of 32 gal (c1.48 hl), but the weights for butter, soap, and their casks were equally important. Generally, the butter bbl weighed 256 lb (116.119 kg) or 26 lb (11.793 kg) for the cask and 230 lb (104.326 kg) for the butter, whereas the soap bbl weighed 280 lb (127.005 kg) or 32 lb (14.515 kg) for the cask and 248 lb (112.490 kg) for the soap. — **1420** Gras 1.506: Pro xxi barellis saponis. **1443** Brokage II.1: Cum iiii barellis saponis; *ibid* 17: 1 barello saponis nigri. *c*1475 Gras 1.193: Of a barel sope. **1502** Arnold 246: The barell of soep, xxx [*sic*] galones. **1507** Gras 1.695: Butter the barelle; *ibid* 702: Sope called blacke sope the barrelle. **1587** Stat. 595: That all maner of sope makers within this realme of England, which shall put to sale anie sope by barrell. *c*1590 Hall 24: The barill of butter waieth, caske and all, 256 poundes waight haberdepoyse; whereof the caske wayeth 26 poundes waight; so ther remaynith in the caske of clean Butter 230 poundes waight haberdepoysse. . . . The barill of sope, caske and all, wayeth 280. . . . The barill of soap empty nowe 32 waight. **1635** Dalton 149: Sope, the barrell . . . shall bee of the same content that ale is. . . . Butter shall be of the same measure that sope is of. **1665** Assize 4: And every Sope-Barrel to hold and contain 32 gallons . . . and shall weigh being empty xxvi pounds of Avoirdupois weight; *ibid* 5: Which is twelve score and sixteen pounds . . . and the barrel of Butter is of like weight. **1682** Hall 30: The Barrells for herrings, Butter and Soape are the same with Ale measures.

A bbl of herrings or eels usually contained 30 gal fully packed (*c*1.14 hl). For salmon, and sometimes for eels, the bbl contained 42 gal (*c*1.59 hl) and was equal to ½ salmon PIPE or $\frac{1}{12}$ salmon LAST. For most other fish, including occasionally herrings and eels, the bbl conformed to the 32 gal capacity of the ale bbl (*c*1.48 hl) except in the case of pilchards or salted mackerel where the capacity was standardized in 1800 at 50 gal (*c*1.89 hl). — **1324** Gras 1.376: Pro vii barellis sturgonum. **1341** *Ibid* 174: xv barrellis de pyk'. *c*1400 *Ibid* 216: De quolibet barello de haddok. **1423** Rot. Parl. 4.256: The barrell of Heryng and Eles, xxx Galons full pakked. **1439** Southampton 2.12: 1 barello salmonum continente 2 dosyn'. **1443** Brokage II.41: Cum ii barellis salmon; *ibid* 105: Cum 1 barello salmon continente xvi salmon. **1482** Rot. Parl. 6.221: The Barell of Salmon XLII Galons. **1507** Gras 1.697: Elys called chaffte ellys the barylle . . . Elys called pymper eles the barelle; *ibid* 699: Hadockes the barrelle; *ibid* 702: Sawlte fyche the barell. **1509** *Ibid* 569: i di. barellus samonis. **1587** Stat. 267: Barels of herring and of eeles. *c*1590 Hall 23: The barill of heringe and eeles ought to be 30 gallons in content fully packed. . . . The but of salmone ought to be 84 gallons fully packed. . . . The last is 6 buttes conteninge 504 gallons; the barill is 42 gallons. **1615** Collect. Stat. 466: Nor barrell of Herring nor of Eeles, unles they contain 30. gallons fully packed. **1616** Hopton 162: And know that the barrell, and halfe barrell of Herrings, and likewise of butter and sope, are the same measure used for Ale. **1682** Hall 29: Barrell fish hath 12 Ale barrels to a Last.

A bbl of gunpowder weighed 1 Cwt of 100 lb (45.359 kg) and was equal to $\frac{1}{24}$ last of gunpowder; a bbl of coals contained nearly 4 Winchester bu (c1.40 hl). — c**1590** Hall 22: The hundred waight of gunpowder is but fyve skore poundes waight, haberdepoyse, to the hundrid. . . . The last . . . is 24 barills. **1603** Henllys 139: Coles are sold by the barrell w[hich] is of Bristoll band, or neere about foure Wynchester bushells.

A bbl of wine generally contained $31\frac{1}{2}$ gal (c1.19 hl) and was equal to $\frac{1}{8}$ wine tun of 252 gal. The oil and honey bbl conformed to the specifications of the wine bbl, as did the tar bbl after 1750. — **1341** Gras 1.174: De lxxii barrellis de tarr'. c**1400** Hall 18: There be also . . . barrells of terre. **1439** Southampton 2.15: Pro 3 barellis de tarr. **1443** Brokage II.8: Cum v barellis tarr'. c**1590** Hall 21: The [wine] barill which is $\frac{1}{8}$ part of a tonne contenyth 31 gallons $\frac{1}{2}$. **1615** Collect. Stat. 467: And euerie [wine] Barrell to containe one and thirtie gallons and an halfe. **1635** Dalton 148: Wine, Oyle, and Honey: their measure is all one. **1682** Hall 29: Wyne, Oyle and Hony Measures: 1 Tunne conteynes . . . 8 Barrells. **1704** Mer. Adven. 243: Ffor the carriage of a barrall of oyl.

The bbl was also used (c1800–75) in England for apples, 3 bu (c1.06 hl); barilla, 2 Cwt (101.604 kg); beef, 32 wine gal (c1.21 hl); candles, 120 lb (54.431 kg); nuts, 3 bu (c1.06 hl); plates (white or black), 300 in number; potash, 2 Cwt (101.604 kg); raisins, 1 Cwt (50.802 kg); and vinegar, 34 gal (c1.29 hl) (Second Rep. 6–7 and Seventh Rep. 62).

The bbl had a number of different uses (c1800) outside England: Guernsey and Jersey, lime, 120 pots or 60 gal (c2.77 hl); Ireland, grain, generally 4 bu of 10 gal each (c1.80 hl), but barley, 16 STONE of 14 lb each or 224 lb (101.604 kg), beans, peas, and wheat, 20 stone (127.00 kg), malt, 12 stone (76.20 kg), oats, 14 stone (88.90 kg), and potatoes, 20 stone (127.00 kg); Isle of Man, lime, 6 Winchester bu (c2.11 hl); Wales, lime in some counties, 3 provincial bu of 10 gal each, equal to 3¼ Winchester bu (*c*1.14 hl), and culms, 4 heaped bu or 40 gal (*c*1.80 hl) (Second Rep. 8).

barrell, barrelle, barrellus. BARREL

barrow [ME *barew, barowe* < OE *bearwe*, basket, handbarrow]. A m-c for salt containing approximately 6 pk (*c*5.29 dkl), used in Cheshire, Worcester, and other places in the salt region in the 1800's. It was a conical wicker case or basket in which salt was put to drain (Leigh 14).

baryll, barylle. BARREL

baskatt. BASKET

basket — 3–9 basket; 4–5 baskett, baskette; 5 baskatt (OED), baskyt (OED); 6 basquette (OED), baszkett (OED), baszkette (OED); 7 basquet (OED) [ME *basket*, prob < ONF *baskot* < (assumed) ONF *baskou* < L *bascauda*, dishpan; *see* WNID3]. A m-c varying in size according to its contents (*c*1700): medlars, 2 bu (*c*7.05 dkl); cherries, Kent, 48 lb (21.772 kg) (Bradley sv). It was usually a wickerwork container made from plaited osiers, cane rushes, or other similar materials.

Baskets used for the following items did not have standard dimensions. — **1420** Gras 1.500: Pro i baskette cum xiiii briste-plates nigr'. **1443** Brokage II.67: iiii baskettys orengys. **1509** Gras 1.565: iiii basketts cum xi [×] c galipotts; *ibid* 568: i parv' basket cum ii dossenis et di. felts . . . i basket cum x dossenis mistel bedes; *ibid* 570: ii basketts cum iiii cases spectakilles . . . ii basketts continent' cv pecias et remanenta teli lini Hasburgh.

baskett, baskette, baskyt, basquet, basquette, baszkett, baszkette. BASKET

bat [prob a special use of *bat*, stick, club]. A m-a in South Wales (*c*1800) containing 1 perch of 11 sq ft (1.022 sq m) (Second Rep. 8).

batten [F *bâton*, stick, staff]. A m-c for straw in Durham (early 1800's) equal to ¹⁄₁₂ THRAVE (Dinsdale 134). It was probably the amount of packed straw in a bundle whose breadth was equal to the length of a certain measuring stick.

bay [ME *bay* < MF *baée*, an opening, < OF *baee* < vb *baer*, to be open]. A m-a of slater's work in Derbyshire (*c*1800) containing 500 sq ft (46.452 sq m) (Second Rep. 8).

bayl. BALE

beatment [perh < vb *beat*, in the sense of a "beating," or quantity to be beaten at once, + -*ment*]. A m-c for grain (*c*1800) in Durham, Newcastle, and Northumberland equal to ¼ pk (*c*2.20 l) (Brockett 22).

belet. BILLET

beryll. BARREL

bescia [F *bêche*, spade, < MF *besche* + -*ia* L ending]. A m-a in Lincolnshire (*c*1400) for turf-cutting on the fens. It represented the amount of land that could presumably be dug annually by one man with a spade between May 1st and August 1st (Prior 150).

beyschell. BUSHEL

billet — 4–6 billette; 5 bylet (OED); 5–6 belet (OED); 6 billett, byllet (OED), byllot; 6–9 billet; 8 billot (OED) [ME *billette* < MF *billete* (F *billette*, *billot*), dim of *bille*, log, round stick]. A m-l of 3 ft 4 inches (1.016 m) for firewood. A single billet had a circumference of 7½ inches (19.050 cm); a cast billet, 10 inches (25.40 cm); and a two cast billet, 14 inches (35.56 cm). — **1559** Fab. Rolls 353: In byllot or shydes. **1587** Stat. 171: And euerie billet to conteine in length three foot and foure inches. *c*1590 Hall 27: The billettes be of like lenghtes, but not of like tycknes. Euery billett ought to be in lenght 3 foott 4 ynches in lenght. The single billet conteyn' 7 ynches about and ½. A billet caled a cast contenith 10 ynches about. Euery billet caled a cast of 2 contenith 14 ynches about. **1616** Hopton 163: All fuell is used by the Statute, of which there be Shids, Billets, Fagots and Coles. **1665** Assize 18: And every Billet named a single, to contain seven inches and a half about . . . every Billet named . . . cast, to contain 10 inches about; and every Billet of two Cast, to contain 14 inches about.

billett, billette, billot. BILLET

bind — 3 L binda, binde, L bynda; 4–6 bynde (OED); 6 bynd; 7–9 bind [ME *binde* < vb *binden*, to bind]. A m-q for eels, consisting of 10 STICKS, or 250 in number. — *c*1253 Hall 12: La binde de anguilles est de x estikes. *c*1272 Report 1.414: Item binda anguillarum constat ex decem stiks. *c*1275 Hall 10: Bynda vero anguillarum constat ex decem stickes; et quelibet sticke ex viginti et quinque anguillis. **1290** Fleta 120: Item lunda [bynda?] anguillarum constat ex x. stikis. *c*1590 Hall 23: A bynd of eeles consistith 10 stikes. **1615** Collect. Stat. 465: A bind of Eeles consisteth of 10. strikes [*sic*] and euerie strike [*sic*] 25. eeles. **1665** Sheppard 61: A Bind of Eels.

binda, binde. BIND

bing [ME *bing,* of Scand origin; akin to ON *bingr,* an enclosure, bin, heap, pile]. A wt of 8 Cwt (406.416 kg) for lead ore in Durham and Northumberland (*c*1800) (Second Rep. 8).

binne — 6 byne; 7 binne [var of BIND]. A m-q for skins, numbering 33. — *c*1590 Hall 28: The Byne consisteth 33 skynns. **1615** Collect. Stat. 465: The Binne of skinnes consisteth of 33. skins.

bodge — 6 bogge (OED); 6–7 bodge [perh < ME vb *bodge,* var of *botch,* to patch clumsily, < F *boce,* protuberance]. A false m-c used illegally by chandlers and others in place of the POTTLE. Since it resembled the pottle, the buyer was deceived into believing that it contained $\frac{1}{2}$ gal or 2 qt (*c*1.89 l) even though its actual capacity was less. — **1588** Hall 46: Instead of the Pottle, falce measures are used, called Bodges, and some woodden measures, made under the halfe pint, most deceiptfull and unlawfull. . . . These measures are most used by chaundlers, milke weomen and diuerse others . . . contrary to the Statute in that case made and provided. *c*1634 *Ibid* 53: In Baskettes called Prickles . . . and sometimes not soe much, which causeth them to sell by Bodges. *See* POTTLE

bogge. BODGE

boillun. BALE

boissel. BUSHEL

bole. BOLL

boll — 4 L bolla; 4–7 bolle; 5–9 boll; 6 bow (OED); 6–7 boule, boull; 7 bole (OED), bowle [ME *bolle* < OE *bolla,* bowl, beaker, measure]. A m-c in northern England and Scotland for grain, coal, and other dry products.

When the Newcastle coal CHALDER weighed 42 Cwt (2133.684 kg), the boll was $\frac{1}{20}$ of that amount or $2\frac{1}{10}$ Cwt (106.684 kg); but when this chalder was increased to $52\frac{1}{2}$ Cwt (2667.105 kg) under Charles II, the boll became $\frac{1}{21}$ of the chalder or $2\frac{1}{2}$ Cwt (127.005 kg) and contained $22\frac{1}{2}$ gal. Finally, when the Newcastle chalder was standardized in 1695 at 72 heaped bu totaling 53 Cwt or 5936 lb (2692.506 kg), the boll equaled $\frac{1}{24}$ of this chalder or $247\frac{1}{3}$ lb (112.187 kg). — **1603** Hostmen 38: Whereas, tyme out of mynde, yt hath been accustomed that all Colewaynes did usuallie cary and bringe Eighte Boulls of Coles to all the Staythes upon the Ryver of Tyne. **1606** *Ibid* 244: Paid for two boulles for the measuringe of keeles . . . paide for 4 bowles. **1608** *Ibid* 245: Paid for foure newe bolles and for the froneinge of them. **1617** *Ibid* 247: The 28 of

March payd to Cuthbert Cutter for B'les [boules] for measuringe of the waynes had of him. *See* HUNDRED

The grain boll on the St. Paul's Estate (*c*1200) contained 1 gal (*c*4.62 1) (St. Paul's cxxxiv), but elsewhere in northern England (*c*1800) it was considerably larger: Durham and Newcastle, 2 bu (*c*7.05 dkl); Northumberland, at Alnwick, barley and oats, 6 bu (*c*2.11 hl), wheat, 2 bu (*c*7.05 dkl), at Hexham, barley and oats, 5 bu (*c*1.76 hl), peas, rye, and wheat, 4 bu (*c*1.41 hl); Westmorland, rye, 2 triple bu (*c*2.11 hl) (Second Rep. 8).

The boll, however, was used principally in Scotland. Under Robert III it was standardized at 12 gal or the capacity of a vessel 9 inches deep and 72 inches in circumference, and later, during the reign of George II, it was fixed at 4 FIRLOTS or 5.9626 Winchester bu (2.101 hl). — *c*1390 Du Cange sv: Bolla debet continere sextarium, videlicet 12. lagenas, et debet esse in profunditate 9. pollicum cum spissitudine ligni utriusque partis. Et in rotunditate superiore continebit 72. pollices, in medio ligni superioris. In rotunditate inferiori 71. pollices. **1609** Skene 2.57: The boll . . . salbe in the deipnes nine inches . . . and in the Roundnes aboue, it sall contein thrie score and twelue inches.

However, there were many exceptions to this standard Scots boll. Geographically, the variations (*c*1800) ran as follows (Second Rep. 8–10). *North* — Caithness: beans, peas, and wheat, 4½ bu (*c*1.58 hl); oats, 6⅛ bu (*c*2.16 hl); oatmeal, 8½ STONE (53.977 kg); potatoes, 16 pk of 1½ stone each (152.406 kg). Sutherland: oats in some places, 5 firlots (2.63 hl). *Northeast* — Aberdeenshire: barley and oats, 4 Aberdeen firlots or 136 pt of 60¼ oz each (232.238 kg); coal, 36 stone or 630 English lb (285.762 kg); lime, 128 Aberdeen pt of 105 cu inches each (2.20 hl). Banffshire: barley, 17 to 17½ stone (107.954 to 111.129 kg). Moray (or Elgenshire) and Nairn: barley meal, 9 to 12 stone (57.152 to 76.203 kg); oatmeal, 8 to 9 stone (50.802 to 57.152 kg). *East* — Angus: meal, 8 stone (50.802 kg); potatoes, 32 stone (203.208 kg); coal, at Dundee, 56 stone (355.614 kg). Kincardineshire: coal, 72 stone (457.219 kg); lime, 128 to 132 pt (2.18 to 2.25 hl); lime shells, 85 Scots pt (1.45 hl). *West* — Argyllshire: lime, 4 to 5 bu (*c*7.05 to *c*8.81 dkl). *Central* — Perthshire: barley meal, 18 stone (114.305 kg); beans and peas, 13 to 14 stone (82.553 to 88.904 kg); oats, 14 to 14½ stone (88.904 to 92.079 kg); wheat, 14 stone (88.904 kg). Stirlingshire: barley, malt, and oats, 133 pt (2.27 hl); wheat, 91 pt (1.55 hl). *Southeast* — Berwickshire: lime, approximately 4 Winchester bu (*c*1.41 hl). Roxburghshire: barley, malt, and oats, 5 firlots (2.79 hl), each firlot 2 pt above the standard; beans, peas, rye, and wheat, 5 firlots of 2275 cu inches each (1.86 hl). Selkirkshire: barley, malt, oats, and potatoes, 5 firlots equal to 16,157 cu inches (2.65 hl); beans, peas, rye, and wheat, 5 firlots of 2286 cu inches (1.87 hl). *Southwest* — Ayrshire: lime, 4 to 5 bu (*c*7.05 to *c*8.81 dkl). Kintyre: lime, 17 pk (*c*1.54 hl) before Patrickmas and afterward 16 pk (*c*1.45 hl). Renfrewshire: beans and peas, 4½ Winchester bu (1.58 hl); oats, 6½ Winchester bu (2.29 hl).

bolla, bolle. BOLL

bolltte. BOLT

bolt — 4–9 bolt; 6 bolltte, bowlte; 9 boult (Morton) [ME *bolt* < OE *bolt;* akin to MLG *bolte*, bolt, piece of linen rolled up]. A m-q (bundled or rolled) for thread, canvas, wood, and various other goods. Its dimensions generally depended on the quality and weight of the goods being shipped. In Berkshire (*c*1850) a bolt of osiers was 42 inches (1.067 m) around and 14 inches (35.56 cm) from the butts (Morton sv). — **1399** trans in Cal. Close 16.371: One whole cloth and 8 'boltes' of 'worstede.' **1507** Gras 1.701: Powlld davys for saylles the bolltte; *ibid* 705: Vlyons for sayles the bowlte. **1509** *Ibid* 577: viii bolts olrons. *c*1550 Welsh 82: 1 bolt canvas . . . 1 bolt Poldavi; *ibid* 107: 2 bolts wood.

boltin. BOLTING

bolting — 8 boltin (OED), bolting, bolton (OED) [*bolt*, bundle, + *-ing*]. A wt of 24 lb (10.886 kg) for straw in Gloucestershire (*c*1800) (Second Rep. 10).

bolton. BOLTING

bomkyn [*]. A small BARREL.

bonch, bonche. BUNCH

bondel, bondell. BUNDLE

boot. BOUT

boschell, bosshell. BUSHEL

botel. BOTTLE[1]; BOTTLE[2]

botele. BOTTLE[2]

botell. BOTTLE[1]; BOTTLE[2]

botella. BOTTLE[1]

botelle, botle, bottel, bottell, bottelle. BOTTLE[1]; BOTTLE[2]

bottle[1] — 4 botel (OED); 5 bottelle (OED); 5–6 botell (OED), L botella (Dur. House), botelle (OED), bottell (OED); 6–7 botle (OED), bottel (OED); 6–9 bottle [ME *botel, botelle* < MF *boteille* < MedL *buticula, butticula,* dim of LL *buttis,* BUTT]. A m-c for liquids: *c*1800, aqua fortis, 4 gal (*c*1.51 dkl), and wine, approximately ⅕ gal (*c*0.76 l) (Second Rep. 10).

bottle[2] — 4 botele; 4–6 botel; 5 bottelle (OED); 5–6 botell (OED), botelle (OED); 5–7 bottell; 6 bottel (OED); 6–9 bottle; 7 botle (OED) [ME *botel* < MF *botel,* dim of *bote,* bundle]. A m-q for hay or straw weighing 7 lb (3.175 kg). — **1365** trans in Memorials 324: And if they sell their hay by boteles, they are to make their boteles in proportion to the same price. **1439** Southampton 2.82: 10 botels. **1474** Cov. Leet 399: And his bottell of haye of an ob. shall way vij lb. and his liter free.

boule, boull. BOLL

boult. BOLT

bounch, bounche. BUNCH

boundell. BUNDLE

boussel, bousshell. BUSHEL

bout — 8–9 bout; 9 boot (OED) [perh a special sense of *bought,* bend or bending]. A m-c for lead ore in Derbyshire (*c*1800) containing 240 DISHES (*c*26.43 hl) (Second Rep. 10).

bout. BUTT

bovat, bovata. BOVATE

bovate — 2–6 L bovata; 3–? bovate; 7 bovatt (OED); 8 bovat (Willis), boviat (OED) [MedL *bovata* < L *bos, bovis,* ox]. A m-a which originally may have referred to the amount of land that an ox and team could plow in a year, but which, in actual practice, varied between 7 and 32 acres (2.835 to 14.160 ha), depending on the quality of the soil in any particular region. Occasionally it was used synonymously with the VIRGATE, equaling ¼ or ½ HIDE, but more often it was reckoned at ½ virgate. — *c*1153 Malcolm 192: In escambio duaram bouatarum terre in Berewyc. **1201** Cur. Reg. 9.53: Scilicet de tercia parte vij. bovatarum terre cum pertinenciis in Waberge. **1202** Feet 1.37: In una bouata terre de predictis duabus bouatis que continet xviij acras terre cum pertinenciis. . . . Alteram bouatam terre cum pertinenciis in Filingham continentem xxviij acras. **1204** Cur. Reg. 10.238: v. bovatas et dimidiam; *ibid* 239: Et Robertum de xv. bovatis terre cum pertinentiis; *ibid* 240: j bovata terre. **1207** Feet 1.110: Ad undecim bouatas terre unde quadraginta bouate faciunt seruicium unius militis pro omni serui- cio. **1219** Eyre 258: Terciam partem ii bouatarum terre. *c*1500 Hall 8: viii [×] xx pertice faciunt acram; duodecim acre faciunt bovatam. . . . ii bovate faciunt virgatam. **1755** Willis 361: From the Terms Hide, Carucate, Bovate, &c. so often occurring in Doomsday-Book, it appears that the primitive Husbandry here consisted chiefly in Tillage or Arable Culture; *ibid* 362: In *Spel- man's Gloss.* an Account is cited from an ancient MS. that viii Bovats made a Carucate, and viii Acres a Bovate; if so, a Carucate must contain lxiv Acres of Arable; but I think otherwise . . . and that a carucate had no fixed Measure. **1777** Nicol. and Burn 610: Bovate . . . of land: as much as one yoke of oxen can reasonably cultivate in a year. *See* OXGANG

bovatt, boviat. BOVATE
bow, bowle. BOLL
bowlte. BOLT
bowsshell, bowsshelle. BUSHEL
box — 5–6 boxe; 6 boxse (OED); 6–9 box [ME *boxe* < OE *box* < LL *buxis* < Gr *pyxis* < *pyxos*, boxtree]. A m-c originally referring to any small receptacle used for drugs and other valuable materials. However, since the eighteenth century it has included containers of any size made for the purpose of holding merchandise and personal property. It generally did not have a standard capacity except (*c*1800) for aloes, 14 lb (6.350 kg); coals, Derbyshire, 2½ striked or leveled bu (*c*8.81 dkl); and salmon, Durham, 8 STONE (50.802 kg) (Second Rep. 10). — **1420** Gras 1.512: iiii box[es] boras[is]; *ibid* 514: i boxe galbannum. **1439** Southampton 2.74: 80 boxis sitronade. **1507** Gras 1.699: Harpe strynges the boxe; *ibid* 703: Shomakyrs heres the boxe.

boxe, boxse. BOX
boyllum, boylun. BALE
boyschel. BUSHEL
bucket [ME *bucket* < AF *buket* < OE *būc*, pitcher, belly]. A m-c for chalk in Buckinghamshire and Hertfordshire (*c*1800) containing 1½ bu (*c*5.29 dkl) (Second Rep. 10).
buisshel. BUSHEL
bunch — 4–6 bunche; 5 bonch, bonche; 5–6 bounche (OED); 6–7 bounch (OED); 6–9 bunch; 7 bunsh (OED) [ME *bunche; see*

WNID3]. A m-q used principally for onions or garlic, 25 heads, and glass, usually equal to $\frac{1}{60}$ WEY or $\frac{1}{40}$ WAW of glass. — [**1290** Fleta 120: Rasus autem alleorum continet xx flones [bunches], et quelibet flonis xxv. capita.] **1439** Southampton 2.8: M. bunchis allei. **1443** Brokage II.1: Cum ix [×] xx bonchys allei; *ibid* 92: Cum iiii [×] xx bonchis allei. **1507** Gras 1.698: Glasse called Flemyche glasse the waw that ys to saye xl bunchys; *ibid* 701: Onyones the C bunches. **1717** Dict. Rus. sv weigh: Of Glas 6[0] Bunches.

The bunch was also used (*c*1800–50) for osiers, Cambridgeshire, a bundle 45 inches (1.143 m) in circumference at the band; reeds, Cambridgeshire, a bundle 28 inches (7.112 dm) in circumference at the band; teasels, Essex, 25 heads, Gloucestershire, 20 heads, and Yorkshire, 10 heads (Second Rep. 10 and Morton sv).

Bunches of the following items did not have standard sizes. — **1396** Gras 1.7: Fanes the bunche; *ibid* 441: C bunches lini. **1402** *Ibid* 556: Pro xx bunche leok. *c*1500 Fab. Rolls 337: Bunchys of lattes.

bunche. BUNCH

bundel, bundell, bundelle. BUNDLE

bundle — 4–7 bundel; 5 bondel (OED), bondell; 5–6 boundell (OED), bundelle; 5–7 bundell; 6 byndle (OED); 7–9 bundle [ME *bundel* < MDu *bondel, bundel;* akin to OE *byndel,* a bundle]. A m-q that varied in number or dimension according to the product, its quality, and weight (*c*1800): barley straw, Devonshire, 35 lb (15.876 kg); bast ropes, 10; birch brooms, 1 or 2 dozen; brown paper, 40 QUIRES; hogshead hoops, Gloucestershire, 36; hoops, Berkshire, 120 to 480; oat straw, Devonshire, 40 lb (18.144 kg); osiers, Gloucestershire, $1\frac{1}{4}$ ft (0.457 m) in circumference, and Hampshire, 42 inches (1.067 m) around the lower band; straw for thatching, Yorkshire, $\frac{1}{12}$ THRAVE; and wheat straw, Devonshire, 28 lb (12.700 kg) (Second Rep. 10–11; 35).

Bundles of the following items had no consistent standard sizes throughout England. — **1443** Brokage II.27: iii bondell' de fryyng pannys. **1507** Gras 1.696: Corke the bundelle for shyppers or ells the C. **1509** *Ibid* 563: iiii [×] xx bundelli papiri nigri. **1524** *Ibid* 195: Pro lx bundelis osyers. **1549** *Ibid* 627: Pro xx bundellis fannes.

bunsh. BUNCH

burden — 2–9 burden; 5 burdon, byrdyn; 5–6 burdyn, burdynge (Dur. House), burthen [ME *burden, burthen* < OE *byrthen; see*

OED]. A wt for steel containing either 6 or 12 sheaves of 30 GADS each and a m-q for fish (ling and mulvel or cod) numbering 20 or 22. — **1443** Brokage II.19: Cum vi byrdyn piscis salsi; *ibid* 40: Et dimidio byrdyn piscis. *c***1461** Hall 17: Also style by gadds; and euery pece of stele in hymselfe is a gadde; and xxx gaddes make a scheff, and xii scheff make a burdon. **1507** Gras 1.703: Stelle the barelle wyche owght to be iiii [✕] xx burden and vi scheffe makythe a burdyn and xxx gaddes makythe sheffe. *c***1550** Welsh 63: 7 burden stile; *ibid* 81: 1 burden fish; *ibid* 275: 4 burthen steel. **1559** Remembrance 67: The xvi[th] of Octobre, John Croche of the cytye of London fyshemonger have maid pryce w[ith] Mr. Mayer . . . for xiis. the burdon of lyngs.

burdon, burdyn, burdynge, burthen. BURDEN
buscel, buscellus, buschel, buschelle, buschellus, busellus. BUSHEL
bushel — 3 L buschellus; 3–4 L bussellum, L busselum; 3–7 L bussellus; 4 boissel, boyschel (OED), buisshel (OED), L buscellus, buschel, busschel (OED), buysshel (OED); 4–5 boussel, bussell, busselle (Hall), buyschel (OED); 4–6 L busellus, busshel, busshell (Prior), busshelle (OED); 4–9 bushel; 5 boschell, bosshell (Southampton 2), buscel (OED), buschelle (Prior), bussel, buysshell, byschelle (OED), byshell (OED); 5–6 bowsshell (OED), bowsshelle (OED); 5–7 bushell; 6 beyschell (OED), bousshell (OED), bushylle (OED), buszhell (OED), buszshel (OED) [ME *busshel, boyschel* < OF *boissel* < *boisse*, a measure of grain]. A m-c for dry products.

In England the standard or Winchester grain bu (35.238 l) contained 4 pk, or 8 gal, or 16 POTTLES, or 32 qt, or 64 pt, and was equal to $\frac{1}{8}$ SEAM or $\frac{1}{80}$ grain LAST. Until the sixteenth century, the bu of wheat was supposed to weigh 64 tow lb, but after the tow lb was abolished, the bu of wheat was sometimes described as weighing 56 avdp lb. — *c***1200** Caernarvon 242: Buschellu londonia hoc est octavam *par*tem quart*er*ii. **1212** Cur. Reg. 13.192: Et j. bussellum bladi. **1220** Cur. Reg. 2.322: Et duos bussellos. **1290** Fleta 119: Et pondus octo librarum frumenti faciunt mensuram ialonis, et octo ialonate frumenti faciunt bussellum, de quibus octo consistit commune quarterium. **1298** Falkirk 1: iii bussellorum frumenti. *c***1300** Mon. Jur. I.80: Cest assavoir que le boissel nest mye ung potel greigneur que lestandarde de la terre. *c***1300** Hall 8: Et viii galones bladi faciunt i bussellum. Et viii buselli bladi faciunt i quarterium. Et bussellus frumenti puri et bene mundati ponderabit xlviii l. sterlingorum. **1351** Rot. Parl. 2.240: Et contiegne le quarter oet bussell *par* l'estandard. **1390** Henry Derby 6: Pro iij bussellis et j pecco auenarum. **1395** York Mem. 2.10: Unum busselum eris, dimidium bussellum et pek ligni. *c*1400 Hall 7: Et viij livres de froument font la galone de vin. Et viii galons de froument font le bussell' de Loundres, qest la oeptisme partie du quarter; *ibid* 12: And viij gallons of wyne make a boschell of whete; *ibid* 36: 8 galones faciunt I buschel; *ibid* 37: Et unus buscellus continet octo lagenas. *c*1400 York Mem. 2.260: Cest assavoir des boussels, demi boussels. **1413** Rot. Parl. 4.14: C'est assavoir, viii Busselx pur la Quartre, & qe chescun Bussell contiendra oept Galons. **1433** *Ibid* 450: Sinoun oept busshels rasez pur le quarter. **1474** Cov. Leet 396: & ij pyntes maketh a quart; & ij quartes maketh a Pottell; & ij Pottels makith a Gallon; & viij Gallons makith a Buysshell, and neyther hepe nor Cantell. *c*1500 Hall 8: xii uncie faciunt libram; viij libre faciunt lagenam; viij lagene faciunt busellum. **1587** Stat. 454: That the measure of the bushell conteine viii. galons of whete, and that euerie galon conteine viii. li. of wheate. **1616** Hopton 162: All kind of graine is measured by . . . a gallon, whereof are made . . . Bushels. **1635** Dalton 145: By Statute the bushell must containe eight gallons, or 64 pounds or pintes of wheat. **1665** Assize 2: But 12 ounces to the pound . . . and 64 pounds to the bushel. **1688** Bernardi 150: Præterea Galonem Frumentarium Angliæ, dimidium Pecci et Octantem Busselli . . . . Pinta denique arida, $\frac{1}{8}$ Galonis, seu congii frumentarii, et $\frac{1}{8 \times 8}$ = $\frac{1}{64}$ Brusselli aut Amphoræ Anglicanæ. **1745** Fleetwood 57–58: For so *quarta*, *quartalis*, and *quartalium*, signifies a Peck, or the fourth Part of a Bushel. **1789** Hawney 310: And 2150.42 solid Inches is a Bushel of Corn-measure.

Local variations of the bu were numerous since it was the principal measure for dry products. Not only did local units vary in capacity, but they also varied in weight. Geographically, these variations (*c*1800) were as follows (Second Rep. 11–13). *North —* Yorkshire: 1 to 3 qt (1.101 to 3.303 1) above the Winchester bu. *Northeast —* Durham: corn, 8 to 8½ gal (*c*3.52 to *c*3.74 dkl). *Northwest —* Cumberland: Carlisle, triple bu of 24 gal (*c*10.57 dkl), and Penrith, barley and oats, 20 gal (*c*8.81 dkl); rye and wheat, double bu of 16 gal (*c*7.05 dkl). Lancashire: potatoes, 90 lb (40.823 kg). *Central —* Bedfordshire: 2 pt above the Winchester bu (3.64 dkl). Derbyshire: potatoes, 90 lb (40.823 kg). Leicester-

27

butt
shire: potatoes, 80 lb (36.287 kg). Staffordshire: barley, beans, oats, and peas, 9½ gal (*c*4.18 dkl). *West central* — Worcestershire: Worcester, 8½ gal (*c*3.74 dkl), Evesham, 9 gal (*c*4.11 dkl), and all other places, 9½ and 9¾ gal (*c*4.18 and *c*4.29 dkl). *West* — Cheshire: barley, 60 lb (27.215 kg); oats, 45 to 50 lb (20.411 to 22.679 kg); wheat, 70 to 75 lb (31.751 to 34.019 kg). Herefordshire: grain, 10 gal (*c*4.40 dkl); malt, 8½ gal (*c*3.74 dkl). Shropshire: barley, peas, and wheat, 9½ to 10 gal (*c*4.18 to *c*4.40 dkl). *South* — Berkshire: corn, 9 gal (*c*3.96 dkl). Oxfordshire: wheat, 9 gal and 3 pt (*c*4.11 dkl). *Southeast* — Middlesex: potatoes, 56 lb (25.401 kg). Surrey: potatoes, 60 lb (27.215 kg). *Southwest* — Cornwall: eastern section, double bu of 16 gal (*c*7.05 dkl), and western section, triple bu of 24 gal (*c*10.57 dkl). Devonshire: barley, 50 lb (22.679 kg); oats, 36 or 40 lb (16.329 or 18.144 kg); wheat, 3 level and 1 heaped pk (*c*3.96 dkl). Gloucestershire: corn, usually 9½ gal (*c*4.18 dkl), sometimes 9, 9¼, and 10 gal (*c*3.96, *c*4.07, and *c*4.40 dkl). Somersetshire: coal, 9 gal (*c*3.96 dkl).

There were also variations (*c*1800) outside England: Scotland, Ayrshire bu, 2 pk (*c*1.81 dkl), Galloway barley bu, 46 to 53 lb (20.865 to 24.040 kg); Wales, Brecknochshire, 10 gal (*c*4.40 dkl), Monmouthshire, 10 to 10½ gal (*c*4.40 to *c*4.62 dkl), Montgomery-shire, 20 gal (*c*8.80 dkl) (Second Rep. 13).

bushell, bushylle, busschel, bussel, bussell, busselle, bussellum, bus-sellus, busselum, busshel, busshell, busshelle, buszhell, buszshel. BUSHEL

but. BUTT

butress [*]. A m-c of undetermined size (*c*1400) for coal (Salzman 1.15).

butt — 5 bout (Southampton l); 5–6 but; 5–7 butte; 5–9 butt [ME *butt* < MF *botte* < OPr *bota* < LL *buttis*, butt, cask]. Equivalent to PIPE. — **1423** Rot. Parl. 4.256: The but of Samon, xx [×] iiii [+] IIII Galons full pakked. **1443** Brokage II.1: Cum ii carectis cum iiii buttis vini; *ibid* 131: Cum i but romeney. **1482** Rot. Parl. 6.221: That every Butt . . . ordeyned for Samon, shuld conteygne . . . xx [×] iiii [+] IIII Galons. *c*1590 Hall 21: The pipe contenith a butt which is ½ of a tunne, 126 gallons; *ibid* 23: The but of salmone ought to be 84 gallons fully packed . . . the last is 6 buttes conteninge 504 gallons. **1615** Collect. Stat. 466: Nor butte of

Salmon, unlesse it contain 84. gallons fully packed. **1665** Assize 4: There is also a certain measure called a Salmon-Butt, which must hold and contain fourscore and four gallons. **1708** Chamberlayne 210: Of these Gallons . . . a Pipe or Butt holds 126. **1717** Dict. Rus. sv: Butt or Pipe of Wine, contains two Hogsheads, or One hundred twenty six Gallons; and a Butt of Currans from Fifteen to Twenty-two Hundred weight. **1725** Bradley sv: Butt, or Pipe, a Liquid Measure, whereof two Hogsheads make a Butt or Pipe, as two Pipes or Butts make one Tun. **1773** Johnson sv: Butt . . . A vessel; a barrel containing one hundred and twenty-six gallons of wine . . . and from fifteen to twenty-two hundred weight is a butt of currans.

butta terræ. BUTT OF LAND

butte. BUTT

butt of land — 7 L butta terræ (Du Cange) [ME *but, butt,* ridge of ground between two furrows, < MedL *butta, buttis; see* OED and WNID3]. A m-a for land, possibly synonymous with the RIDGE or SELION, being a strip of land or pathway between two parallel furrows of the open field. — **1688** Holme ii §32: Smaller parcells according to that quantity of ground it containeth, both for length and breadth . . . 3 Ridges, Butts, Flats, Stitches or small Butts, Pikes.

buyllon. BALE

buyschel, buysshel, buysshell. BUSHEL

bylet, byllet, byllot. BILLET

bynd, bynda, bynde. BIND

byndle. BUNDLE

byne. BINNE

byrdyn. BURDEN

byschelle, bysshell. BUSHEL

C

C. CENT

caas. CASE

cabot [OF *cabot* (F *chabot*), perh < *cabo, capo,* head, +-*ot*]. A m-c for wheat in Jersey equal to approximately ¾ English bu (*c*2.64 dkl). There was also (*c*1800) a smaller cabot, 4 of which made 3 standard cabots, used for barley and corn (Second Rep. 13).

cade — 4–6 L cadus; 4–9 cade; 6 gag (Dur. House), gage, gagge (Dur. House) [ME *cade* < L *cadus,* a large vessel usually of earthenware, a wine jar, a liquid measure]. A m-c, a small bbl or keg, for fish and other products: herrings, 500 to 620; sprats, 1000. — **1392** Henry Derby 97: Et per manus eiusdem pro j cade allecium rubrorum. **1393** *Ibid* 208: Item in xij cadis; *ibid* 222: Item pro j cado pro vergws imponendo. **1443** Brokage II.89: Cum xii cades allecii relute; *ibid* 99: Cum xii cades shot allecii rubei. **1456** trans in Fountains xxiii: Tar, 1s. a gallon, 6s.8d. to 12s.2d. a cade; *ibid* 258: Cadus corei. **1502** Arnold 263: Xx. cadis rede hering is a last, v.C. in a cade, vi. score iiij. heringis for the C. **1532** Finchale ccccxxi: One gage of eels. *c*1550 Welsh 217: 20 cados wheat . . . barley . . . oat malt. **1717** Dict. Rus. sv: Cade, a Cag, Cask, or Barrel . . . . Cade of Herrings, a Vessel or Measure containing the quantity of five Hundred red Herrings, or of Sprats a Thousand.

cadge. CAGE

cadus. CADE

cage — 5 kage (OED); 6 cadge (OED), kaig (OED); 6–9 cage [OF *cage* < L *cavea,* cavity, cage, < *cavus,* hollow]. A m-q, generally without a fixed value, for animals: quails, sometimes 28 dozen. — **1509** Gras 1.568: i cage cum xxviii dossenis quailles.

cais. CASE

cantel — 5–7 cantel, cantell [ME *cantel* < ONF *cantel* (MedL *cantellus*), dim of *cant,* edge, corner]. A shallow measure in which the contents did not reach the rim. Either the vessel was purposely filled this way or the merchant or seller compressed its contents. The shallow measure was limited for use in selling oats, malt, and meal by the same Edwardian statute that limited the use of the heaped measure (*see* Appendix II: Edward II, 1325). — **1474** Cov. Leet 396: And viij Buysshelles makith a Quarter, striken with a Rasid stryke, and neyther hepe nor Cantell. **1587** Stat. 77: No maner of graine shall be sold by the heape or Cantell, except it be otes malt and meale. **1603** Henllys 137: In all these bushells, oates and oaten mault is pressed and wrunge downe in the pecke. **1615** Collect. Stat. 464: And that the Toll bee taken by stricke, and not by heape or Cantell.

cantell. CANTEL

canter [*]. A m-c for ale in Bedfordshire (*c*1800) equivalent to a qt (*c*1.15 l) (Second Rep. 13).

caracca, carack, caract, caracte. CARAT

carat — 6 caracte (OED), carette (OED), carret (OED), carrotte (OED), charect (OED); 6–7 carrect (OED), karect (OED); 6–9 caract; 7 L caracca, carack (OED), caratt (OED), carrack (OED), charact (OED), charat (OED), charract (OED), corrat (OED); 7–8 carract (OED), carrat (OED), karat; 7–9 carat [prob < MedL *carratus* < Ar *qīrāt*, bean or pea shell, a weight of 4 grains, a carat]. A wt of 4 gr (0.259 g) for precious stones. — **1678** Du Cange sv caracca: Parvum pondus quatuor granorum, quibus utuntur in ponderandis lapidibus pretiosis, Gallis et Anglis, Carat. **1728** Chambers 1.360: The Moneyers, Jewellers, &c. have a particular Class of Weights for Gold and Precious Stones, viz. Caract, Penny-weight and Grain. **1778** Diderot XXVI.422: Pour peser l'or et pour les pierreries, ils se servent du karat et du grain. **1784** Ency. meth. 404: Le carat se divise en 4 grains.

carat. CHARGE[2]

caratt. CARAT

carcha. CARK

carecta, carectata, carectatum. CHARGE[2]

caretell. CAROTEEL

carette. CARAT

caritas [L *caritas*, charity]. A m-c for wine (*c*1300): Evesham, ¾ gal (*c*2.84 l); Abingdon, 1½ gal (*c*5.67 l); and Worcester, 2 gal (*c*7.56 l) (Prior 155). However, the caritas or "charity" probably originated as an allotment of wine given by an abbot to his monks over a certain period of time rather than as a definite capacity measure.

cark — 4–5 carke (OED), kark (OED), karke (OED); 4–8 cark; ? L carcha (Prior), karre (Prior) [ME *cark, carke*, load, burden, < ONF *carque; see* CHARGE[1]]. A wt for spices of 3 or 4 Cwt (136.077 or 181.436 kg), and a m-c for wool equal to $\frac{1}{30}$ SARPLER (11.340 kg). — **1665** Sheppard 64: A Cark of Wooll is said to be a quantity, whereof 30 make a Sarplar. **1717** Dict. Rus. sv: Cark, a certain Quantity of Wooll, the thirtieth part of a Sarplar. *See* HUNDRED

carke. CARK

carnock — 5–8 carnok; 6–7 cornock; 7 cornook (OED), cornooke; 8 carnock, curnock [*see* CRANNOCK]. Equivalent etymologically to CRANNOCK but metrologically to COOMB. — *c*1600 Ricart 84: So that every sak be tryed and provid to be and holde a carnok, and the ij. sakkes to holde a quarter. **1616** Hopton 12: Whereof are made . . . Cornookes, Coombes, or halfe Quarters. **1682** Hall 30: 1 Last conteynes: 10 Quarters, 20 Cornookes . . . 80 Bushels. **1688** Holme 260: A Cornock is 2 strikes or 4 Bushels. **1708** Chamberlayne 109: 4 Bushels the Comb or Curnock; *ibid* 212: 2 Curnocks make a Quarter, Seam or Raff. **1716** Harris 2. sv measures: Carnock or Coom. **1728** Chambers 1.519: Carnock or Coom. **1778** Diderot XXI.677: Carnok ou Coom.

carnok. CARNOCK

caroteel — 5 caretell; 5–8 caroteel; ? caroteele (OED), caroteelle (OED) [ME *caroteel*, perh < Ar *qirṭāl*, coll of *qirṭālat, qartillat*, ass' burden, basket]. A m-c for cloves, 4 to 5 Cwt (181.436 to 226.795 kg); currants, 5 to 9 Cwt (254.010 to 457.218 kg); mace, approximately 3 Cwt (*c*152.00 kg); nutmegs, 6 to $7\frac{1}{2}$ Cwt (293.928 to 367.410 kg); and oil, $\frac{1}{8}$ TUN (*c*1.19 hl). — **1439** Southampton 2.55: Pro 4 caretell' olei continentibus 1 pipam. **1717** Dict. Rus. sv: Caroteel of Cloves 4 to 5 C. Weight. Currans 5 to 9 C. Mace, about 3 C. Nutmegs 6 to 7 and a half, C. **1721** Bailey sv: Caroteel, a quantity of some Commodities; as of Cloves, [from 4 to 5 Hundred Weight. *See* HUNDRED

caroteele, caroteelle. CAROTEEL

carrack, carract. CARAT

carrat. CARAT; CHARGE[2]

carrata. CHARGE[2]

carrect. CARAT; CHARGE[2]

carrecta. CHARGE²
carrectata. CARUCATE; CHARGE²
carret. CARAT
carretate, carriata. CHARGE²
carrotte. CARAT
carruca, carrucat, carrucata. CARUCATE
cartload [ME *cart, carte* +LOAD]. A m-c which generally did not have standard dimensions, but which referred to an arbitrary amount of goods loaded on a cart. Occasionally equivalent to FOTHER.
caruca. CARUCATE
carucata. CARUCATE; CHARGE²
carucate — 1–7 L carucata; 2–3 L carrucata; 3 L carruca, L caruca; 3–? carucate; 6 carrucat (OED); 7 L carrectata [ME *carucate* < MedL *carucata, carrucata,* plowland, plowgate, < *caruca, carruca,* plow]. Equivalent to HIDE. — **1200** Feet 2.109: De una carrucata terre cum pertinentiis in Thornham. **1201** Cur. Reg. 9.52: j. carucata terre cum pertinentiis in Laleford'. . . . vj carucatas terre cum pertinentiis in Pihtesle. . . . j. carucate terre cum pertinentiis in Serdredesee. **1214** Cur. Reg. 14.283: Robertus filius Maudredi per Robertum de Munceys atornatum suum petit versus Rogerum Pantolf medielatem viij. carrucatarum terre cum pertinenciis in Laweford'. **1220** Cur. Reg. 3.151: Ad quatuordecim bovatas unde xiiij. carucate terre faciunt feodum j. militis. **1222** St. Paul's 135–36: Warinus de Bassingbourne tenet unam carucam terræ continentem ix [×] xx acras terræ arabilis; *ibid* 136: Warinus de Brantone tenet unam carucam continentem vii [×] xx acras cum prato et bosco. *c*1500 Hall 8: viii [×] xx pertice faciunt acram; duodecim acre faciunt bovatam; ii bovate faciunt virgatam; ii virgate faciunt carucatam. **1635** Dalton 71: But a plow-land, or Carve of land, is called in Latine, *Carucata terræ,* that is, *quantum aratrum arare potest in æstivo tempore.* . . . And so this definition or description of *Carucata terræ,* sheweth that it is not of any certaine content. **1678** Du Cange sv carrectata: Carrectata terræ, Modus agri. **1755** Willis 358: Some hold an Hide to contain 4 yard Land, and some an 100, or 120 Acres; some account it to be all one with a Carucate or Plough-Land. **1777** Nicol. and Burn 610: Carucate of land, from *caruca* a plough, signifies as much land as can reasonably be tilled in a year by one plough.

carue — 1–? carue (OED); 7 carve [ONF *carue*, plowland, < L *caruca*, plow]. Equivalent to HIDE. — **1635** Dalton 71: That a Carve, or Hyde of land (or a plow-land) which is all one, is not of any certaine content, but so much as one plow may plow in one yeer; and so in some Countrey [= district] it is more, and some other it is lesse (according to the heavinesse of their soile) . . . . Also a Carve of land (or a Plow-land) may containe house, meadow, pasture, and wood.

carve. CARUE

cas. CASE

cascate. CASKET

case — 4 caas (OED), kase (OED); 4–5 cas; 4–6 cass (OED); 4–9 case; 5 L cassa, kace (OED); 5–6 casse; 6 cais (OED) [ME *case*, *cass* < ONF *casse* < L *capsa*, chest, box, case]. A wt, or occasionally a superficial measure, for many products: Normandy glass, 120 sq ft (11.148 sq m); ordinary glass, generally 1¾ Cwt (88.903 kg) or 196 lb based on the 112 lb Cwt; sinopia, approximately 5 Cwt (*c*254.00 kg); steel, approximately 1 Cwt (*c*50.00 kg); and vermillion, approximately 2½ Cwt (*c*127.00 kg). — **1420** Gras 1.511: xii cases canette. **1439** Southampton 2.34: 1 case saponis albi; *ibid* 55: Pro 1 cassa de sinapio pond. 5 C. sotile; *ibid* 86: 1 case de inde; *ibid* 89: 3 casys de canella; *ibid* 96: Pro 2 casys de vermylon' pond. 500 lb.; *ibid* 97: 5 casys de vermylon' pond. 1,250 lb. **1443** Brokage II.109: Cum iiii cas' suger; *ibid* 251: Cum X casys suger dymyter; *ibid* 269: iii casys triacle kery. **1507** Gras 1.698: Glasse called Normandy the casse. **1509** *Ibid* 570: ii basketts cum iiii cases spectakilles. **1530** *Ibid* 196: Pro sex cases de glasse. *c*1550 Welsh xlvii: Steel, the case (= 1 Cwt.). *c*1590 Hall 27: The casse of glass is a hundrid and ¾ in waight, after 112 to the 100, so that the casse must be, after this ratte, 196 poundes waght haberdepoysse. **1717** Dict. Rus. sv: Case, of Normandy Glass, a quantity consisting of 120 Foot. *See* HUNDRED

cask — 6–7 caske (OED); 6–9 cask [Sp *casco*, potsherd, skull, helmet, cask, < *cascar*, to break, < L *quassare*, to break]. A m-c (*c*1700 and 1800) for almonds, approximately 3 Cwt (*c*152.00 kg); butter, Caithness, 72 to 84 lb (32.658 to 38.101 kg); cider, Gloucestershire, 110 gal (*c*4.16 hl); cloves, mace, and nutmegs, approximately 300 lb (*c*136.00 kg); pilchards, 50 gal (*c*1.89 hl); red herrings, generally 450; sugar, 8 to 11 Cwt (391.904 to 538.868 kg); tobacco, 224 lb

(101.604 kg); and wheat flour, 2 Cwt (101.604 kg) (Dict. Rus. sv and Second Rep. 13).

caske. CASK

casket — 5–9 casket; 6 caskytt (OED); 7 cascate (OED); 9 casquet (OED) [ME *casket,* modif of MF *cassette; see* CASSET]. A m-c smaller than a CHEST, often used for precious gems and other valuable items. — **1467** Eng. Gilds 379: The same quayer to be put in a boxe called a Casket.

caskytt, casquet. CASKET

cass, cassa, casse. CASE

casset [MF *cassette,* dim of ONF *casse,* case]. Equivalent to CASKET. — **1435** Southampton 1.84: Casset . . . suchre candy.

cast [ME vb *casten* < ON *kasta,* prob akin to L *gestare, gerere,* to bear, carry]. A m-c (*c*1800) containing 8 gal (*c*3.03 dkl) (Second Rep. 13).

castrel. COSTREL

cek. SACK

celder, celdra, celdre. CHALDER

ceme. SEAM

cent — 3 cent, cental (Gras 1), cente, centeine, centeyne; 3–7 L centena; 4 It centinaio; 4–6 L centum; 5–9 L C.; 7 L centanarium [L *centum,* hundred]. Equivalent to HUNDRED. — **1228** Gras 1.163: De cent de canevas. *c*1253 Hall 11: La centeine de bord, caneuaz et de lengeteile' est de cent aunes, et checun cent de vi [×] xx. . . . Le last de arang' est de xM., et checun mil est de X Cent, et chescun cent de vi [×] xx. . . . La centeine de cire, sucre, peyuer, cumin, almand, et de alume, si est de xiii peris et di., et checune pere de viii li. . . . La sume de lib. en la centeyne, cent viii li. *c*1272 *Ibid* 10: Item centena zucari, cere, piperis, cimini, amigdalorum, et allume continet tresdecim petras et dimidiam; et quelibet petra continet octo libras. *c*1275 Gras 1.227: i cente de peaus lanes. **1290** Fleta 119: Centena vero canabi, tele . . . consistit ex sexies viginti; *ibid* 119–20: Centena vero ferri ex quinquies viginti peciis; *ibid* 120: Centena autem muluellorum et durorum piscium consistit ex octies viginti piscibus. *c*1303 Gras 1.159: De centum bordis . . . centum ulne de canobo . . . centum minute tele. **1323** *Ibid* 209: De centum pellibus leprorum . . . de una centena cuniculorum. *c*1340 Pegolotti 255: Canovacci vi si vendono a centinaio, d'alle 120 per 1 centinaio. **1443** Brokage II.7: iiii c canvas. *c*1461 Hall 17: Also

stocke fyssche ys sold by vi [×] xx. . . . But the rule of Doggermen
ys to sell vi [×] xx and iiij fysschys for a C. **1474** Cov. Leet 396:
And to *th*is day *th*e C. ys trewe after xx [×] v for the C. . . . xx [×]
v for the C, the wich kepes weyght & mesure 1 li. the halfe C, xxv
li. the quartern. *c*1475 Hall 16: Also fysshis, fowles, and bestes be
sold by numbyr and by dyuers C. **1524** Gras 1.194: Pro uno centum
cole fysch. **1549** *Ibid* 630: Pro centum horse shoes. **1678** Du Cange
sv centanarium: Pondus centum librarum . . . . Centena ceræ,
zuccari, piperis, cumini . . . apud Anglos, continet 13. petras
et dimidiam: et quælibet petra continet 8. libras. Summa ergo
librarum in centena 108; *ibid* sv centena: Ferri, ex 100. petris.
1708 Chamberlayne 205: Cod-fish, Haberdine, Ling, etc. have 124
to the C. . . . Herrings 120 to the C.

**cental, centanarium, cente, centeine, centena, centeyne, centinaio,
      centum.** CENT

ceroon. SERON

cest. CHEST

cester, cestre, cestron. SESTER

chaarge. CHARGE[1]

chaftmonde. SHAFTMENT

chairge. CHARGE[1]

chalder — 2–7 L celdra; 5 L celdre (Gras 1), chaldre, schaldre (Fab.
      Rolls), sheldra (Hatfield); 5–9 chalder; 6 chalderne, chaudder
      (OED), chawlder (OED); 6–9 chaldron; 7 chauder (OED); 8
      chaldern, chaudron; ? celder (Prior), chaldra (Prior), cheldra
      (Prior), childyr (Prior), seldra (Prior) [ME *chalder, chaldre* < MF
      chaldere, kettle, pot, < LL *caldaria*, caldron]. A m-c for coal, coke,
      and grain in England, Wales, and Scotland.
      In England the standard chalder of coal, first regulated in 1421
      under Henry V, contained 32 bu, totaling 1 ton or 2000 lb (907.180
      kg), and was equal to $\frac{1}{20}$ KEEL of 20 tons. In 1676–77 it was in-
      creased to 36 heaped bu, totaling 1 ton of 2240 lb (1016.040 kg) or
      20 Cwt of 112 lb each. However, the chalder of sea coal varied
      from these standards, generally containing 48 bu (*c*21.62 hl) or 12
      sacks of 4 heaped bu each. — *c*1400 Gras 1.214: De qualibet
      chaldre carbonum maris. **1406** trans in Cal. Close 19.159: He shall
      bring to London and nowhere else 70 'chaldres' of coal. **1421** Rot.
      Parl. 4.148: & *vo*tre Custume ent est prise solonc le portage de xx
      Chaldres. **1439** Southampton 2.8: 2 chaldr' carbonum. **1443**

Brokage II.5: Cum i chalder carbonis. **1503** Gras 1.649: Pro vi chaldriis see colys. **1555** York Mer. 155: Item, a chalder of coles to the marchaunts owne use. **1562** *Ibid* 168: A chalder of coles for the merchauntes own house, meanyng so many coles as ye will spend yearlye, iiis. *c***1590** Hall 24: The chalderne of sea cooles is 12 sackes of sea coole, every sacke ought to conteyne 4 bushells watter measurs, the bushell hepid as much as yt will stand, so that the chalderne is 48 bushells in grosse. **1603** Henllys 139: Coles are sold by the barrell [in Wales] . . . and not by the Chaldron as ys used in other partes of this Realme. **1708** Chamberlayne 213: 36 Bushels are a Chaldron of Coals. **1717** Dict. Rus. sv chaldern: Or Chaldron, a dry English Measure consisting of four Quarters or thirty-six Bushels heap'd up according to the seal'd Bushel, kept at Guild Hall, London. **1773** Johnson sv: Chalder, Chaldron, Chaudron . . . A dry English measure of coals, consisting of thirty six bushels heaped up . . . . The chaldron should weigh two thousand pounds. **1784** Ency. meth. 139: Le score de charbon donne à bord du navire, 21 chaldrons; mais il en désigne seulement 20 . . . . Le chaldron de charbon est de 36 bushels.

The Newcastle coal chalder contained 72 heaped bu totaling 53 Cwt or 5936 lb (2692.510 kg) and was equal to $\frac{1}{8}$ keel. This chalder, standardized at the above specifications in 1695, equaled 2 standard English chalders of 36 heaped bu each. Prior to 1695 it had weighed 42 Cwt (2133.684 kg). — *c***1580** Hostmen 5: To w[hich] is answered that for the space of these seven yeres last past, a chalder of Coles Newcastell measure hath not ben raysed in price above two shillings, w[hich] is 16d. in a London Chalder. **1600** *Ibid* 18: And so manye Chaldron and Chaldrons of Sea Cole, Stone Cole, or pytt Cole. **1650** *Ibid* 91: Mr. Ralph Davison, of this Towne, and Free Brother of this Companie, hath sould Eight Chalder of Coles to A man of warr. **1695** *Ibid* 39: And three such wains or six such carts shall be reckoned for one chaldron and no more. **1703** *Ibid* 164: For every chaldron of Coles. **1784** Ency. meth. 138: Le keel, de 8 chaldrons.

The chalder was also used in England (*c*1800) for products other than coal: lime, Cambridgeshire, 40 bu (*c*14.09 hl), Derbyshire, 32 heaped bu (*c*14.41 hl), Surrey and Yorkshire, 32 bu (*c*11.28 hl); grindstones, Durham, 1 to 36 in number depending on their size (Second Rep. 14).

In Scotland the corn chalder contained 16 BOLLS of 4 FIRLOTS each, totaling approximately 12 Winchester SEAMS (c33.62 hl). — **1159** Malcolm 193: Et in molendinis .xx. celdras inter farinam & frumentum. **1298** Falkirk 2: Videlicet pro celdra frumenti ij s. et celdra avene xij d. **1678** Du Cange sv celdra: Mensuræ species apud Scotos.

chaldern, chalderne, chaldra, chaldre, chaldron. CHALDER
chappin. CHOPPIN
char. CHARGE²
charact, charat. CARAT
chardge. CHARGE¹
charect. CARAT
charge¹ — 4 chaarge (OED); 5 charge; 6 chairge (OED), chardge (OED); 7 L chargia [ME *charge* < OF *charge* < *chargier*, to load, < LL *carricare* < L *carrus*, wagon]. A m-c for salt generally weighing 1¼ Cwt (63.502 kg), but occasionally equaling 2¼ Cwt or 9 quarter Cwt (114.304 kg). — **1439** Southampton 2.53: 15 charg' salis. **1678** Du Cange sv chargia: Pondus definitum, statuta mensura. *See* HUNDRED
charge² — 3 L carrata, L carrectata (Gras 1), L carriata (Battle), charge, charre, L charrus; 3–4 L carectatum (Gras 1); 4 L carectata, L carrecta (Swithun), L carucata (Fab. Rolls), It ciarrea; 4–5 L carecta; ? carat (Hewitt), carrat (Prior), carrect (Prior), carretate (Salzman 1), char (trans in Fleta), charret (Prior) [*see* CHARGE¹]. Equivalent to and eventually (c1350) supplanted by FOTHER. — **1249** Close 5.202: Quatuor carratas plumbi. *c*1253 Hall 11: Fet asauer ke la charge de plum est de xxx fotmaux, et checun fotmal est de vi pers, ii lib. meyns; checun pere est de xii lib. *c*1270 Report 1.420: Duodecim pondera faciunt unam carratam majorem. *c*1272 Hall 9: Charrus plumbi debet ponderare et constat ex triginta fotmellis, et quodlibet fotmellum continet [vi] petras, exceptis duabus libris . . . [et] petra constat ex duodecim libris; *ibid* 10: Et tunc est summa petrarum in le Charre octies viginti et octo petre. **1290** Fleta 119: Item charrus plumbi consistit ex xxx. fotmellis et quodlibet fotmellum continet vj. petras minus duabus libris, et quelibet petra ponderat xij. libras. . . . Et magnas charrus ex octies viginti et xv. petris. *c*1300 Hall 8: Summa librarum carecte Londonie: duo milia et centum libras. **1323** Gras 1.209: De i carectata plumbi. *c*1340 Pegolotti 255: Piombo vi si vende a

ciarrea, e ogni ciarrea si è di peso la montanza del peso in somma di 6 sacca peso di lana, di chiovi 52 per 1 sacco e di libbre 7 per 1 chiovo. **1678** Du Cange sv charrus: Mensuræ [vel ponderis] species apud Anglos.

chargia. CHARGE[1]

charract. CARAT

charre, charret, charrus. CHARGE[2]

chast, chaste. CHEST

chaudder, chauder, chaudron, chawlder, cheldra. CHALDER

chest — 1 cest (OED), cyst (OED); 3–5 chiste; 3–6 cheste; 3–9 chest; 4–7 chist (OED); 5 chast (OED), chaste (OED), ciste (Southampton 2); 5–6 chyst (OED) [ME *chest, chist* < OE *cest, cist, cyst* < L *cista* < Gr *kistē*, box, chest]. A m-c which did not have a standard size (*c*1800) for products other than cochineal, $1\frac{1}{2}$ Cwt (76.203 kg), and isinglass, $3\frac{1}{2}$ Cwt (158.756 kg) (Second Rep. 14). — **1443** Brokage II.50: Et iii chestes candell' de cera; *ibid* 111: 1 chiste cum diversis haberdasshe. **1524** Gras 1.196: Pro quinque chests de glasse. *c***1550** Welsh 50: 4 chests sugar; *ibid* 83: 1 chest dry wares. *See* HUNDRED

cheste. CHEST

chide. SHIDE

childyr. CHALDER

chist, chiste. CHEST

chopin, chopine, choppen. CHOPPIN

choppin — 3 schopin (OED); 4 chopyn; 6 choppen (OED), choppyne (OED); 7–8 chopine (OED); 7–9 chopin, choppin; 8 chappin (OED) [ME *chopyn* < MF *chopine*, a liquid measure, < MLG *scōpe, scōpen*, scoop]. A m-c in Scotland containing 2 MUTCHKINS or $\frac{1}{2}$ Scots pt (0.853 l). — **1310** trans in Memorials 78: And they will make no false measures, such as the measures called 'chopyns' and 'gylles'. **1773** Johnson sv chopin: A term used in Scotland for a quart, of wine measure. **1820** Second Rep. 14: Chopin or Choppin . . . Scotland: $\frac{1}{2}$ a pint, 2 mutchkins = $52\frac{1}{2}$ cubic inches, about 2 English pints.

choppyne, chopyn. CHOPPIN

chudreme — 2 chudreme, L cudrinus [*]. A m-c for cheese in Scotland. — **1164** Malcolm 262: Et viginti cudrinis de caseis redditus mei de Sterling. . . . Triginta caseos quorum quilibet facit Chudreme.

chyde. SHIDE
chyfe. SHEAF
chyst. CHEST
ciarrea. CHARGE²
cipha. SIFE
ciste. CHEST
cistern, cistra. SESTER
claue, clava, clave, clavus, claw, clawe, cleaue, cleave, clou, cloue.
CLOVE

clove — 3–4 L clava, L clavus; 3–9 clove; 5 claw, clawe, clou (Southampton l); 5–7 cloue; 6 claue, clave; 7 cleaue, cleave [AF *clou*
(MedL *clavus*) < L *clavus*, a nail]. A wt of 6½, 7, or 8 lb (2.948,
3.175, or 3.629 kg) for cheese, wool, metals, and other agricultural
and nonagricultural goods. It was commonly called a half-stone.
— **1228** Gras 1.157: 1 clove de tasels. **1290** Rot. Parl. 1.47: Unde
clavus ponderat vi li. et demid, et si deficiat dim' li. perdunt
clavum. *c*1300 Hall 40: Et clavi tot sunt quot sunt septimane in
anno. **1304** Gras 1.303: Pro xxxii clavis lane. **1430** Rot. Parl. 4.381:
Que le pois d'une weye de formage, puisse tener xxx & ii cloues;
c'est assavoir, chescun cloue vii li. *c*1461 Hall 13: Also woll is
weyd by this weyght, butt itt is nott rekynnyd soo, for ytt is
bowght odyr by the nayle. . . . vij lb. make a nayle; *ibid* 19: For
thai use to by or sell most comynly odyr by the Clawe, the Nayle
. . . . The clawe amountythe in poundes vii . . . . That ys to say
. . . Claw content' vij. **1540** Recorde 203: In Cheese . . . the verye
weightes of it are Cloues and Weyes: so that a Cloue shoulde
contayne 7 pounde. *c*1590 Hall 23: 7 poundes waight haberdepoyse
is the halfe stonne or clave of woole, or nayle. . . . 7 pounds
daberdepoyse [*sic*] is the claue or nayle of woole. . . . 7 poundes
waight haberdepoise is the clove of cheesse. **1606** *Ibid* 38: A cloue
is 7 pounde. **1616** Hopton 164: And a cleaue is halfe a Stone. **1635**
Dalton 149: A weigh of cheese must containe 32 cloves, and every
clove 8. l. of averdepois weight. **1665** Assize 5: And every Clove to
be seven pounds of Avoirdupois-weight. **1665** Sheppard 61: The
Wey of Cheese must contain 32 cloves, and every Clove 8 pound of
Averdepoys weight. **1678** Du Cange sv clava: Pondus quoddam
apud Anglos, nimus petra. Affine videtur voci Clove, de qua sic
Skinner in Etymol. Anglic.: Clove pondus quoddam casei octo
libris constans. **1682** Hall 31: A cleave half a stone. **1696** Jeake

80: Beef, in 1 Nail, 8 Pounds of common use. **1708** Chamberlayne 207: Wooll is Weigh'd by the clove, which is seven Pounds. . . . In Essex, they Weigh Cheese and Butter by eight Pounds to the Clove. **1710** Harris 1. sv weigh: And each Clove 8 Pound, tho' some say but 7. **1717** Dict. Rus. sv: But in Essex, 8 pounds of Cheese and Butter go to the Clove. *See* NAIL

clue [ME *clewe, clue* < OE *cliewen*, a ball, a globular body; akin to OHG *kliuwa*, a ball]. A m-l (*c*1800) of 4800 yd (43.872 hm) for yarn or hemp (Second Rep. 14).

coard, coarde. CORD

cobyte. CUBIT

coddus [perh L form of OE *codd*, small bag]. A m-c of uncertain size for grain. — **1678** Du Cange sv: Mensura annonaria, Anglis. Vetus Charta tom. 1. Monast. Anglic. pag. 175: De Ecclesia Hamptona 11. denarios, et 2. Coddos bladi.

coeme. COOMB

coffer — 4–6 coffre; 6–9 coffer [ME *coffre* < OF *cofre, coffre* < L *cophinus*, basket, < Gr *kophinos*]. A m-c similar in size and application to a CHEST or trunk. — **1509** Gras 1.571: i coffre cum xx peciis brussel. *c*1550 Welsh 65: 6 coffers drywares; *ibid* 79: 1 coffer containing 35 tin; *ibid* 136: 7 coffers and fforsets of dry wares.

coffin — 4 coffyn (Memorials), L cophinus; 4–9 coffin (OED); 5 cofyn [ME *coffin*, a basket, receptacle, < MF *cofin* < L *cophinus*, basket; *see* COFFER]. A m-c similar in size and application to a CHEST or trunk. — **1303** Gras 1.161: Cophinus racemorum . . . Cophinus sucre. **1439** Southampton 2.74: 1 cofyn de scamanye.

coffre. COFFER

coffyn, cofyn. COFFIN

colbrond [*]. A m-c of uncertain size (*c*1400) for coal in Cheshire (Hewitt 189).

comb, combe. COOMB

comble — 2–7 L cumulata (mensura); 4–9 comble; 5 coumble [MF *comble* < L *cumulus*, heap, summit, crown]. A heaped measure which contained an amount of grain extending above the rim. The actual amount in excess of a level measure depended on the proportions of the vessel, and it was restricted by statute in 1325 (*see* Appendix II) for use only in selling oats, malt, and meal. — *c*1200 Rameseia III.159: Quæ mensura, sexies impleta et rasata, facit unam mensuram cumulatam. **1299** Liber xxv: Mensura cumulata. **1351** Rot. Parl. 2.240: Et soit chescune mesure de blee rasee, sanz comble. **1362** *Ibid* 269: & brees pur les ditz trois Hostelx soient mesurez p*ar* mesure acordant a l'Estandard, rasee & nient comble. **1390** Rot. Parl. 3.281: & oept Busselx pur le Quarter rasez & nient comblez. **1413** Rot. Parl. 4.14: Par force de queux Ordinaunces tiel Mesure ad este use, ove un Bussell du dit Quarter comble. **1415** *Ibid* 81: Q'il ne preigne pur le quarter si noun viii busselx tant soulement, racez & nient comblez. **1444** Rot. Parl. 5.103: Mesurez p*ar* mesure accordant a l'Estandard, rase & nient coumble. **1587** Stat. 77: No maner of graine shall be sold by the heape [comble] or cantell, except it be otes malt and meale. *c***1590** Hall 24: Every sacke ought to conteyne 4 bushells watter measurs, the bushell hepid as much as it will stand. *c***1634** *Ibid* 53: Item, hee further sheweth that the Sackes or Baggs for Lyme ought to conteine a Bushell heapt.

come, coom. COOMB

coomb — 3 L cumba; 5–6 combe (OED); 5–9 comb; 6 coeme, come (OED), koome (OED); 6–7 coome; 6–9 coomb; 7 coombe, coumb (OED); 8 coom; ? cowme (Prior) [ME *combe* < OE *cumb*, vessel, measure; *see* WNID3]. A m-c for grain generally containing 4 bu (*c*1.41 hl) and equal to ½ SEAM. It was commonly called a half-quarter. — **1202** Feet 2.178: Ad quamlibet firmam sexdecim cumbas brasio auene et iiij cumbas et dimidiam de grudo . . . et viginti quatuor cumbas frumenti; *ibid* 180: Sexdecim cumbas de braseo auene. **1573** Tusser 36: Ten sacks whereof euerie one holdeth a coome . . . A Coeme is halfe a quarter. *c***1600** Ricart 84: So that every sak be tryed and provid to be and holde a carnok, and the ij. sakkes to holde a quarter. **1616** Hopton 12: Whereof are made . . . Cornookes, Coombes, or halfe Quarters. **1635** Dalton 144: 4 Bushels maketh the Coombe. **1665** Sheppard 7: Four Bushells make a Coomb; Two Coombs make a Quarter. **1682** Hall 30: 1 Last conteynes: 10 Quarters, 20 Cornookes . . . 80 Bushels. **1688** Holme 260: A Cornock is 2 strikes or 4 Bushels. **1708** Chamberlayne 109: 4 Bushels the Comb or Curnock; *ibid* 212: 2 Curnocks make a Quarter, Seam or Raff. **1716** Harris 2. sv measures: Carnock or Coom. **1717** Dict. Rus. sv: Coomb or Comb . . . four Bushels, or half a Quarter. **1728** Chambers 1.519: Carnock or Coom. **1778** Diderot XXI.677: Carnok ou Coom.

See CARNOCK

coombe, coome. COOMB

coorde. CORD

copa. COPE

cope — 4–6 L copula; 5 cupe; 5–6 L cupa; 6 L copa (Finchale), cope, copule, copynett [ME *cupe, cope,* perh < (assumed) OE *cȳpa,* basket]. A m-c of uncertain size for grain, fish, and other products. — **1303** Gras 1.351: Pro cciiii [×] xx [+] ii copulis i quarteron et di. ficuum et racimorum. **1304** *Ibid* 172: Pro xxi copulis ficorum. **1395** trans in Cal. Close 15.324: 850 . . . (copulas) of figs and raisins. **1402** trans in *ibid* 17.545: 42 . . . (cupas) of hides. **1404** trans in *ibid* 18.264: 309 . . . (copulas) of fruit. *c*1475 Gras 1.193: Of a cupe waad. **1530** Finchale ccccxxiiiv: One cope ficuum . . . One copynett ficuum. *c*1550 Welsh xlvii: Irish cod fish, the copule . . . ling, the copule; *ibid* 58: 30 copules linges . . . 20 copules codfish.

cophinus. COFFIN

copula, copule, copynett. COPE

cord — 4–5 coorde (OED); 4–7 corde (OED); 4–9 cord; 6 coarde (OED); 7–8 coard (OED) [ME *cord* < OF *corde* < L *chorda,* catgut, chord, cord, < Gr *chordē*]. A m-q for wood, originally determined as the amount encompassed by a length of cord or string, equal to a double cube of 4 ft or 128 cu ft (3.624 cu m), but there were local variations (*c*1800): Derbyshire, 128, 155, and 162½ cu ft (3.624, 4.389, and 4.601 cu m), and Sussex, 126 cu ft (3.568 cu m) (Second Rep. 14).

corde. CORD

corf — 5 corffe (OED); 7–9 corfe (OED); 8–9 corf; 9 corve (OED) [ME *corffe* < MDu *corf,* prob < L *corbis,* basket]. A m-c for coal (*c*1800) in Durham that contained 4 bu totaling 3¼ Cwt (165.106 kg) and in Derbyshire, 2¼ bu or 2 Cwt (101.604 kg) (Second Rep. 14). It was a large basket used by miners to carry coal from the underground veins to the surface. *See* HUNDRED

corfe, corffe. CORF

cornock, cornook, cornooke. CARNOCK

corrat. CARAT

corve. CORF

costerell. COSTREL

costrel — 3 costret (error for costrel); 4–5 costrell (OED), costrelle (OED), costril (OED), costrille (OED); 4–9 costrel (OED); 5 costerell (OED), costrele (OED), costrylle (OED); 6 kostorell (OED); 7 castrel (OED) [ME *costrel* < MF *costerel* < *costier*, at the side, < *coste*, rib, side; hence, vessel carried at a man's side]. A m-c for wine that was made of leather, wood, or earthenware. — **1298** trans in Memorials 40: Be it remembered, that Walter of Caile, near Brestolle, came . . . and acknowledged that he was altogether ignorant of the usage of the City; and that he had been attached by the taking of . . . one costret.

costrele, costrell, costrelle, costret, costril, costrille, costrylle. COSTREL

coture. COUTURE

coumb. COOMB

coumble. COMBLE

count [ME *counte* < MF *compte, conte* (F *compte*) < LL *computus*, a computation, < L *computare*, to reckon, compute]. Equivalent to TALE. — **1858** Shuttleworths 792: Tale or Count. By this are counted fish, hides, paper, parchment, sables, &c.

courtceldra [*court*, a var of *quart*, for *quarter* < OF *quartier* < L *quartarius*, a fourth part, < *quartus*, the fourth, +*celdra* CHALDER; hence, a fourth part of a chalder]. Equivalent to SEAM (c1300) (Prior 165).

couture — 4–5 coture, couture [MF *couture* < L *culter*, knife; hence, the blade or spike (coulter) on the plow which cut the roots of old vegetation or weeds during the process of plowing]. Equivalent to FURLONG. — c**1400** Henley 8: Byen sault ke vne coture deyt estre de quarante perches de long. . . . Ore en arrant alet xxx foys entur pur fere le reon plus estreyt e kant le acre ert pararre a donkes estes all lxxij coutures ke sunt vj lywes kar ceo fet asauoyr ke xij cotures sunt vne lywe.

cowme. COOMB

cran [Sc *cran* < Gael *crann*, a lot, a measure]. A m-c for herrings (c1800) equal to approximately 34 wine gal (c1.29 hl) (Second Rep. 14). A standard but bottomless 30 gal herring bbl was heaped full and the bbl then lifted, leaving the herrings in a pile on the ground or floor.

crannacus, crannoc, crannoca. CRANNOCK

crannock — 3–4 L crannocus; 4–9 crannock; 6 creneoke (OED), crenneke, crennock (Shuttleworths), crenoke, crineoke, cryneoke (OED), crynoke, krenneke, krennock (Shuttleworths); 6–7 cranok (Henllys), cranoke; 7 L crannoca; 8 crannoc (Ireland), crannok, cranock (Liber), cronnog (Liber); ? L crannacus (OED), crannoke (Prior), crennoc (Prior) [MedL *crannocus*, of Celt origin; akin to W *crynog*, crannock]. A m-c used principally for grain in England, Wales, Scotland, and Ireland. In Ireland the crannock of wheat varied from 8 pk to 8 bu (*c*0.70 to *c*2.82 hl) and of oats, from 7 to 14 bu (*c*2.47 to *c*4.93 hl), while in Wales the crannock generally contained 10 bu (*c*3.52 hl) although variations from 10 to 12 bu (*c*3.52 to *c*4.23 hl) were not uncommon. — **1228** Close 1.52: Cepit de eadem abbatia c oves et xxviij crannocos frumenti. **1297** trans in Cal. Just. I.178: And took a crannoc[us] of oats. **1315** Ireland xxxv: Quinque crannocos frumenti torelliati, boni, sicci et mundi, de mensura septem bussellorum cumulatorum pro quolibet crannoco. . . . Quinque crannocos avenarum, boni et mundi bladi, quindecim bussellos cumulatos, pro quolibet crannoco. **1319** *Ibid* xxxv: Crannoco [frumenti], videlicet, mensurato per septem bussellos rasos et octavum bussellum cumulatum . . . . Quolibet, videlicet, crannoco [frumenti] continente octo pecks, cumulatos . . . . Quilibet crannocus [avenarum] continebit quindecim pecks cumulatos boni et mundi bladi . . . . Quiquidem crannocus [avenarum] continebit sexdecim pecks cumulatos boni . . . . Crannoco [avenarum] videlicet mensurato per septem bussellos cumulatos. **1322** *Ibid* xxxv: Pro quolibet crannoco avenarum per quatuordecim bussellos cumulatos. **1586** Shuttleworths 558: 2½ krennekes of salt at the North Wyche. **1587** *Ibid:* Two krennekes of salt 22s. **1588** *Ibid:* A crenneke of salt. **1589** *Ibid:* Four crenokes of salt. **1590** *Ibid:* Two crineokes of salt 31s. **1591** *Ibid:* 3½ crynokes of salt 54s. **1603** Henllys 137–38: Neither ys the Cranoke or Wey measures used in the selling thereof. **1678** Du Cange sv crannoca: Mensuræ genus apud Hibernos. **1787** Liber xxv: An Irish-measure, called a Crannok, containing two quarters, is mentioned.

crannocus, crannok, crannoke, cranock, cranok, cranoke, creneoke, crenneke, crennoc, crennock, crenoke, crineoke. CRANNOCK

cronn — 3 L cronnus (Prior); ? cronn (Prior) [*]. A m-c for grain at Worcester (*c*1250) containing 4 bu (*c*1.50 hl) (Prior 165).

cronnog. CRANNOCK

cronnus. CRONN

cryneoke, crynoke. CRANNOCK

cubet, cubete, cubette, cubide. CUBIT

cubit — 1–7 L cubitus; 4 cupet (OED), cupyde (OED); 4–7 cubite

(OED); 4–9 cubit; 5 cobyte (OED), cubete (OED), cubital; 5–6 cubet (OED), cubette (OED), cubyt (OED), cubyte (OED); 7 cubide (OED) [ME *cubite* < L *cubitus*, elbow, cubit]. A m-l, originally the distance from the elbow to the extremity of the middle finger, which was generally taken as 18 inches (4.572 dm), or 6 PALMS or 2 SPANS. — *c*1075 Hall 2: Quarum haec sunt nomina: digitus, uncia, palmus, sextas, pes, cubitus; *ibid* 3: Cubitos in pedes; *ibid* 4: Qualis erat cubitus quo Archa Testamenti, quam Moises iussu Dei fecerat, fuerat mensurata. Alius cubitus, qui et maior dicitur, quo Archa Noe demetita esse dinoscitur, qui brachio extenso toto cubito capiti prelato se esse demonstrat. *c*1100 *Ibid* 5: Cubitus fit ex pede et semis. *c*1300 *Ibid* 7: Pes et dimidius faciunt cubitum usualem. **1395** York Mem. 1.142: Unus pes et dimidius, cubitum usualem. *c*1400 Hall 6: Tres cubiti vel quinque pedes faciunt passum. **1440** Palladius 119: And cubital let make her longitude. **1682** Hall 28: A Cubit is a foote and half. **1688** Bernardi 221: Virga Anglica. 3 Pedes, 12 Palmi, 2 Cubiti. **1708** Chamberlayne 207: 1 Foot and an half makes a Cubit.

cubital, cubite, cubitus, cubyt, cubyte. CUBIT
cudrinus. CHUDREME
cumba. COOMB
cumulatus. COMBLE
cupa, cupe. COPE
cupet, cupyde. CUBIT
curnock. CARNOCK
cut [*]. A m-l for yarn (*c*1800): Northern England, $\frac{1}{12}$ HANK (42.656 m worsted yarn and 63.980 m cotton yarn); Scotland, Clydesdale, 120 threads (274.20 m), each thread $2\frac{1}{2}$ yd in length (Second Rep. 15 and Brockett 89).
cwaer. QUIRE
cyst. CHEST
cyvar [*]. A m-a in Wales (*c*1800): North Wales, Anglesey and Caernarvon, 3240 sq yd (2709.063 sq m); South Wales, in some parts, 2821 sq yd (2358.725 sq m) or 192 LLATH of $11\frac{1}{2}$ sq ft (Second Rep. 15).
cyvelin [*]. A m-l for cloth in North Wales (*c*1800) equal to 9 ft (2.743 m) (Second Rep. 15).

D

dacra, dacre, dacrum, daiker, daker, dakir, dakker, dakrum, dakyr.
DICKER

dale [OE *dāl*, portion, allotment]. A m-c of unknown size used (*c*1400) for salt at Worcester (Prior 166).

daugh [*]. A m-a for land in Scotland (*c*1800) varying in size according to the quality of the soil in any region (Second Rep. 15).

decker, deker. DICKER

desone. DOZEN

dicar, dickar. DICKER

dicker — 3 L dakrum; 3–6 dacre, daker, dakir, diker, dyker; 3–7 L dacrum; 4–5 dakyr (York Mem. 1); 4–7 L dacra; 5 dykur, dykyr; 5–6 dycer, dycker (OED); 6 daiker, deker (OED), dickar (OED), dikar (OED), dikkar (OED), dykker; 6–8 decker; 6–9 dicker; 7 dicar (OED); 8 dakker (OED) [ME forms akin to MLG *dēker*; all < L *decuria*, a division or parcel of ten, < *decem*, ten]. A m-q for a variety of goods: hides, 10; horseshoes, 10 pairs; gloves, 10 pairs; and necklaces, 10 bundles, each bundle containing 10 necklaces. — *c*1243 Select Cases 3.lxxxvi: vj. lesta correi, ij. dakeres minus. *c*1253 Hall 11: Le daker de gaunz est x peyre. Le dakir de fers de chival est de xx fers. *c*1272 *Ibid* 10: Last vero coriorum ex viginti dikeres; et quodlibet diker constat ex decem coriis. . . . Item diker cirothecarum constat ex decem paribus |cirothecarum. **1276** Gras 1.227: ii dakers des quirs. **1290** Fleta 119: Item lastus coreorum consistit ex x. dacris, et quodlibet dakrum ex x. coreis. Dacrum vero cirotecarum ex x. paribus. Dacrum vero ferrorum equorum ex xx. ferris. **1304** Gras 1.170: Pro iiii dacris coriorum. **1305** *Ibid* 304: Pro i lasto i dacro coriorum. **1321** *Ibid* 248: 1 lasta v dacre. **1323** *Ibid* 209: De quolibet lasto coreorum siccorum unde xx dacres faciunt lastum et x corea faciunt 1 dacrem. **1324** *Ibid* 251: i lastam et i dacram et ix coria coriorum. *c*1350 *Ibid* 179: De x et di. dakeris coreorum. **1381** trans in Cal. Close 13.440: 29 dakers of

47

oxhides and cowhides. *c*1400 Gras 1.214: De qualibet dycer corei tannati. **1439** Southampton 2.24: Pro 1 dykur de hud'. **1443** Brokage II.57: 11 dyker' coriis bovinis; *ibid* 170: Cum v dykyr' et ix coriis bovinis. *c*1461 Hall 17: And x hydes make a dyker. *c*1475 Gras 1.192: Of a daker calf' skynns tanned. **1507** *Ibid* 702: Rede hydes containing x hydes to the decker. **1509** *Ibid* 565: vii dyker rasours. **1547** trans in Cal. Pat. 19.399: To export 300 "dykkers" of tanned leather and calf skins. **1548** trans in Cal. Pat. 19.401: Licence to Edward Vaughan . . . to export 200 "dyceres" of leather or tanned leather hides or backs. *c*1590 Hall 23: Every dicker consistith 10 skynns. **1597** Skene 1. sv serplaith: Ten hides makis ane daiker, and twentie daiker makis ane last. **1615** Collect. Stat. 465: And euerie dicker consisteth of ten skins. **1616** Hopton 164: There is also . . . Hides, Dickers, and Lasts. **1678** Du Cange sv dacra: Vel Dacrum, consistit ex 10. coriis. **1708** Chamberlayne 205: Of Hides, 10 are a Dicker; 20 Dickers a Last . . . of Gloves, 10 Pair a Dicker. **1717** Dict. Rus. sv: Dicker of Leather, is ten Hides or Skins . . . of Gloves, ten Pair; of Neck-laces ten Bundles, each Bundle containing ten Neck-laces. **1784** Ency. meth. 139: Le last de petites peaux, est de 10 deckers, ou 200 dites. . . . Le decker de gands, 10 paires, ou 20 dites.

digit — 1–7 L digitus; 6–9 digit (OED) [L *digitus*, finger]. A m-l, originally a unit of body measurement, a finger's breadth, which was equal to $\frac{1}{4}$ PALM, $\frac{1}{12}$ SPAN, $\frac{1}{16}$ ft, $\frac{1}{24}$ CUBIT, $\frac{1}{40}$ STEP, and $\frac{1}{80}$ PACE. Based on the ft of 12 inches, the digit was made equal to $\frac{3}{4}$ inch (1.905 cm). — *c*1075 Hall 2: Quarum haec sunt nomina: digitus, uncia, palmus; *ibid* 3: Palmus autem iiij digitos habet. *c*1400 *Ibid* 5: Digitus rotundus est xvi pars pedis. Uncia est digitus et eius tercia pars; *ibid* 6: Quattuor digiti faciunt palmum.

digitus. DIGIT

dikar, diker, dikkar. DICKER

dish [ME *dish* < OE *disc*, plate, < L *discus*, dish, disc, quoit, < Gr *diskos*, quoit, platter, < *dikein*, to throw]. A m-c for lead ore in Derbyshire (*c*1800) that varied between 14 and 16 pt (1.101 to 1.258 dkl), each pint containing 48 cu inches (Second Rep. 15).

disson, dizzen. DOZEN

dodd — 3 dodd (St. Paul's), L dodda [perh < ME vb *dod*, to beat, to thresh]. A m-c for grain on the St. Paul's Estate containing 1.125

Colchester SEAMS (*c*3.96 dkl). — **1222** St. Paul's 47: Doddas
avenæ; *ibid* trans lxxvi: 24 doddæ equal 27 Colchester quarters.

dodda. DODD

doleum. DOLIUM

dolium — 3–4 L doleum; 3–6 L dolium [L *dolium*, large jar]. Equivalent to TUN. — **1228** Gras 1.157: 1 doleum vini. *c*1270 Report
1.420: Dolium cervisiæ continet ccxl gallones. **1290** Fleta 120:
Doleum vini lii sextaria vini puri continere et quodlibet sextarium
quatuor ialones. **1306** Rot. Parl. 1.207: Quod omnia ligna doleo-
rum vini. *c*1500 Hall 8: In dolio vini sunt ccl lagene.

**doosen, doozen, dosain, dosan, dosand, dosayn, dosayne, dosein,
dosen, dosene, doseyn, doseyne, dosin, dossand, dossein, dossen,
dosseyn, dossin, dosson, dossyn, dosyn, dousaine, dousayne, dousen, douzaine, douzein, douzeine, douzen.** DOZEN

dozen — 2 duzeinne (OED); 3 douzeine, duzeynne; 4 dosain (OED),
dosene (OED), dozyne (OED); 4–5 doseyn, doseyne (OED), dozeyn (OED), dozeyne (OED); 4–6 dosayn (OED), dosayne (OED),
dosein (OED), L duodenum; 4–7 dosen (OED), L duodena; 5
disson (OED), dossyn, dozene (Southampton 1), dusan (OED),
dusane (OED), dussen (OED), duzan (OED), duzsein; 5–6 dosan,
dossen, dosyn; 6 desone (OED), doosen (OED), dosand (OED),
dosin (OED), dossand, dosseyn (OED), dossin (OED), dosson
(OED), dousaine (OED), dousayne (OED), douzaine (OED),
douzein (OED); 6–7 dousen (OED); 6–9 dozen; 7 doozen (OED),
dossein (OED), L dozena, dozzen (OED), L duodecim; 7–8 douzen (OED), L dudena; 8 dizzen (OED); ? duone (Durham), dusein
(Prior), dussein (Prior), dusseine (Prior), duze (Langtoft) [ME
forms < OF *dozaine* < *doze*, twelve, < L *duodecim* < *duo*, two,
+ *decim* < *decem*, ten]. A m-q consisting of 12 of any item. —
*c*1253 Hall 11: La douzeine de gaunz et de parchemine et de suterie
si est de xii peus. . . . La duzeynne de fer est de vi [*sic*] pecis. **1308**
Gras 1.362: Adduxit xxi duodenas arcarum. **1393** *Ibid* 528: Pro xl
duodenis capparum. **1396** *Ibid* 440: X duodenis redelassh'. *c*1400
Ibid 213: De qualibet duodena pellium de jenetts; *ibid* 214: De
qualibet duodena nigri vel albi panni monachalis. **1414** Rot. Parl.
4.52: & de chescun sis Duzseines. **1418** Wills 4: It*em* . . . ii doseyn.
1420 Gras 1.456: Et v dossenis pellium vitulinarum tannatarum.
1439 Southampton 2.2: 5 dosyn caligarum; *ibid* 76: 2 dosyn'

candelebrorum. **1443** Brokage II.15: iiii dosyn ropys oynyns. *c*1475 Hall 13: That is ix dossyn. **1507** Gras 1.695: Bottells the dossen; *ibid* 700: Lether for cousschenes the dossen; *ibid* 701: Olld shettes called packyng shetts the dossen. **1509** *Ibid* 570: ii dossenas napkins; *ibid* 572: Di. dossenam cours cusshens. **1524** *Ibid* 196: Pro un' dosan rolls bokerams. *c*1549 York Mer. 144: Item, paid for vj dossand bread. **1554** Mer. Adven. 96: And for everi two hoolle clothes or doble dossens so shipte or sowlde. *c*1590 Hall 25: The parchement rowle is 5 dossen, conteninge 60 skynns. **1616** Hopton 164: The skins of Goats are numbered by the kippe . . . and Calues by the dozen 12. **1665** Sheppard 57: The Dozen of Iron consisteth but of six [*sic*] Pieces. **1678** Du Cange sv dozena: Duodecim, duodeni . . . . Dudena, pro Duodena.

dozena, dozene, dozeyn, dozeyne, dozyne, dozzen. DOZEN
drachime, drachm, drachme, dragm, dragme. DRAM
dram — 4–8 dragme; 6 drachime (OED); 6–7 drachme, dragm (Hopton); 7–8 drachm; 8–9 dram [ME *dragme* < MF *dragme* < LL *dragma* < L *drachma* < Gr *drachmē*, a handful]. A unit of wt in the ap and avdp systems.

An ap dr contained 3 s (3.888 g) of 20 gr each and was equal to ⅛ ap oz of 480 t gr. — *c*1600 Hall 36: Scrupuli is 20 barley cornes. . . . 3 scrupules contain a drachme. **1688** Bernardi 137: Vel more Pharmacopolarum: Libra de Troy, 12 Unciæ ℥, 96 = 12 × 8 drachmæ ℥. **1708** Chamberlayne 205: The Apothecaries reckon 20 Grains Gr. make a Scruple ℈, 3 Scruples 1 Drachm ℨ, 8 Drachm 1 Ounce ℥. **1716** Harris 2. sv weight: Grains 20. Scruples 3. Drachms 8. Ounce. **1717** Dict. Rus. sv: Dram or Drachm, the just Weight of sixty Grains of Wheat . . . the eighth part of an ounce.

The avdp dr contained 27.344 t gr (1.772 g) and was equal to 1/16 avdp oz of 437½ t gr. However, in many medieval and early modern sources the avdp dr was confused with the ap dr: either the avdp dr to avdp oz ratio of 16 was incorrectly taken as the ap ratio of 8, or the ap conversion factor of 60 for dr to gr was erroneously used instead of the avdp conversion factor of 27.344; sometimes both errors were made together. — **1682** Hall 29: Aver-du-pois conteynes: every pound, 16 ounces; every ounce, 8 drgmes [*sic*]; every dragme, 3 scruples; every scruple, 20 graines. **1688** Bernardi 135: Insuper uncia Avoirdupois pro mercibus caducis explicat 8

drachmas aut 3 × 8 = 24 scripulos Avoirdupois. **1717** Dict. Rus.
sv: Dram or Drachm, the just Weight of sixty Grains of Wheat; in
Avoir-du-pois Weight, the sixteenth part of an ounce. **1790** Jefferson 1.985: The pound is divided into 16 ounces; the ounce into 16
drachms.

draught [ME *draught, draht* < OE *dragan*, to draw]. A wt of 61 lb
(27.669 kg) for wool in Sussex (*c*1850). It was ¼ PACK of wool
weighing 240 lb (108.862 kg), with 1 lb allowed for the turn of the
scale (Cooper 42).

drop [ME *drope* < OE *dropa; see* WNID3]. A wt in the Scots t
system (*c*1890) equaling 29.72 gr (1.926 g), or ¹⁄₁₆ oz of 475½ gr
(Chaney 27).

**dudena, duodecim, duodena, duodenum, duone, dusan, dusane,
dusein, dussein, dusseine, dussen, duzan, duze, duzeinne, duzeynne,
duzsein.** DOZEN

dycer, dycker, dyker, dykker, dykur, dykyr. DICKER

E

el, eline. ELL

ell — 1–7 eln; 2–9 elne; 3–6 ellen; 3–7 L alna, L ulna; 4 ellyn (OED); 5–7 elle; 5–9 ell; 6 el (OED), eline (OED) [ME *ellen, eln, elne* < OE *eln*; akin to L *ulna*, elbow, ell]. A m-l for cloth generally containing 45 inches (1.143 m) or ⁵⁄₄ yd of 36 inches, although ells of 54 inches (1.372 m) in Shropshire, 48 inches (1.219 m) in Jersey, and 37½ English inches (*c*0.95 m) in Scotland were also used. In the twelfth through fourteenth centuries L *ulna* was used ambiguously to indicate both ell and YARD. — *c*1272 Hall 7: Et xij pollices faciunt pedem; et tres pedes faciunt ulnam. **1308** Gras 1.365: Et xxx ulnas panni mixti coloris. *c*1350 Eng. Gilds 352: And *t*hat euerich chaloun ouer *th*re ellen of leng*the* out of a-syse be forfeted. *c*1400 Hall 41: Nota quod tres pedes regii faciunt ulnam Regis. **1439** Southampton 2.6: 60 ulnis panni linii. **1443** Brokage II.245: iiii c dimidio ulnas de canvas. *c*1461 Hall 14: And xii ynchis make a fote; and iij fote make a yard; and the Ynglysh ell go V gr. [quarters] off yard. **1474** Cov. Leet 397: The Elle to be v quarters of the yarde in lengthe. **1502** Arnold 204: Item a Fll [Flemish] ell conteyneth iii q't's of an Eng. yarde, and v. q't's of *the* Fll ell makith an Eng. ell. **1507** Gras 1.696: Canvas called Vytory' canvas the bale containing ii [×] c elles. **1540** Recorde 207: 3 Foote and 9 Ynches, make an Elle. *c*1590 Hall 27: The English ell is 5 quarters of an Englishe yard in lenght, conteninge 45 ynches in lenght. **1616** Hopton 165: Also an English mile is . . . 1408 Elles. **1635** Dalton 150: Three foot and nine inches make an Ell. **1665** Sheppard 16: 3 foot and 9 Inches an Eln. **1678** Du Cange sv alna: Ulna, certæ longitudinis virga, qua telas pannosque metiuntur. **1682** Hall 28: An Elle is a yard and 9 inches. **1688** Bernardi 197: Pes est . . . 1²⁄₄₅ Ulnæ Anglicæ; *ibid* 221: Virga Anglica . . . ⅘ Ulnæ Anglicæ. **1708** Chamberlayne 207: 1 Yard and a Quarter makes an Ell. **1717** Dict. Rus. sv: Ell, a long Measure, consisting of 3 Foot and 9

Inches. **1805** Macpherson I.642: The parliament of Scotland decreed [in 1427], that the elne should contain thirty-seven [*sic*] inches, agreeable to the law of King David I. **1820** Second Rep. 15: Ell . . . Shropshire: of linen cloth, 6 quarters = 54 inches . . . Jersey: 4 feet = 48 inches . . . Scotland: the standard is 37 inches = 37½ English.

elle, ellen, ellyn, eln, elne. ELL

ench, enche. INCH

ende — 5 L *fynes* (for L *finis*, end; Southampton 2); 6 ende [ME *ende* < OE *ende; see* WNID3 sv end]. A wt for iron equal to $\frac{1}{112}$ or $\frac{1}{132}$ ton (9.072 or 7.711 kg). — *c*1500 Southampton 2.120: 112 endes makyth a tunne yryn and yn the kyngys custome they alowe 132 endes to the tun.

enoforium. OENOPHORUM

escheppa, eschippa, eskippa. SKEP

estarium, esteria. STRIKE

estik, estika, estike. STICK

estricha, estricum. STRIKE

F

faat. FATT

factus [*]. A m-c on the St. Paul's Estate containing 17 bu (*c*5.99 hl), or 2 SEAMS of 8½ bu each. — **1283** St. Paul's 164: Per factum bracini.

fad — 7 fawde (Best); 9 fad, faud [*]. A m-q of straw equal to $\frac{1}{12}$ THRAVE. — **1829** Brockett 110: Fad, faud, a bundle of straw, twelve of which make a thrave.

fadam, fadame, faddam, faddom, faddome, fademe. FATHOM

fadge [ME *faige*, perh < (assumed) OF *fais*, bundle]. A m-q for sticks (*c*1800), as a bundle of undesignated size (Brockett 110).

fadim, fadme, fadmen, fadom, fadome, fadowme, fadum, fadym, fædm. FATHOM

fæt, fætt. FATT

fagate, fagatt, faget, fagett, faggat, fagget. FAGGOT

faggot — 4 fagate, faget (OED), fagett (OED); 4–6 faggott; 4–7 fagot; 5 fagatt (OED), fagott (Finchale), ffagott; 5–9 faggot; 6 faggat (OED), fagget (OED) [ME *fagot* < MF *fagot*, prob < OPr *fagot*, perh < VL *facus*, modif of Gr *phakelos*]. A measure for firewood, 3 ft (0.914 m) in length and 24 inches in circumference; and a wt for steel, 120 lb (54.431 kg). — **1350** trans in Memorials 254: Also, — that the cart which brings firewood, [for] talwode, shall take for the hundred, at Crepulgate 6d., and for the hundred of fagates 4d. **1474** Cov. Leet 399: And his ffagott of wodde of an ob. schal-be iij schaftmond and a halfe a-bout and a yerde of lenthe. And his ffagott of j d. schal-be vij schaftmond a-bout, kepyng the same lenght. **1587** Stat. 171: And euerie fagotbed to conteine in length three foot. And the band . . . to be of foure and twentie inches about, besides the knot. *c*1590 Hall 28: Euery faggot, bend or sticke ought to conteyne, in lenght, 3 foott; and the bond of euery such faggott ought to be 24 ynches about, besydes the knott. **1616** Hopton 163: Fagots should be three foot long, and the band beside the knot 24 inches made round. **1635** Dalton 149: Talwood, billet, and fagot. **1665** Assize 18: Item, every Faggot-band to contain in length three foot, and the band of every such Faggot to be 14 [*sic*] inches about besides the knot. **1682** Hall 30: Fagots must be 3 foote long, and the band 24 inches round, besides the knot. **1708** Chamberlayne 207: A Faggot of Steel is 120 Pounds. *See* SHAFTMENT

faggott, fagot, fagott. FAGGOT

fal. FALL

faldom, faldome. FATHOM

fall — 6 fal (Finchale); 7 fall [< vb *fall; see* second citation]. A m-l containing 6 ELLS (6.858 m) and a m-a containing 36 sq ells (47.544 sq m). — **1665** Sheppard 19: 6 Elns long make a Fall, which is the common lineal measure. And six Elns long, and six broad, make a square and superficial Fall of measured Land; *ibid* 19–20: And it is to be understood, That one Rodd, one Raip, one lineal Fall of Measure, is all one; for each one of them containeth six Elns in length. Howbeit, a Rodd is a Staff or Pole of wood; a Raip is made of Towe or Hemp; And so much Land as falleth under the Rodd or Raip at once, is called . . . a Fall of Measure or a linear fall, because it is that measure of the line or length only as the superficial Fall is the measure both of length and breadth.

fan [ME *fan* < OE *fann* < L *vannus*, fan, van for winnowing grain]. A m-c for chaff in Cambridgeshire (*c*1800) containing 3 heaped bu (*c*1.35 hl) (Second Rep. 16).

fardal. FARDEL[1]

fardel[1] — 4–5 L fardellus; 4–6 fardele (OED); 4–7 fardel (OED), ferdel (OED), ferdell (OED), ferdelle (OED); 5 fardille (OED); 5–6 fardell; 6 ferdle (OED); 6–7 farthel (OED), farthell (OED), farthelle (OED); 6–9 fardle (OED); 7 fardal (OED); ? fardelle (Prior), ferdall (Prior) [ME *fardel* < MF *fardel* < OF *fardel* < *farde*, bundle, prob < Ar *fardah*, bundle]. A m-c for cloth and other items assembled as a bale or bundle of no standard dimensions. — **1308** Gras 1.361: Adduxit iiii fardellos canabi. **1324** *Ibid* 386: Pro ii fardellis gladiorum. **1392** *Ibid* 541: Pro xl worsted' in i fardello. **1420** *Ibid* 456: Pro i fardello cum viii vergis panni largi sine grano. **1439** Southampton 2.13: 2 fardell' de napere; *ibid* 42: 2 fardell' pellium coniculorum continentibus 10 C. pelles; *ibid* 68: i fardell' de peletory continente ii mantellis de lebard. **1443** Brokage II.25: Cum ii fardellis canvas; *ibid* 67: i fardello de cerico;

ibid 69: ii fardellis fetherbeddes; *ibid* 134: ii fardellis flokkys; *ibid* 271: ii fardellis pellium. *c*1550 Welsh 52: 16 fardels linen cloth; *ibid* 61: 4 fardels merchandise; *ibid* 67: 6 fardels frise; *ibid* 74: 1 fardel mercery wares; *ibid* 97: 3 fardels grocery, mercery and haberdashe wares. *c*1555 Remembrance 72: For a fardell of canvas from the Watergat into any place above the Newe Corner or into Saynte Mihells paroche: ii d.

fardel[2] — 2 ferdel (Prior); 4 L fardellum, L ferdellum; 6–? fardel (OED); ? fardell (Prior), L ferdella (Prior), L ferdellus (Prior) [ME *ferdel* < *ferde*, fourth, < OE *fēartha*, *fēortha*, fourth, + *del*, part, < OE *dǣl*, part]. A m-a of land equal to 10 statute acres (4.050 ha) or ¼ VIRGATE of 40 acres. Equivalent to and superseded by FARTHINGDALE (*c*1400–1500). — **1338** Langtoft 600: Decem acræ faciunt ferdellum. Quatuor fardella faciunt virgatam unam.

fardele. FARDEL[1]

fardell. FARDEL[1]; FARDEL[2]

fardelle. FARDEL[1]

fardellum. FARDEL[2]

fardellus, fardille. FARDEL[1]

fardingdeal, fardingdeale. FARTHINGDALE

fardingland. FARTHINGLAND

fardle. FARDEL[1]

farlet. FIRLOT

farthel, farthell, farthelle. FARDEL[1]

farthendale, farthendel, farthendele, farthing. FARTHINGDALE

farthingdale — 5 forthingdole (OED); 6 farthendel; 6–7 farthendele; 6–? farthingdale; 7 farthendale, farundel; 7–8 fardingdeal (OED), fardingdeale, farthingdole (OED), farundell; 8 farundale; ? farthing (Gras 2), farundele (Prior), L furchendellus (Prior), L furthendellus (Prior) [ME *ferthing* < OE *fēorthung* < *fēortha*, fourth, +*dale*, part, < OE *dāl*, part, portion]. A m-a for land with two very different dimensions, one fortyfold the other. Because of its general meaning of "a fourth part," it came to be used interchangeably with FARDEL[2] and FERLING and ultimately supplanted them totally in indicating 10 statute acres (4.050 ha) or ¼ VIRGATE of 40 acres. It also was used as the equivalent of a ROOD or ¼ acre of 40 sq perches (0.101 ha). — **1542** Recorde 208: A Rod of lande, which some call a roode, some a yarde lande, and some a farthendele, 4 Farthendels make an Acre. **1600** Hylles 67: A farthendele or roode of lande. **1665** Sheppard 24: And that a Fardingdeale alias

Farundell of Land (*Quadranta terræ,* in Latine) signifieth the fourth part of an Acre. **1678** Du Cange sv roda: Anglis, Quarta pars acræ, quæ et Farding deale, seu Farundel dicitur, juxta Cowellum, ex Anglico Rodd, Pertica. **1682** Hall 29: A Roode or a Farthendale conteynes 10 day workes; that is, one pearch in breadth and 40 in length. **1717** Dict. Rus. sv farding-land: Farundale of Land; is the fourth part of an Acre. *See* FARTHINGLAND

farthingdole. FARTHINGDALE

farthingland — 8 fardingland; ? farthingland (Gras 2), ferthinland (Prior), forland (Prior), L forlandus (Prior) [ME *ferthing* < OE *fēorthung* < *fēortha,* fourth, + *land*]. Equivalent to both dimensions of FARTHINGDALE. — **1717** Dict. Rus. sv farding-land: Farding-land or Farundale of Land; is the fourth part of an Acre.

farundale, farundel, farundele, farundell. FARTHINGDALE

fat, fate. FATT

fatham, fathem. FATHOM

fathom — 1 fædm (OED); 2–4 fedme (OED); 3 fadim (OED), fadum (OED), fathum (OED); 4 fademe (OED); 4–5 fadme (OED); 4–6 fadom; 4–7 fadome; 5 fadmen (OED), fadym (OED), vathym (OED), vetheym (OED), vethym (OED); 5–6 fadam (OED), fadame (OED), fadowme (OED), fathem (OED), fawdom (OED), fawdome (OED); 6 faddam (OED), faldom (OED), faldome (Durham), fatham (OED), fauddme (Dur. House), faudom (OED), feddom (OED), vadome (OED); 6–7 fathome (OED); 7 faddom (OED), faddome (OED), L fathomus; 7–9 fathom; 8 ffatham [ME *fadme* < OE *fædm, fæthm,* fathom, the arms outstretched]. A m-l generally containing 6 ft (1.829 m), but occasionally 7 ft (2.134 m). — **1392** Henry Derby 158: Et pro xx fadom cordez. **1393** *Ibid* 242: Et eidem pro xl fadome corde. **1635** Dalton 150: Seven foot maketh a fadome. **1665** Sheppard 16: 7 foot a fathom. **1682** Hall 28: A Fadome is two yards. **1688** Bernardi 202: Pes Anglicus . . . ⅙ Fathomi. **1704** Mer. Adven. 245: Ffor sorting and laying up every ffatham of lathwood. **1717** Dict. Rus. sv: Fathom, a Measure of six Foot, generally taken for the space comprehended by the utmost stretching of both arms.

fathome, fathomus, fathum. FATHOM

fatt — 1 fæt (OED), fætt (OED); 2–4 fet (OED), vet (OED); 3 feat (OED); 4–6 fat; 4–8 fatt, fatte; 5 faat; 5–7 fate [ME *fat, fatt* < OE *fæt, fætt*]. A m-c for grain generally containing 9 bu (*c*3.17 hl), and

a m-q for other products: bristles, 5 Cwt (254.010 kg); coal, ¼
CHALDER (c3.17 hl); isinglass, 3¼ to 4 Cwt (147.417 to 181.436 kg);
unbound books, 4 bales equal to ½ MAUND; wire, 20 to 25 Cwt
(1016.040 to 1270.050 kg); and yarn, 220 or 221 bundles. — **1413**
Rot. Parl. 4.14: Et auxint les Marchauntz et Citezeins de la Citee de
Loundres usent de prendre de chescun Vendour pur la Quarter de
Furment noef Busselx par une Mesure use deins la dit Cite appelle
le Faat. **1420** Gras 1.459: Pro 1 barello i fat. **1433** Rot. Parl. 4.450:
Achatours des Blees en plusours autres Citees, Villes, Burghs, et
Countees d' Engleterre, continuelment de jour en autre, achatont et
preignont noef Bushels [fatt] pur le quarter. **1509** Gras 1.562: ii
fatts i pipa cum xii grossis papiri. **1555** York Mer. 156: A fat of
eles, foure pence. **1562** *Ibid* 168: A fatte of eles, vi d. **1587** Stat. 244:
And the marchants and citizens of London do use to take of euerie
seller for the quarter of wheate ix. bushels by the measure . . .
called the fate. **1615** Collect. Stat. 466: The Purveyors of Corne for
the kings household haue taken nine bushels for the quarter. . . .
And the Citizens of London also do the like by a measure called the
fate. **1717** Dict. Rus. sv: Fat of Ising-glass, a quantity from three
hundred Weight and a quarter to four hundred Weight: Of unbound books half a Maund or four bales: Of Wire from 20 to 25
C. Weight: Of Yarn, from 220 to 221 Bundles. *See* HUNDRED

fatte. FATT
faud. FAD
fauddme, faudom. FATHOM
fawde. FAD
fawdom, fawdome. FATHOM
fearlot. FIRLOT
feat. FATT
feddom, fedme. FATHOM
feirtlett. FIRLOT
feodum. KNIGHT'S FEE
ferdall. FARDEL[1]
ferdekyn. FIRKIN
ferdel. FARDEL[1]; FARDEL[2]
ferdell. FARDEL[1]
ferdella. FARDEL[2]
ferdelle. FARDEL[1]
ferdellum, ferdellus. FARDEL[2]

ferdkyn. FIRKIN
ferdle. FARDEL[1]
ferken, ferkin. FIRKIN
ferlig. FERLING
ferling — 3 L ferlingus; 3–4 L ferlingata; 3–5 ferling; ? ferlig (Prior), L ferlingatum (Gras 2) [ME *ferling* < OE *fēorthling*, a fourth part]. A m-a of land equal to 10 statute acres (4.050 ha) or $\frac{1}{4}$ VIRGATE of 40 acres. Equivalent to and superseded by FARTHINGDALE (c1400–1500). — **1200** Cur. Reg. 8.257: Alanus de Bocland' petit versus priorem de Plinton iij. ferlingatas terre et dimidiam in Bocl' et dimidiam ferlingatam terre in Hoo ut jus suum. **1214** Cur. Reg. 14.166: j. hide terre et dimidie et j. ferlingi terre cum pertinentiis. **1220** Cur. Reg. 2.226: De placito tercie partis xij. ferlingatarum terre cum pertinentiis. **1227** trans in Cal. Char. 1.17: Four ferlings of land in Kingeston held by Walter. **1262** trans in *ibid* 2.42: And one ferling and a half which Robert de Bosco holds. c1310 Nicholson 81: Decem acræ faciunt ferlingatam; quatuor ferlingatæ faciunt virgatam. **1393** trans in Cal. Close 15.145: And a messuage and one ferling of land in Treuynek co. Cornwall. **1411** trans in *ibid* 20.244: One ferling of land in Denepriour.
ferlingata, ferlingatum, ferlingus. FERLING
ferlong. FURLONG
ferlot. FIRLOT
ferrekyn, ferthekyn. FIRKIN
ferthelett. FIRLOT
ferthinland. FARTHINGLAND
fertleitt, fertlett. FIRLOT
fesse [perh ME *fesse* < MF *fesse, faisse* < L *fascia*, band]. A m-q for hay, originally referring to a cord used to bind hay, smaller than a TRUSS of 56 lb (25.401 kg) but larger than a bottle of 7 lb (3.175 kg). — **1327** trans in Memorials 167: It was agreed that hay belonging to foreigners, coming to the said city [London] by land or by water, should in future not be sold in the same city by *boteles*, but only wholesale by shiploads . . . as also, by cartloads, and *fesses* for horses. *See* BOTTLE[2]
fet. FATT
ffagott. FAGGOT
ffatham. FATHOM
fflaggon, fflagon. FLAGON

ffocher. FOTHER
ffoott. FOOT
ffother. FOTHER
ffotmel. FOTMAL
ffyrkyn. FIRKIN
fhote. FOOT
fidder. FOTHER
finger [ME *finger* < OE *finger; see* WNID3]. A m-l for cloth which originally was a unit of body measurement equal to 2 NAILS or ½ SPAN. Based on the ft of 12 inches, it was generally expressed (*c*1500) as 4½ inches (1.143 dm) (Nicholson 58).
firikin, firken. FIRKIN
firkin — 5 ferdekyn (OED), ferdkyn (Memorials), ferken (OED), ferthekyn; 5–6 firkyn; 6 ferrekyn (OED), ffyrkyn, firken (OED), firkine, firkyne, fyrken (OED), fyrkin (OED), fyrkyn, fyrkyne, fyrkynge; 6–8 ferkin; 6–9 firkin; 7 firking (OED); 9 firikin (OED) [ME *ferdkyn* < (assumed) MDu *veerdelkijn, vierdelkijn*, dim of *veerdel, vierdel*, fourth, fourth part]. A m-c for ale, beer, butter, fish, and soap.

The ale firkin contained 8 gal (*c*3.70 dkl) and was equal to ½ ale KILDERKIN or ¼ ale bbl. — **1517** Hall 49: And viii galons to the ale ffyrkyn. **1587** Stat. 595: And euerie ferkin for ale viij. gallons of the kings standard gallon. **1635** Dalton 148: Ale, the measure thereof, is . . . Firkin, 8. **1665** Assize 9: It was also ordained in Anno 23 Hen. 8 that the Ale-Firkin should hold and contain eight gallons.

The beer firkin contained 9 gal (*c*4.16 dkl) and was equal to ½ beer kilderkin or ¼ beer bbl. — *c***1517** Hall 50: That there shuld' be no lesse assyse for bere than . . . ix galons to the fyrkyn' of the kynges standard'. **1539** Dur. House 338: Of Master Hylton: 1 barell syngyll beyr and 1 fyrkynge doubyll beayre, 4s. 4d. **1587** Stat. 595: And euerie ferkin for beere nine gallons of the kings standard gallon. *c***1590** Hall 22: Beare measures: The firkyn contenyth 9 galons: the kilderkyn . . . 18 gallons: the barill contenith 36 gallons. **1635** Dalton 148: Beere, the measure thereof . . . Firkin, 9. **1665** Assize 9: The Beer-Firkin shall hold and contain nine gallons.

The firkin of butter or soap conformed to the 8 gal capacity (*c*3.70 dkl) of the ale firkin, but equally important was the weight of the cask: generally 6½ lb (2.948 kg) before 1662 and generally

8 lb (3.629 kg) afterward. — *c***1500** Mer. Adven. 56: Anie firkine or firkins of sope. *c***1590** Hall 24: The fyrkyne wayeth of butter, caske and all, 64 poundes haberdepoise, whereof the caske wayeth 6 pounde ½. **1635** Dalton 149: The empty firkin not to weigh above 6 pound and an halfe; and to containe 8 gallons. **1665** Assize 4: And every Sope-Barrel . . . 32 gallons . . . and every Firkin empty shall weigh vi pound and a half . . . and shall hold and contain eight gallons. **1673** Stat. Charles 159: The Firkin . . . ought to weigh Sixty and four pounds, viz. Fifty and Six pounds of good and Merchantable Butter Neat, and the Cask Eight pounds.

The firkin of salmon, and occasionally of eels, contained 10½ gal (*c*3.97 dkl); of herrings and eels, 7½ or 8 gal (*c*2.84 or *c*3.03 dkl); and of most other fish, 8 gal ale-firkin capacity (*c*3.70 dkl). — **1443** Brokage II.98: viii ferthekyns allecii. **1482** Rot. Parl. 6.221: That every . . . half Barell, ordeyned for Samon, shuld conteygne . . . XXI Galons . . . . Also it hath ben used, that every Barell for Elys, shuld hold and conteigne XLII Galons, the half Barell, and Firkyn, after the same rate. *c***1590** Hall 23: The barill [of salmon] is 42 gallons; the kilderkin . . . 21 gallons; the firkyne 10 galons ½. **1717** Dict. Rus. sv: Firkin, a sort of Liquid measure, the fourth part of a Barrel, containing eight Gallons of Ale, Soap, or Herrings . . . and 10½ Gallons of Salmon or Eels.

firkine, firking, firkyn, firkyne. FIRKIN

firlot — 5 ferlot (OED); 6 feirtlett (OED), ferthelett (OED), fertleitt (OED), fertlett (OED), furlet (OED), fyrlot (OED); 6–9 firlot; 7–8 furlot (OED); 8 farlet (OED); 9 fearlot (Hunter) [ME *ferlot* < ON *fjörthi*, fourth, + *hlutr*, *hlotr*, lot, share, part]. A m-c for grain in Scotland.

The Edinburgh firlot was the standard (*c*1800) for wheat, 21¼ Scots pt (3.628 dkl) of 104.2 cu inches each, and the Linlithgow firlot, 31 Scots pt (5.253 dkl), was the standard (*c*1800) for barley, oats, and malt (Second Rep. 16).

In some of the shires (*c*1800), however, both the capacity and the number of pt making up the firlot varied (Second Rep. 16–17). *North* — Caithness: barley, 5 to 7½ per cent above the Linlithgow standard (5.516 to 5.647 dkl). Ross-shire: barley, 32 pt (5.464 dkl). *Northwest* — Inverness: barley, 7 per cent above the Linlithgow standard (5.621 dkl). *East* — Angus: barley, 31¼ to 32½ pt (5.336 to 5.549 dkl); wheat, 22 to 22½ pt (3.756 to 3.842 dkl).

Kincardineshire: barley, 33 pt (5.635 dkl); wheat, 22 pt (3.756 dkl). *Central* — Perthshire: barley, 3 per cent above the Linlithgow standard (5.410 dkl). *West central* — Dumbartonshire: barley, 6½ per cent above the Linlithgow standard (5.594 dkl). *Southeast* — Berwickshire: barley, 5 to 7½ per cent above the Linlithgow standard (5.516 to 5.647 dkl). Roxburghshire: wheat, 22 pt (3.756 dkl). Selkirkshire: wheat, 22⅒ pt (3.773 dkl).

flaccon, flaccone, flaccoun, flackoun, flagan, flaggon. FLAGON

flagon — 5 flagan (OED), flakon (OED); 5–9 flaggon; 6 flaccon (OED), flaccone (OED), flaccoun (OED), flackoun (OED), flagone (OED); 6–9 flagon; 7 fflaggon, fflagon [ME *flakon* < MF *flacon*, drinking vessel, small keg, < LL *flasco, flasconis*, bottle]. A m-c for liquids, generally containing 1 gal (*c*3.78 l). — **1500** Relation 95: Spent, 259 flaggons . . . of which, to the Lord, half a flaggon. *c*1634 Hall 52: Item hee hath found out diuerse kindes of falce Measures made by Turnors and by Crooked Lane men, by Porters and by diuerse others, that is to saie 1. The Winchester Quart measure. 2. The Wine quart measure. 3. The fflaggon, Crooked Lane measure. 4. The Juggs. 5. Black pottes. 6. Woodden Canns. 7. Bottles wherein beere and aile are mixed togeather, which is not only wastfull, but alsoe very unholsome for mens' bodies that drink it. . . . 9. Siluer fflagons, and many other unlawfull measures . . . which . . . are neither marked nor sealled. **1745** Fleetwood 81: I have observ'd before, that Lagena (a Flaggon) holds 4 Quarts . . . . Now an 132 Flaggons must, at that rate make 528 Quarts.

flagone, flakon. FLAGON

flasce. FLASK

flask — 1 flasce (OED), flaxe (OED); 6–7 flaske (OED); 6–9 flask; 7 flasque (OED) [MF *flasque*, powder flask, prob modif of OSp *frasco*, powder flask, flask for liquids; akin to OE *flasce, flaxe*, bottle; *see* WNID3]. A m-c for liquids, generally (*c*1800) containing 3 pt (*c*1.42 l) (Second Rep. 17).

flaske, flasque, flaxe. FLASK

flicce, flicch, flicche, flick, flickke, flik. FLITCH

flitch — 1 flicce (OED); 5 flickke (OED), flykke (OED); 5–6 flicche, flik (OED), flyk (OED), flyke (OED); 6 flicch (OED), flycke (OED); 6–7 flick (OED), flytche (OED); 6–9 flitch [ME *flicche* < OE *flicce;* akin to MLG *vlicke*, flitch]. A m-q for cured hog meat, namely, a side. — **1509** Gras 1.581: Pro xl flicches bakonis. *c***1550** Welsh 31: 2 flitches bacon.

flycke, flyk, flyke, flykke, flytche. FLITCH

focher, fodar, fodder, foder. FOTHER

fodmell. FOTMAL

fodre, fodyr. FOTHER

fontinell. FOTMAL

fooder. FOTHER

foot — 1–7 L pes; 3 fhote (OED), fott (OED); 3–4 fot (OED); 3–6 fote, fut (OED); 3–9 foot; 4–7 fute (OED); 5 fowte (OED), foyte (OED); 5–6 fotte (OED); 5–7 foote; 6 ffoott, fuit (OED); 6–7 foott [ME *fot, foot* < OE *fōt; see* WNID3]. A m-l of 12 inches (0.305 m) or ⅓ yd which originated as a unit of body measurement equal to 4 PALMS. — *c***1100** Hall 6: Quattuor palmi faciunt pedem. *c***1300** *Ibid* 7: 3 palme et 3 grana ordei faciunt pedem. . . . Pes et dimidius faciunt cubitum usualem. **1395** York Mem. 1.142: Notandum quod tria grana ordei sicca et rotunda faciunt pollicem; et xij pollices faciunt pedem. *c***1400** Hall 6: Pes cum duabus terciis faciunt cubitum; *ibid* 7: Et xij pollices faciunt pedem. **1440** Palladius 86: iii foote or iiii in heght. *c***1461** Hall 14: And xii ynchis make a fote. **1474** Cov. Leet 396: Also hitt was ordeyned at the same tyme that iij barley-Cornes take out of the middes of the Ere makith a Inche; and xij Inches makith a foote. *c***1475** Nicholson 77: And xij enchis makyth a foote. **1537** Benese 2: A foote conteyneth .xii. ynches in lengthe. *c***1590** Hall 27: Dymension longitudes of the ynche, ffoott, yard . . . . The foott in length is 12 inches. **1603** Henllys 137: Yet doeth yt agree in the ynche, foote, and yard. **1615** Collect. Stat. 464: xij. ynches make a foot. **1616** Hopton 165: Three barley cornes make an Inch, 12 Inches a foote, 3 foote a yard. **1635** Dalton 150: Twelve inches make a foot. **1647** Digges 1: Twelve inches, a Foote. **1678** Du Cange sv alna: Pes Regius est 12. pollicum. **1682** Hall 28: A Foote is 12 inches. **1688** Bernardi 202: Pes Anglicus . . . 12 Unciæ aut pollices. **1708** Chamberlayne 207: 3 Hand a Foot. **1717** Dict. Rus. sv: Foot, a long Measure of 12 Inches.

foote. FOOT

foother. FOTHER

foott. FOOT

forelang, forelange, forelong, forelonge. FURLONG

forland, forlandus. FARTHINGLAND
forlang, forlange, forlong, forlonge. FURLONG
formel, formell, formella. FOTMAL
forpet. FORPIT
forpit — 8–9 forpet, forpit [for *four part* or *fourth part*]. The fourth
part of a pk. Equivalent to LIPPY. — **1820** Second Rep. 17: Forpet
or Forpit . . . Scotland: the fourth part of a peck, otherwise called
a lippie.
forthingdole. FARTHINGDALE
fot, fote. FOOT
fother — 4 fothir, fozer; 4–6 fothyr (OED), futher (OED), futhir
(OED); 4–9 fother; 5 fothre, fouthre (Southampton 1), fuddyr; 5–6
foder, fodre (OED), fodyr (OED), fouther; 5–7 fudder, fuddir
(OED), fuder (OED), fudyr (OED); 5–9 fodder; 6 fodar (OED),
fowther (OED); 6–7 fidder (OED); 7 fooder (OED), foother; ?
ffocher (Prior), ffother (Prior), focher (Prior) [ME *fother* < OE
fōther, a cartload]. A wt for lead generally of 2100 lb (952.539 kg),
used interchangeably with and eventually (*c*1350) superseding
CHARGE². It was reckoned in four different ways: 30 FOTMALS of
70 lb each (31.751 kg), or 168 STONE of 12.5 lb each (5.670 kg), or
175 stone of 12 lb each (5.443 kg), or 12 WEYS, each wey of 175 lb
(79.378 kg). Occasionally fothers of 1950 lb (884.061 kg), 2000 lb
(907.194 kg), 2184 lb (990.640 kg), 2250 lb (1020.593 kg), and 2340
lb (1061.401 kg) were also used.— **1350** trans in Memorials 265:
Bought one *fozer* of lead. **1391** Henry Derby 59: Pro j fothir. *c*1432
Finchale ccccxxx: Lead £5 6s.8d. per "fothre." **1435** Southampton
1.2: Fouther de plumb. **1443** Brokage II.257: Cum vi fother plumbi
in v waynes. *c*1461 Hall 13: Also lede ys sold by the fudder, xix
c[wt] and dim make a fuddyr, after v [×] xx [+] xii to the C. *c*1475
Gras 1.192: Of a foder lead. **1555** York Mer. 156: A fother of
leade, taken in at the crayne, twelve pence. *c*1580 Hostmen 5: To
pay 12d. for every Fother. *c*1590 Hall 23: The fodder at the King's
Beame 19 hundred [weight] ½, and every 100 is 120 poundes waight,
haberdepoyse, contenith 2280 [*sic*]. **1603** Hostmen 39: Shall for
every foother so ledd and teamed att his Stayth beinge iustlie
proued paye xii d. **1615** Collect. Stat. 464–65: The load of lead doth
consist of 30. formels, and euerie formell containeth 6. stone, except two pound: and euerie stone doth consist of 12 pound. **1616**
Hopton 163: Lead by the pound, hundred, and fodder. **1635**

Dalton 149: Lead, the content of the pound, the stone, and the load. **1665** Assize 5: There is also a load of Lead, which consisteth of thirty Formels, and every Formel containeth six Stone wanting two pounds. **1682** Hall 30: A Fodder conteynes 19 hundred-[weight] and an halfe;˙and 2184 pounds. **1708** Chamberlayne 207: The Tun is Twenty Hundred Weight of every thing but Lead, of which there is but Nineteen Hundred[weight] and an half to the Tun or Fodder. **1717** Dict. Rus. sv fodder: Or Fother of Lead, a Weight containing 8 Pigs, and every Pig 23½ Stone, which is about a Tun or a common Wain or Cart-load: In the Book of Rates, a Fodder of Lead is said to be 2000 pound Weight; at the Mines 'tis 2200 and an half; and among the Plummers at London, 1900 and an half. *See* CARTLOAD; HUNDRED; LOAD; TON

fothir, fothre, fothyr. FOTHER

fotinel, fotinell, fotinellum, fotmæl. FOTMAL

fotmal — 3 L fotinellum (error in manuscript often made), L fotmella, L fotmellum, L fotmellus (Prior); 3–8 fodmell; 3–9 fotmal; 4–7 fotmel; 7 formel, formell, L formella; 8 fotinell; ? ffotmel (Prior), fontinell (Thor. Rogers 1), fotinel (Salzman 1), fotmæl (Thor. Rogers 1), L fotmelus (Prior) [OE *fotmæl*, foot measure; *see* OED]. A wt for lead of 70 lb (31.751 kg) equal to ⅟₃₀ FOTHER of 2100 lb (952.539 kg). — **1230** Close 1.348: Godricus de Novo Castello lator presentium, regi liberavit apud Portesmue vij [×] xx et j fotmella plumbi. *c*1253 Hall 11: Fet asauer ke la charge de plum est de xxx fotmaux, et checun fotmal est de vi pers, ii lib. meyns; checun pere est de xii lib . . . la sume de lib. en le fotmal, lxx lib. *c*1269 Report 1.420: Carrata minor continet xxiv fodmelles, unum fodmell continet LXX libras. *c*1272 Hall 9: Charrus plumbi debet ponderare ex constat ex triginta fotmellis, et quodlibet fotmellum continet [vi] petras, exceptis duabus libris . . . petra constat ex duodecim libris. **1290** Report 1.419: Item charrus plumbi consistit ex triginta fotinellis, et quodlibet fotinellum continet sex petras minus duabus libris. *c*1375 Prior 91: Sex Waxpunde makiet. j. ledpound. xij. ledpunde. j fotmel. **1615** Collect. Stat. 465: The load of lead doth consist of 30. fotmels, and euerie formell containeth 6 stone, except two pound. **1665** Assize 5: There is also a load of Lead, which consisteth of thirty Formels, and every Formel containeth six Stone wanting two pounds. **1678** Du Cange sv formella: Ponderis genus apud Anglos. **1758** Report

1.420: Seventy Pounds make a Fotinell or Fodmell. **1805** Macpherson I.471: 5 stones 10 pounds . . . 1 fotmal.

fotmel, fotmella, fotmellum, fotmellus, fotmelus. FOTMAL

fott, fotte. FOOT

fourlonge. FURLONG

foust. FUST

fouther, fouthre. FOTHER

fowte. FOOT

fowther. FOTHER

foyte. FOOT

fozer. FOTHER

fraell, fraelle, fraellus, fraiel. FRAIL

frail — 4 L fraellus; 4–5 fraell (OED), fraelle (OED), fraiel (OED), frayel (OED); 4–6 frayle; 4–9 frail; 5–6 frale (OED); 6 fraile (OED), frayl; 7 freal (OED) [ME forms < MF *fraiel, freel, frael; see* WNID3]. A m-c for fruit and small manufactured items. It was a basket, made of rushes, that could generally hold between 30 and 75 lb (13.608 to 34.019 kg) of merchandise. — **1304** Gras 1.169: Pro vi fraellis ficorum. **1394** trans in Cal. Close 15.324: They laded in a ship called 'la Petre' of Caen, Peter Robert of Caen master, 850 barrels . . . of figs and raisins, two frails thereof making always a barrel. *c***1550** Welsh 98: 1 frayle spurs . . . 1 frayl horseshoes.

fraile, frale, frayel, frayl, frayle, freal. FRAIL

frundel, frundele. FURENDAL

fudder, fuddir, fuddyr, fuder, fudyr. FOTHER

fuit. FOOT

furchendellus. FARTHINGDALE

furelang, furelange, furelonge. FURLONG

furendal — 7–8 frundel; 8 furendal; ? frundele (Prior) [prob < OE *fēortha*, fourth, + *dāl*, part, portion]. A m-c in northern England generally containing 2 gal (0.881 dkl) and equal to ¼ bu. — **1717** Dict. Rus. sv: Furendal or Frundel of Corn, contains two Gawns or Gallons, i.e. the fourth part of a Bushel.

furlang, furlange, furleng. FURLONG

furlet. FIRLOT

furlong — 1 furlang (OED), furlung (OED); 2 furleng (OED); 3–5 furelang (OED), furelange (OED), furlange (OED); 4 ferlong (OED), fourlonge (OED); 4–5 forelang (OED), forelange (OED),

forlang (OED), forlange (OED), furelonge (OED), furlonge
(OED); 4–6 forelonge (OED), forlong (OED), forlonge (OED);
4–9 furlong; 5 forelong; 7 L furlongus [ME *furlong* < OE *furlang*,
the length of a furrow, <*furh*, furrow, +*lang*, long]. A m-l equal
to $\frac{1}{8}$ mi and generally containing 660 ft (2.012 hm) or 40 PERCHES
of $16\frac{1}{2}$ ft each. — *c*1400 Henley 8: Byen sault ke vne coture deyt
estre de quarante perches de long. *c*1461 Hall 14: And there go viij
forelonges to a myle, in Yngland. **1616** Hopton 165: Also an English mile is 8 Furlong. **1635** Dalton 150: Fortie pole in length
maketh a furlong. **1665** Assize 6: Plinie Lib. 2. Cap. 23. deriveth
Stadium to be a furlong. **1682** Hall 29: A Furlong is 40 pearches in
length. **1688** Bernardi 202: Pes Anglicus . . . $\frac{1}{660}$ Stadii aut
Furlongi, et $\frac{1}{5280}$ Milliaris Anglici. **1708** Chamberlayne 207: 40
Perch make a Furlong. . . . 16 Foot and a half make a Perch. **1717**
Dict. Rus. sv: Furlong, a Measure which in most Places contains
40 Poles or Pearches in length, being the eighth part of a Mile.
1784 Ency. meth. 138–39: La mille d'Angleterre, suivant un édit
du roi Henri VII, est de 8 furlongs, 1760 yards, ou 5280 pieds
(feet) de longueur. **1805** Macpherson II.203: Each furlong containing forty poles or perches, and every pole to contain sixteen
feet and a half in length. *See* COUTURE

furlonge, furlongus. FURLONG
furlot. FIRLOT
furlung. FURLONG
furthendellus. FARTHINGDALE
fust — 5–? fust; 6 foust (OED) [OF *fust*, cask, log, tree trunk, < L
fustis, stick, staff]. A m-c for wine (*c*1450), a cask of unknown size
(Shipley 287).
fut, fute. FOOT
futher, futhir. FOTHER
fynes. ENDE
fyrken, fyrkin, fyrkyn, fyrkyne, fyrkynge. FIRKIN
fyrlot. FIRLOT

G

gad — 4–7 gadd; 4–9 gad; 5–6 gadde; 8–9 gaud (OED), gawd (OED) [ME *gad, gadd* < ON *gaddr*, a string, nail, spike]. A wt for steel of uncertain poundage equal to $\frac{1}{30}$ SHEAF, and a m-l for land varying from 9 to 25 ft (2.743 to 7.620 m) and synonymous with the PERCH. — *c*1461 Hall 17: Also style by gadds; and euery pece of stele in hymselfe is a gadde; and xxx gaddes make a scheff. **1502** Arnold 173: In dyvers odur placis in this lande they mete ground by pollis gaddis and roddis some be of xviij. foote some of xx fote and som xvi fote in length. **1507** Gras 1.703: And xxx gaddes makythe sheffe. **1696** Phillips sv: Gad, or Geometrical Pearch, a Measure of Ten Foot, and in some places but Nine Foot.

gadd, gadde. GAD

gag, gage, gagge. CADE

gait [perh a special use of *gate*, a way, < ME *gate* < ON *gata*, road, path]. A m-c for water in Northamptonshire (*c*1850) containing 2 buckets (*c*2 bu or *c*70 l) (Sternberg 39).

gallandde, gallande, gallante. GALLON

gallon — 3 L ialon, L jalo (Swinfield); 3–4 galun (OED); 3–7 L galo, L galona; 4–5 galoun (OED); 4–7 galon; 5 galone, galown (OED); 5–9 gallon; 6 gallandde, gallande, gallond (OED), gallonde (OED), gallone, gallunde (OED), galne (OED), galond (OED), galonde (OED); 7 gallante (OED); 9 gaun, gawn; ? gullyn (Prior), jalon (Prior) [ME *galon, galun*, a liquid measure, < ONF *galon* < MedL *galeta*, jug, pail, a liquid measure, of obscure origin]. A m-c for many liquid and dry products.

The ale gal, of varying dimensions prior to its standardization at 282 cu inches (4.621 l) under Elizabeth I, contained 4 qt or 8 pt and was equal to $\frac{1}{8}$ ale FIRKIN, $\frac{1}{16}$ ale KILDERKIN, and $\frac{1}{32}$ ale bbl. — **1390** Henry Derby 6: Clerico Buterie super servisia, per manus diuersorum pro v galonibus servisie, x d. **1392** *Ibid* 157: xxiiij galones, galo ad j d. ob., xij s. *c*1517 Hall 49: That nevyr shalbe no lesse than viii pyntes to the galon'. *c*1549 York Mer. 144: Item, paid for xxx gallanddes ayell, x s. **1682** Hall 29: But Ale hath no more than 32 gallons to the barrell. **1789** Hawney 310: That 282 solid Inches is a Gallon of Ale.

The beer gal, also of varying dimensions until it was standardized at 282 cu inches (4.621 l) under Elizabeth I, contained 4 qt or 8 pt and was equal to $\frac{1}{9}$ beer FIRKIN, $\frac{1}{18}$ beer KILDERKIN, and $\frac{1}{36}$ beer bbl. — **1682** Hall 29: 1 Barrell conteynes: 2 Kilderkins, 4 Firkins, 36 Gallons, 72 Pottles, 144 Quarts, 288 Pints. **1708** Chamberlayne 210: 2 Pottles make a Gallon, a Gallon of Beer, or the Measure containing 282 Solid Inches, and holds of Rain Water 10 Pounds, 3 Ounces $^{240}\!/_{1000}$ Avoirdupois.

The corn or grain gal was standardized at 268.8 cu inches (4.404 l) under Elizabeth I. Although it usually contained 4 qt or 8 pt and equaled $\frac{1}{2}$ pk, $\frac{1}{8}$ bu, or $\frac{1}{64}$ SEAM, its actual capacity varied from approximately $272\frac{1}{4}$ to 282 cu inches (*c*4.46 to *c*4.62 l) before its standardization. — *c*1272 Report 1.414: Et octo libre frumenti faciunt galonem. **1290** Fleta 119: Et pondus octo librarum frumenti faciunt mensuram ialonis. **1351** Rot. Parl. 2.240: Soient les Mesures, c'est assaver bussell . . . galon. *c*1400 Hall 36: 8 libre faciunt I galon', 61,440 grana. **1413** Rot. Parl. 4.14: & qe chescun Bussell contiendra oept Galons. **1474** Cov. Leet 396: & ij Pottels makith a Gallon; & viij Gallons makith a Buysshell. **1540** Recorde 204: 8 pounde (or 8 pyntes) doe make a Gallon. **1587** Stat. 454: And that euerie galon conteine viii. li. of wheate of troie weight. *c*1590 Hall 20: 2 galons makith a pecke . . . . So that 8 gallons . . . makith the bushell. **1615** Collect. Stat. 468: And euery gallon contain eight pounds of wheat, of Troy weight. **1635** Dalton 144: 8 pintes/4 quarts/2 pottles maketh the gallon. **1665** Assize 3: The full and just weight of xii. ounces Troy in Wheat do make a concave or hollow measure, named a pint; and viii. of the same pints do make the gallon for . . . Corn. **1688** Bernardi 150: Præterea Galonem Frumentarium Angliæ, dimidium Pecci et Octantem Busselli . . . . Aediles autem et moderatores fori eundem Galonem siccum unciis pedis Anglici $272\frac{1}{4}$ in. solidum construunt. . . . Pinta denique arida, $\frac{1}{8}$ Galonis, seu congii frumentarii et $\frac{1}{8} \times 8 = \frac{1}{64}$ Brusselli. **1717** Dict. Rus. sv dry measure: To measure dry things, as Corn, or Grain, we have first the Gallon, which is bigger than the Wine-Gallon, and less than the Ale or Beer-

Gallon; containing 272 and a quarter cubick Inches, and 9 Pounds, 13 Ounces, 12 Drams and a half of Avoirdupois-Weight. **1789** Hawney 310: 268.8 solid Inches is a Gallon . . . of Corn-measure. **1805** Macpherson I.471: 8 pounds of corn 1 gallon, 8 gallons 1 bushel of London.

The wine gal was standardized in 1707 at 231 cu inches (3.785 l). Although usually containing 4 qt or 8 pt and equaling $\frac{1}{18}$ RUND-LET, $\frac{1}{42}$ TIERCE, $\frac{1}{63}$ HOGSHEAD, $\frac{1}{84}$ PUNCHEON, $\frac{1}{126}$ PIPE, or $\frac{1}{252}$ TUN, its actual capacity varied prior to 1707, with 282 cu inches (4.621 l) and 224 cu inches (3.671 l) being the most common. The oil and honey gal conformed to the specifications of the wine gal, as did those for beef, fish, and pork. — *c***1200** Caernarvon 242: Et octo libræ frumenti faciunt galonem Vini. *c***1300** Hall 8: Et viii libre ponderant unam galonem vini. *c***1461** *Ibid* 7: Et viii livres de froument font la galone de vin; *ibid* 12: And xii unces make a lb. of Troy: and of all thys weyghts viij lb. make a galon of wyne. *c***1549** York Mer. 144: Item, for x gallandes wyne, xiij s. iiij d. *c***1590** Hall 22: 8 pound troy is a gallone in waighte, or 4 quartes. **1665** Sheppard 7: Of liquor, 12 ounces make a pound; 8. pound make a Gallon of Wine. **1678** Du Cange sv galo: Galona, Mensura liquidorum apud Anglos, quarum unaquæque octo continet pintas Anglicanas. **1688** Bernardi 149: Quinetiam Galonem vinarium in pedis Anglici corporeas uncias 231. **1707** Seventh Rep. 36: That any round vessel, commonly called a cylinder, having an even bottom and being 7 inches diameter throughout, and 6 inches deep from the top of the inside to the bottom, or any vessel containing 231 cubical inches and no more, shall be deemed and taken to be a lawful wine gallon. **1708** Chamberlayne 210: So that 4 Gallons of Beer Measure are almost 5 Gallons of Wine . . . and each Gallon of Wine is 231 Cubical Inches, 8 Pound, 1 Ounce, and 11 Drachms Avoirdupois of Rain-Water. **1710** Harris 1. sv measures: The Beer and Ale Gallon is larger than the Wine Gallon, in proportion to the excess of the common Pound Averdupois above the true Pound Troy; that is, as 12 · 231 :: so $141\frac{2}{20}$ to $281\frac{1}{2}$, which is very near the Cubick Inches in the Ale Gallon. **1717** Dict. Rus. sv winemeasure: The English Wine-Measures are smaller than those of Ale and Beer, and hold proportion as about 4 to 5 . . . and each Gallon of Wine is 231 cubical Inches.

Locally, the butter gal weighed 12 lb (5.443 kg) at Shropshire and in Wales and 16 lb (7.257 kg) at Bridgenorth. — **1820** Second Rep. 18: Gaun or Gawn. Shropshire and Wales: a corruption of gallon, applied to butter containing 12 lbs . . . Bridgnorth: of butter, 16 lbs.

gallond, gallonde, gallone, gallunde, galne, galo, galon, galona, galond, galonde, galone, galoun, galown, galun. GALLON

garb — 3 L garba; 3–7 garbe; 6–9 garb [ONF *garbe* (OF *jarbe*), of Gmc origin; *see* OED]. A wt for 30 pieces of steel. It was of uncertain poundage and perhaps was synonymous with the GAD. — *c*1253 Hall 11: La garbe de ascer est xxx pecis. *c*1272 Report 1.414: Garba afferis constat ex triginta peciis. **1820** Second Rep. 18: Garb . . . of steel, 30 pieces. 31 Ed.1.

garba, garbe. GARB

gaud. GAD

gaun. GALLON

gawd. GAD

gawn. GALLON

gill — 4 gille (OED), jille (OED); 4–5 gylle; 6 gyll (OED); 7–9 gill; 9 jill (Dinsdale) [ME *gille*, perh < MF *gille, gelle*, vat, tub; *see* WNID3]. A m-c for liquids generally equal to $\frac{1}{4}$ pt (*c*0.12 1) or $\frac{1}{32}$ gal. In some of the shires, however, it equaled $\frac{1}{2}$ pt (*c*0.24 l) and the measure of $\frac{1}{4}$ pt was called a jack. — **1310** trans in Memorials 78: Such as the measures called "chopyns" and "gylles." **1790** Jefferson 1.982: The gill, four of which make a pint.

gille. GILL

glanet [*]. A wt for 30 pieces of steel (*c*1350). It was of uncertain poundage and perhaps was synonymous with the GAD (Hewitt 190).

glean — 8–9 glen; 9 glean, glene [MF *glene, glane; see* WNID3 vb glean]. A m-q comprising 25 herrings and equal to $\frac{1}{15}$ REES. In Essex and Gloucestershire it was a m-q for teasels, consisting of one bunch. — **1805** Macpherson I.471: 25 herrings 1 glen, 15 glens 1 rees. **1820** Second Rep. 18: Glean, Glen, Glene of teazles, Essex and Gloucestershire; a bunch.

glen, glene. GLEAN

goad — 4–6 gode (OED); 5 goode (OED); 6 goade (OED); 7 goad [ME *gode* < OE *gād*, goad, arrowhead, spear point]. A m-l for cloth, containing $4\frac{1}{2}$ ft (1.371 m). Occasionally it was a m-l for land synonymous with the PERCH. — **1696** Jeake 65: In I Goad . . . $4\frac{1}{2}$ Feet, a Measure in some places for Land and Cloth received by Custom.

goade, gode. GOAD
goney. GUNNY
goode. GOAD
grain — 3–6 greyn (OED), greyne (OED); 3–7 L grana, L granum; 4 grein (OED), greine (OED); 4–7 grayn (OED), grayne; 5 grane (OED); 5–9 grain; 6 grene (OED); 6–7 graine [ME *grain, grein* < MF *grain,* grain, kernel, seed, < L *granum,* grain, seed]. The smallest unit of wt (*c*0.06 g), equal to $\frac{2}{875}$ avdp oz, $\frac{1}{450}$ merc and tow oz, $\frac{2}{951}$ Scots t oz, and $\frac{1}{480}$ ap and English t oz. It was also used as the basis for the standardization of the inch, which was defined as the length of 3 medium-sized barleycorns placed end to end (*c*2.54 cm). — *c*1200 Caernarvon 242: xxx . . . & duo g[ra]na frumenti in medio spici. *c*1272 Hall 7: Sciendum quod tria grana ordei, sicca et rotunda, faciunt pollicem. **1290** Fleta 119: Sterlingus . . . qui debet ponderare xxxij. grana frumenti medio-cra. *c*1461 Hall 14: The lengythe of iii barly cornys make an ynche, so that barly growe in comyn soyle, not to lene, nodyr to muche compost abowte. **1474** Cov. Leet 396: *th*at xxxij graynes of whete take out of the mydens of the Ere makith a sterling o*th*er-wyse called a peny. . . . And hitt was ordeyned . . . that iij barley-Cornes take out of the middes of the Ere makith a Inche. **1540** Recorde 202: After the statutes of Englande, the least portion of waight is commonly a Grayne, meaning a grayne of corne or wheate, drie, and gathered out of the middle of the eare. *c*1600 Hall 36: Grana . . . a grain is a barley corne taken in the midst of the eare. **1616** Hopton 159: And this Troy weight containes in euery pound 12 ounces, euery ounce 20 peny weight, euery peny weight 24 graines. **1635** Dalton 150: Three barley cornes measured from end to end (or 4 in thicknesse) maketh one inch. **1678** Du Cange sv granum: Grana, Angl. Grain. **1688** Bernardi 135: Uncia Anglica de Troy . . . 480 grana argenti triticive. **1708** Chamber-layne 205: In Troy-Weight, 24 Grains of Wheat make a Penny-Weight Sterling. **1717** Dict. Rus. sv troy-weight: The smallest Denomination is a Grain, which is the Weight of a Grain of Wheat, gathered out of the middle of the Ear well dryed. *See* BARLEYCORN
graine, grana, grane, granum, grayn, grayne, grein, greine, grene, greyn, greyne. GRAIN
groce, groos, gros, grose. GROSS
gross — 5 groos (OED); 5–7 groce (OED); 5–9 grose; 6 gros (OED); 6–7 grosse; 6–9 gross [ME *groos, groce* < MF *grosse* < fem of

gros, thick, coarse]. A m-q of any item, generally consisting of 12 dozen or 144 in number. — *c*1461 Hall 17: Also there ys a Numbyr that ys called a Grose, and itt cont[aineth] xij doss[en]; and thereby be sold poynyes, laces, purces, knyvys, balles, strenges and odyr dyuers thynges mo. **1507** Gras 1.696: Coper gowle the grose; *ibid* 698: Gyrdelles of thred the grosse; *ibid* 703: Sporres the grosse. **1524** *Ibid* 194: Pro un' grosse knythose; *ibid* 196: Pro iiii grosse de cards . . . Pro sex grosse de combes. *c*1550 Welsh 64: 1 gross girth web. **1717** Dict. Rus. sv: A Gross, is the quantity of Twelve Dozen.

grosse. GROSS

gullyn. GALLON

gunny — 8 goney (OED); 8–9 gunny [Hind *goṇī* < Skr *goṇī*]. A m-c (*c*1800) for saltpeter, ¼ Cwt (12.700 kg), and cinnamon, ¾ Cwt (36.741 kg), contained in a sack (Second Rep. 18). *See* HUNDRED

gwaith [*]. A m-a for peat in North Wales (*c*1800), containing 150 sq ft (13.935 sq m) (Second Rep. 18).

gwyde [perh < W *gwyniad*, a white-fleshed fish, < *gwyn*, white]. A m-q for eels containing 10 STICKS or 250 in number. — *c*1461 Hall 17: Also Elys be sold by the stike, that ys xxv elys; and x styckys make a gwyde.

gybe [perh < E dial *gib*, a hooked stick]. A m-c for wool (*c*1430) containing 2 POKES or bundles (Southampton 1.88).

gyll, gylle. GILL

H

habardepayce, habardepayse, habardepayx, habardepoix, habardypeyse, haberdepase, haberdepayes, haberdepoies, haberdepois, haberdepoysse, habertypoie, haburdepeyse, haburdypoyse. AVOIRDUPOIS

hakere. ACRE

half-barrel. KILDERKIN

half-coomb. STRIKE

half-quarter. COOMB

half-quartern. STONE

half-stone. CLOVE

hamper — 4–5 hampere (OED); 6 hampier (OED); 6–9 hamper; 7 hampire (OED) [ME *hampere*, alter of *hanaper* < MF *hanapier*, a case to hold hanaps, < *hanap*, a drinking vessel, + -*ier*]. A m-c for dry goods. It was a large basket of wickerwork, usually with a cover, used as a packing case. — c1550 Welsh 172: 1 hamper 6 bags dry wares; *ibid* 264: 1 trunk and 1 hamper household stuff; *ibid* 282: 2 trunks 4 hampers felts.

hampere, hampier, hampire. HAMPER

hanc, hanck, hancke. HANK

hand — 1–5 hond (OED); 1–9 hand; 4 haunde (OED), hoond (OED), hoonde (OED); 4–6 honde (OED); 4–7 hande; 7–8 handful [ME *hand* < OE *hand, hond; see* WNID3]. A m-l, originally a unit of body measurement, made equal to 4 inches (10.16 cm). — 1561 Eden xviii: Foure graines of barlye make a fynger: foure fingers a hande: foure handes a foote. 1635 Dalton 150: Foure Inches maketh an handful. 1665 Sheppard 16: 4 inches a handful. 1708 Chamberlayne 207: 4 Inches make a Hand. 1717 Dict. Rus. sv handful: A Measure of four Inches. 1728 Chambers 1.520: The Measure for Horses, is the Hand or Handful; which, by the Statute, contains four Inches.

hande, handful. HAND

hank — 4–9 hank; 6 hanc (OED); 6–7 hanke (OED); 7–9 hanck (OED), hancke (OED) [ME *hank*, of Scand origin; cf Dan *hank*, handle, Sw *hank*, a band or tie, ON *hanki*, clasp, *hönk*, *hangr*, hank, coil, skein]. A m-q for yarn (*c*1800) containing 12 cuts or 560 yd (5.121 hm) for worsted and 840 yd (7.681 hm) for cotton (Brockett 89).

hanke. HANK

haunde. HAND

haverdupois. AVOIRDUPOIS

heap [ME *heep*, *hepe*, heap, multitude, < OE *hēap*]. A m-q for limestone in some parts of Scotland (*c*1800) containing 4¼ cu yd (3.249 cu m) and weighing 5 tons (Second Rep. 20).

hīd, hida. HIDE

hide — 1 hīd (OED); 1–9 hyde; 1–? hide; 2–7 L hida; 3–7 L hyda [ME *hide*, *hyde* < OE *hīd*, *hīgid*, originally land enough to support a family, < stem of *hīwan*, *hīgan*, members of a household]. A m-a which probably originated as an amount of land needed to support a peasant family for a period of one year and, at the same time, as a unit for tax assessments. But, beginning in the eleventh century, the hide was usually expressed in terms of acres, with 60 (*c*24.30 ha), 64 (*c*25.92 ha), 80 (*c*32.40 ha), 100 (*c*40.50 ha), 120 (*c*48.60 ha), 140 (*c*56.70 ha), 160 (*c*64.80 ha), and 180 (*c*72.90 ha) acres being the most common. Seldom was it larger than 180 acres. In addition, it was occasionally expressed as a division of land containing a certain number of VIRGATES, most often as one of the following: a hide of 2 virgates, each virgate containing 2 BOVATES of 12 acres each, and thus 48 acres (*c*19.44 ha) in all; a hide of 3 virgates, no standard acreage established for the virgate; a hide of 4 virgates, each virgate generally containing 15 (*c*6.07 ha), 20 (*c*8.10 ha), 24 (*c*9.72 ha), 30 (*c*12.15 ha), or 40 acres (*c*16.20 ha); a hide of 4 virgates, each virgate containing 4 FARTHINGDALES of 10 acres each, and thus 160 acres (*c*64.80 ha) in all; and hides of 5, 6, 7, and 8 virgates, no standard acreage established for the virgate. — *c*1100 Bello 11: Octo itaque virgatæ unam hidam faciunt. **1200** Cur. Reg. 8.145: De duabus hidis et dimidia in Pepewell' et in Waresle . . . . j. hide terre cum pertinenciis in Leghe. **1201** Cur. Reg. 9.53: Unde xxvij. hide faciunt feodum j. militis. **1204** Cur. Reg. 10.209: Jordanus filius Avicie petit versus Rogerum filium Berte j. hidam terre et xxviij. acras cum pertinentiis in Crikeshee sicut jus suum et hereditatem. **1220** Cur. Reg. 3.151: De viginti et una hidis terre cum pertinentiis . . . . Ad quatuordecim bovatas unde xiiij. carucate terre faciunt feodum j. militis. **1222** St. Paul's 135–36: Warinus de Bassingbourne tenet unam carucam terræ continentem ix [✕] xx acras terræ arabilis; *ibid* 136: Warinus de Brantone tenet unam carucam continentem vii [✕] xx acras cum prato et bosco. *c***1250** Rameseia III.208: In Comitatu Huntingdoniæ. Upwode, cum Ravele . . . Viginti acræ faciunt virgatam. Quatuor virgatæ faciunt hidam. Wistowe . . . Triginta acræ faciunt virgatam. Quatuor virgatæ faciunt hidam. . . . Haliwelle . . . Octodecim acræ faciunt virgatam. Et quinque virgatæ faciunt hidam. Soca de Slepe . . . Sexdecim acræ faciunt virgatam. Et quinque virgatæ faciunt hidam. Hougtone, cum Wittone . . . Octodecim acræ faciunt virgatam. Sex virgatæ [faciunt] hidam. In Wittone. Viginti acræ [faciunt] virgatam. Quinque virgatæ [faciunt] hidam; *ibid* 209: Hemmingforde . . . Sexdecim acræ faciunt virgatam. Et sex virgatæ [faciunt] hidam. Dillingtone . . . Triginta et tres acræ et dimidia faciunt virgatam. Sex virgatæ faciunt hidam. Westone . . . Viginti et octo acræ faciunt virgatam. Et quatuor virgatæ faciunt hidam. Bringtone . . . Triginta et quatuor acræ faciunt virgatam. Et quatuor virgatæ faciunt hidam. Bitherne . . . Quadraginta et quatuor acræ faciunt virgatam. Et quatuor virgatæ faciunt hidam; *ibid* 210: Elingtone . . . Viginti et quatuor acræ faciunt virgatam. Sex virgatæ faciunt hidam. . . . Stiveclee . . . Viginti et quatuor acræ faciunt virgatam. Et quatuor virgatæ faciunt hidam; *ibid* 211: Bernewelle . . . Triginta et sex acræ faciunt virgatam. Septem virgatæ faciunt hidam. . . . Cranfelde . . . Quadraginta et octo acræ faciunt virgatam. Quatuor virgatæ faciunt hidam; *ibid* 212: Shittlingdone cum Pekesdene . . . Duodecim acræ faciunt virgatam. Quatuor virgatæ faciunt hidam; *ibid* 213: In comitatu Hertfordiæ. Therfelde . . . Sexaginta et quatuor acræ faciunt virgatam. Et quatuor virgatæ faciunt hidam. In comitatu Suff[olciæ]. Laushulle . . . Quinquaginta acræ faciunt virgatam. Tres virgatæ [faciunt] hidam. In comitatu Norff[olciæ]. Brauncestre . . . Quadraginta acræ faciunt virgatam. Quatuor virgatæ [faciunt] hidam; *ibid* 214: In comitatu Cantebr[igiæ]. Ellesworthe . . . Triginta acræ faciunt virgatam. Quatuor virgatæ [faciunt] hidam. *c***1283** Battle xiii: Quatuor virgatæ seu wystæ faciunt unam hydam. *c***1289** Bray 9–10: Memorandum quod in campis de Herleston sunt viginti septimae virgatae terrae per hidam, quarum de ffeodo domini regis quatuor virgatae et dimidia, de ffeodo de Berkhamsted duae virgatae, de ffeodo de Doddesforde decem virgatae, de ffeodo de Neubotle decem virgatae et dimidia. **1338** Langtoft 600–01: Decem acræ faciunt ferdellum. Quatuor fardella faciunt virgatam unam. Quatuor virgatæ faciunt hidam unam; *ibid* 601: Fardellum Acræ X / virgata XL. / hida. CLX. **1635** Dalton 71: An Hyde of land doth containe . . . 480 acres; *ibid* 150: One hundred acres is an hide of land. **1665** Sheppard 22: And again, some say, Eight Hides are 800 Acres. **1678** Du Cange sv hida: Hida, et Hyda, ex Saxon. hyd, Terræ portio, quantum sufficit ad arandum uni aratro per annum. **1708** Chamberlayne 208: An Hundred Acres are accounted an Hide of Land. **1755** Willis 358: Some hold an Hide to contain 4 yard Land, and some an 100, or 120 Acres; some account it to be all one with a Carucate or Plough-Land. *See* CARUCATE; CARUE; PLOWLAND

hlæst. LAST

hobaid. HOBED

hobed — 8–9 hobaid, hobed [perh akin to E dial *hobbet, hobbit*, a measure of 2 or more bu]. A m-c in South Wales for lime, 4 pedwran of 5 or 6 qt each (*c*2.20 to *c*2.64 dkl), and in North Wales for lime, 2 STOREDS or 4 bu (*c*1.41 hl), and for wheat, approximately 173 lb (78.471 kg). — **1820** Second Rep. 19: Hobaid or Hobed of lime: S. Wales, 4 pedwran, or quarters, of 5 or 6 quarts each . . . Anglesia and Caernarvonshire: 2 storeds = 4 bushels; *ibid* 31: N. Wales: of wheat, 1½ hobaid, to weigh 260 lb.

hogeshed, hogesheved, hoggeshead, hoggeshed, hoggeshedde, hoggeshede, hoggesheed, hoggesyde, hoggishede, hoggisheed, hoggyshead, hoggyshed, hoggyshede. HOGSHEAD

hogshead — 4 hoogeshed; 4–6 hoggeshed; 5 hogesheved (Finchale), hoggeshede, hoggesyde (OED), hoggishede (OED), hoggyshead, hoggyshed, hoggyshede, hogyshede; 5–6 hogyshed; 6 hogeshed, hoggeshedde, hoggesheed (OED), hoggisheed (OED), hogshed, hogsheed (OED); 6–7 hoggeshead (OED); 6–9 hogshead; 7 hogshede (OED) [ME *hoggeshed* < *hogges*, poss of *hogge*, hog, + *hed*, head; the reason for the name is uncertain]. A m-c for many products: ale, 48 ale gal (*c*2.22 hl) equal to 1½ bbl, or 3 KILDERKINS, or 6 FIRKINS; beer, 54 beer gal (*c*2.49 hl) equal to 1½ bbl, or 3 kilderkins, or 6 firkins; cider, Guernsey and Jersey, 60 gal (*c*2.27

hl), Herefordshire and Worcestershire, 110 gal (c4.16 hl); honey, oil, and wine, 63 wine gal (c2.38 hl) equal to ½ PIPE, or ¼ TUN; and molasses, 100 gal (c3.78 hl). — **1391** Henry Derby 23: Clerico panetrie per manus Fyssher pro ij barellis et j hoogeshed vacuis per ipsum pro floure imponendo xviii d. **1423** Rot. Parl. 4.256: The Hoggeshede xx [×] iii [+] III galons. **1439** Southampton 2.11: 1 hoggyshed de glassis; *ibid* 50: 1 pipa et 1 hoggyshed de alym . . . 3 hoggyshedys . . . de haberdasshe . . . 1 hoggyshead de naperye; *ibid* 62: Pro 6 hoggyshedys sulfuris. **1443** Brokage II.42: Et i hogyshede saponis; *ibid* 46: Cum iii hogyshedys hony; *ibid* 49: Cum hogyshede de horsseshoue . . . cum 1 hogyshede olei; *ibid* 171: 1 hogyshede caudorons veteris . . . 1 hogyshede pelewys. **1444** Rot. Parl. 5.114: That every Tonne contene xx [×] xii and XII Galons, and every Pipe xx [×] vi [+] VI Galons . . . and every Hoggeshede LXIII Galons. **1507** Gras 1.699: Iryne wyer the hoggeshed. **1509** *Ibid* 590: Pro iii hog[eshedes] beere. **1517** Hall 49: And the contente of the Gascoyne hoges[hed'] shuld' be, yf hyt kepe gawge, iii [×] xx & iii galons. **1547** Cal. Pat. 19.397: Buttes, pypes, hoggesheddes, pontions or barrelles. **1572** Mer. Adven. 97: By hoggeshed or hoggesheds. **1587** Stat. 267: The tunne of wine CC.lii. galons. the pipe C.xxvi. galons . . . the hoggeshed three score and three galons. c**1590** Hall 21: The hogshed which is ¼ of a tunne contenith 63 gallons. **1615** Collect. Stat. 467: And euerie Hogshead to containe threescore and three gallons. **1635** Dalton 148: Wine, Oyle, and Honey: their measure is all one . . . Hogshead, 63. gallons. **1682** Hall 29: I Tunne conteynes . . . 2 Pipes or Butts . . . 4 Hogsheads. **1708** Chamberlayne 210: 1 Barrel and half, or 54 Gallons make a Hogshead. **1717** Dict. Rus. sv: Hogshead, a Measure or Vessel of Wine or Oil, containing the fourth part of a Tun or 63 Gallons; two of these Hogsheads make a Pipe or Butt. **1820** Second Rep. 19: Hogshead . . . Formerly of ale 48 gallons; of beer 54 . . . of mollasses, 100 gallons . . . Herefordshire and Worcestershire: of cider, 110 gallons . . . Guernsey and Jersey: of cider, 120 pots, 60 gallons.

hogshed, hogshede, hogsheed, hogyshed, hogyshede. HOGSHEAD
hond, honde. HAND
honderd, hondered, hondert, honderte, honderyd, hondird, hondred, hondret. HUNDRED
hoogeshed. HOGSHEAD

hoond, hoonde. HAND

hoop — 3 L hoppa (St. Paul's); 5 hop, hope; 6–9 hoop [ME *hop,
hoop* < OE *hōp;* akin to MDu *hoep*, ring, band, hoop]. A m-c for
grain: Durham, ¼ pk (*c*2.20 l); Montgomeryshire, 5 gal (*c*2.20
dkl); Shropshire and Worcestershire, 1 pk (*c*8.81 l); and St. Paul's
Estate, 1 bu (*c*3.52 dkl). — **1467** Cov. Leet 334: Also they have
ordenyd that the wardens Make ij strikis, ij halfe strykis, ij hopes,
& let the salters have hem with-owt eny money. . . . Also they woll
that no retaylers in the Cete take no hyr for the lone of strykis,
half-strykis nor hopus lande [loaned] to the salters. **1820** Second
Rep. 19: Hoop—Durham, ¼ peck, Shropshire, a peck, Montgomeryshire, 5 gallons, called also a peccaid.

hop, hope, hoppa. HOOP

houndred, houndret, hunderd, hundered, hunderet, hunderit, hundird.
HUNDRED

hundred — 1–9 hundred; 3 hunndredd (OED); 3–4 hondret (OED),
houndret (OED), hundret (OED); 3–5 hondred (OED); 3–7
hundered (OED); 4 hondird (OED), houndred (OED), hunderet
(OED), hunderit (OED), hundird (OED), hundryd (OED); 4–6
hundride (OED), hundyrd (OED); 4–8 hunderd (OED); 4–9
hundrid; 5 honderd (OED), hondert (OED), honderte (OED),
hundurd (OED), hundyrt (OED); 5–6 hondered (OED), honderyd
(OED); 6 hundrede, hundreth, hundrethe (OED); 7 L hundredus
[OE *hundred* < stems of *hund*, hundred, + *-red*, akin to Goth
rathjo, number, reckoning]. A m-q, the CENT (C), and a wt, the
Cwt, for many products.

The C generally numbered 100, but larger amounts were not
uncommon: 106, lambs and sheep in Roxburghshire and Selkirkshire; 120, the long-hundred for canvas, eggs, faggots, herrings,
linen cloth, nails, oars, pins, reeds, spars, stockfish, stones, and
tile; 124, cod, ling, haberdine, and saltfish; 132, herrings in
Fifeshire; 160, "hardfish"; and 225, onions and garlic. — **1519**
Mer. Adven. 57: And of every hundreth shepe skynnes, ij d., and
of every hundreth lam fells, j d. **1555** York Mer. 156: A hundreth
waynescotts, six shillings and eyght-pence. *c*1590 Hall 27: The
hundred of canvas and of lynnen clothe is and contenith 120 to the
hundrid; *ibid* 28: The Hundred consisteth of 15 ropes and euery
rope 15 heades; so that the 100 of onyons and garlike consisteth
225. **1603** Henllys 139: Hearings are sold freshe by the meise,

w[hich] is five hundred, eche hundred contayninge vj [×] xx.
1615 Collect. Stat. 465: A hundred of Garlik consisteth of 15.
ropes, & euery rope containeth 15. heads. **1616** Hopton 162:
Herrings . . . at 120 to the hundred; *ibid* 164: Ling, Cod, or
Haberdine hath 124 to the hundred. **1635** Dalton 149: Six score
herrings shall goe to the hundred. . . . The hundred of hard fish
must containe eight score; *ibid* 150: Also all other headed things, as
nailes, pins, &c. are sold six score to the hundred. **1678** Du Cange
sv centena: Ferri, ex 100. petris. **1682** Hall 29: Ling, Cod or
Haberdine, 124 to the Hundred; *ibid* 30: Coney, Kid, Lambe
Bulge, Catt, etc.: 5 Skore to the hundred. **1704** Mer. Adven. 245:
Ffor sorting and laying up every hundred hogshead staves belonging to a ffreeman. **1708** Chamberlayne 205: Cod-fish, Haberdine,
Ling, etc. have 124 to the C . . . . Herrings 120 to the C . . . .
Filches, Grays, Jennets, Martins, Minks, Sables, 40 Skins is a
Timber . . . other Skins, five Score to the Hundred. **1805** Macpher-
son I.471: 120 herrings 1 hundred. **1820** Second Rep. 19: Hundred
. . . eggs, oars, spars and stone, 120 . . . of mullets, 8 score = 160
. . . of faggots, 6 score . . . of bunches of reeds, 6 score . . .
Fifeshire: of herrings, 132 . . . Roxburghshire and Selkirkshire:
of sheep or lambs, sometimes 106.

The Cwt generally weighed 112 lb (50.802 kg) and was equal to
$\frac{1}{20}$ ton of 2240 lb (1016.040 kg), but, like the C, it had several
variations: 100 lb (45.359 kg), aloes, angelica, annatto, asafetida,
capers, copal, cotton, down, gentian, ginseng, gum guaiac, gunpowder, indigo, isinglass, manna, myrrh, pepper (long), pimento,
plums, raw linen, saccharum, sarsaparilla, tobacco, turmeric, and
verdigris; 104 lb (47.173 kg), filberts in Kent; 108 lb (48.988 kg),
almonds, alum, cinnamon, nutmegs, pepper, sugar, and wax; and
120 lb (54.431 kg), iron at the king's scales in Cornwall. — *c*1253
Hall 11: La centeine de cire, sucre, peyuer, cumin, almand, et de
alume, si est de xiii peris et di., et checune pere de viii li. . . . La
sume de lib. en la centeyne, cent viii li. *c*1272 *Ibid* 10: Item centena
zucari, cere, piperis, cimini, amigdalorum, et allume continet
tresdecim petras et dimidiam; et quelibet petra continet octo libras.
1290 Fleta 119: Item centena cere, xucarii, piperis, cumini,
amigdolarum et aloigne continet xiij. petras et dimidiam, et
quelibet petra continet octo libras. *c*1340 Pegolotti 255: Mandorle,
e riso . . . e stagno . . . e ferro, e tutte cose grosse si vendono in

Londra a centinaio, di libbre 112 per 1 centinaio. *c*1461 Hall 13:
And by this weyght [112 lb] be all maner of merchaundyse bought
and sold, as tynne, lede, iron, coper, style, wode . . . madder . . .
laces, sylks, threde, flex, hempe, ropys, talowe. . . . Also lede ys
sold . . . after v [×] xx [+] xii to the C. . . . And other warys that
be sold by the lb., as peper, saffryn, clowys, mace, gynger and
other suche, thes be called Sotyll Warys and they wold be rekynnyd
after v [×] xx to the C. **1474** Cov. Leet 396: And to *th*is day *the* C.
ys trewe after xx [×] v for the C. . . . xx [×] v for the C, the wich
kepes weyght & mesure 1 li. the halfe C, xxv li. the quartern.
*c*1590 Hall 22: The hundred waight of gunpowder is but fyve skore
poundes waight, haberdepoyse, to the hundrid; *ibid* 23: The 100 of
tynne at the marchantes of London is but 112 poundes haberdepoyse; *ibid* 24: But at the Kings beame at Cornwall yt is 120
poundes waight [for iron] to the 100; *ibid* 25: Item waxe . . .
sugare, peper, cinamond, nuttmegs contaynith 13 stone $\frac{1}{2}$; and
euery stonne 8 to the hundrid; so that the hundrid contenith 108;
ibid 27: The load of hay is but 18 hundredes . . . and euery
hundred 112 poundes waight. . . . The casse of glasse is a hundrid
and $\frac{3}{4}$ in waight, after 112 to the 100. **1615** Collect. Stat. 465:
A hundred of ware, sugar, pepper, cynamome . . . containeth . . .
108 l. **1616** Hopton 163: Tinne, Copper, and Lattine haue 112
pounds to the hundred. **1635** Dalton 149: Sugar, spices, and wax
. . . 108. li. maketh the hundred. . . . Hops, five score and twelve
pounds maketh the hundred. **1665** Assize 5: But the weight of the
Wey of Essex-Cheese or Butter, is three hundred pounds weight,
after the rate of five score and twelve pounds of Avoirdupois-
weight. . . . The sack of Woll is three hundred twenty eight
pounds, and a hundred and twelve pounds to every hundred
weight. **1678** Du Cange sv centanarium: Pondus centum librarum
. . . . Centena ceræ, zuccari, piperis, cumini . . . apud Anglos,
continet 13. petras et dimidiam: et quælibet petra continet 8.
libras. Summa ergo librarum in centena 108. **1688** Bernardi
137–38: Libra equidem Avoirdupois . . . $\frac{1}{112}$ Hundredi. **1820**
Second Rep. 20: Hundred-Weight . . . properly 112 lbs = 4
quarters = 8 stone; but of aloes, angelica, annatto, asafaetida . . .
capers, cotton, down, gentian, ginseng . . . gum guaicum, indigo,
isinglass, manna, myrrh, long pepper, pimento, plums, saccharum
. . . sarsaparilla, tobacco, turmeric, verdigris and raw linen yarn,

100 lbs are to be reckoned a hundred weight. . . . Kent: of filberts,
104 lbs. *See* CENT

**hundrede, hundredus, hundret, hundreth, hundrethe, hundrid,
   hundride, hundryd, hundurd, hundyrd, hundyrt, hunndredd.**
HUNDRED

hutch [ME *huche* < OF *huche, huge* < LL *hutica; see* OED]. A m-c
in Renfrewshire (*c*1800), a chest or coffer containing 2 Cwt
(101.604 kg) of copperas or pyrite stone (Second Rep. 20). *See*
HUNDRED

hyda, hyde. HIDE

hyle [perh a special sense of *hill* < ME *hill, hul* < OE *hyll;* hence,
a large pile or stack]. A m-c for flax in Hampshire (*c*1800) containing 10 sheaves (Second Rep. 20).

I

ialon. GALLON

iarre. JAR

ince. INCH

inch — 1 ince (OED), ynce (OED); 1–7 L pollex, L uncia; 3 unche (OED); 4–6 ench, enche (OED); 4–7 ynch, ynche; 4–9 inch; 5–6 inche; 6 insch (OED), intch, unch (OED), ynsh [ME *inch, inche, ynch* < OE *ince, ynce* < L *uncia*, the twelfth part, inch, ounce]. A m-l (2.54 cm) which originally was a unit of body measurement commonly associated with a thumb's breadth. In the Roman duodecimal system it was equal to $\frac{1}{12}$ ft. During the Roman occupation it was introduced into Britain, where it became part of the English system of weights and measures. Throughout the Middle Ages and the early modern period the inch was defined as the length of 3 medium-sized barleycorns placed end to end. — *c*1075 Hall 2: Quarum haec sunt nomina: digitus, uncia, palmus; *ibid* 4: Tantum enim precellit pes manualis pedem naturalem, quantum pollex in longitudinem protendi potest. **1220** Clerkenwell 140: Prima occidentalis cum solario continet in fronte iuxta vicum regium in latitudine tres vlnas et duos pollices. *c*1272 Hall 7: Sciendum quod tria grana ordei, sicca et rotunda, faciunt pollicem . . . . xij pollices faciunt pedem. *c*1300 *Ibid* 7: Nota quod tria grana ordei de medio spice faciunt pollicem. **1395** York Mem. 1.142: Notandum quod tria grana ordei sicca et rotunda faciunt pollicem. *c*1400 Hall 5: Uncia est digitus et eius tercia pars. *c*1461 *Ibid* 14: The lengythe of iij barly cornys make an ynche. **1474** Cov. Leet 396: Also hitt was ordeyned . . . that iij barley-Cornes take out of the middes of the Ere makith a Inche. *c*1475 Nicholson 77: It is to mete that iij Barly Cornys in the myddis of the Ere makyth one ynche, And xij enchis makyth a foote. *c*1500 Hall 7: iii grana ordei, de medio spice, faciunt pol*l*icem. **1537** Benese 3: Therefore ye shall take the lengthe of an ynche moost trulye upon an artificers rule, made of two foote in length, after the standarde of London, the which rule doth conteyne xxiiii ynches in lengthe. *c*1550 Remembrance 23: Item under xx ynshis goth iii fisshis for one . . . Item under xx intches three goeth for one. *c*1590 Hall 27: Dymension longitudes of the ynche, ffoott, yard . . . accordinge to the statut and standart of England . . . . The inche. 3 grayns of Barly, dry and rotund. **1603** Henllys 137: Yet doeth yt agree in the ynche, foote and yard. **1615** Collect. Stat. 464: It is ordained that three graines of barley drie and round do make an ynch. **1616** Hopton 165: Three barley cornes make an Inch, 12 Inches a foote. **1635** Dalton 150: Three barley cornes measured from end to end (or 4 in thicknesse) maketh one inch. **1647** Digges 1: Wherein is ordained three Barly cornes dry and round to make an Inch. **1665** Assize 6: Uncia est in pede pars XII. **1678** Du Cange sv alna: Pes Regius est 12. pollicum. **1688** Bernardi 192: Uncia. Pollex transversus. $\frac{1}{12}$ Pedis eujusque. **1708** Chamberlayne 207: The smallest Applicative Measure is a Barley-Corn, whereof three in length make a Fingers breadth or Inch. **1717** Dict. Rus. sv: Inch, a known Measure, the twelfth part of a Foot, containing the space of three Barley-corns in length.

inche, insch, intch. INCH

J

jag — 6–9 jagg; 8–9 jag (OED); 9 jaug (OED)[*]. A m-c for hay; it was smaller than a load of 20 Cwt or 2240 lb (1016.040 kg). — **1717** Dict. Rus. sv load: Load of Hay, contains about two thousand weight, being a good load; but a small load of Hay is called a Jagg.

jagg. JAG

jalo, jalon. GALLON

jar — 4 L jarda; 5 jare (Southampton 1), jarre; 5–8 jarr; 6–7 iarre (OED); 7–9 jar [MF *jarre* < OPr *jarra* < Ar *jarrah*, earthen water vessel]. A m-c for dry and liquid products: green ginger, 100 lb (45.359 kg); oil, 12 to 26 gal (*c*4.54 to *c*9.84 dkl); green vinegar, 100 lb (45.359 kg); and wheat, 52 lb (23.587 kg). — **1303** Gras 1.356: Pro ii jardis olei . . . pro 1 jarda olei. **1443** Brokage II.30: Cum ii jarrys olei; *ibid* 67: iiii jarrys lymons; *ibid* 156: i jarre olei continente xii lagenas; *ibid* 226: i jarr' vini. **1509** Gras 1.563: 1 parv' jarres olei. **1717** Dict. Rus. sv jarr: Of Oil, an earthen Vessel containing from 18 to 26 Gallons. A Jarr of green Ginger, is about 100 Pounds weight. **1820** Second Rep. 20: Jar . . . of Lucca oil, 25 gallons . . . of green vinegar, 100 lbs . . . of wheat, 52 lbs.

jardum, jare, jarr, jarre. JAR

jaug. JAG

jill, jille. GILL

jugum terre. YOKE OF LAND

K

kace. CASE
kage, kaig. CAGE
karat, karect. CARAT
kark, karke, karre. CARK
kase. CASE
keaver. KIVER
keel — 5–7 keill (OED), kele; 5–8 keil; 6 keyle (OED); 6–7 keele, keile; 7 keell; 7–9 keel; 8 kiell (OED) [ME *kele* < MDu *kiel*, ship, boat]. A m-c for coal, the capacity of a barge or flat-bottomed ship. It was commonly called a barge-load.

When the CHALDER was standardized in 1421 at a capacity of 32 bu totaling 1 ton of 2000 lb (907.180 kg), the keel contained 20 of these chalders or 20 tons (18,143.600 kg). After the chalder was increased in 1677 to 36 heaped bu totaling 1 ton of 2240 lb (1016.040 kg), the number of chalders in the keel was changed to 16 (35,840 lb or 16,256.640 kg). — **1421** Rot. Parl. 4.148: & sont ascuns gentz qi ont tielx Keles del portage de XXII ou XXIII Chaldres, & vo*t*re Custume ent est prise solonc le portage de XX Chaldres tant soulement, en deceite de Vous, tres soverain Sr. **1555** York Mer. 155: Peter Hudelesse, Richard Plaskett . . . of the saide cytye of Yorke, owners of certeine keles, bootes, and lighteners.

The Newcastle chalder, however, was much larger than the standard chalder, and when it weighed 42 Cwt (2133.684 kg), 10 Newcastle chalders or 420 Cwt (21,336.840 kg) made a keel. After this chalder was fixed at a capacity of 72 heaped bu totaling 53 Cwt (2692.510 kg) in 1695, the capacity of the keel was changed to 8 chalders totaling 424 Cwt or 47,488 lb (21,540.177 kg). — **1603** Hostmen 19: No free brother of the saide ffelloshipp of Hostmen, shall from henceforth sell or lode in any shipp . . . any kynde of Coles, by lesser or greater measure then the true and accustomed measure of the Keeles or Lighters; *ibid* 36: And that from henceforth there shall no Coles att all be brought from aborde of any shipp, Hoie, or other vessell in any Keele or Lighter whatsoever, except yt be the sweepings, and that not to exceed in any one Keell or Lighter above two smale maunds. **1604** *Ibid* 54: To the said owners of Keles. **1650** *Ibid* 91: Whereas it appeareth by good and sufficient Testimonye that Gilbert Ellet . . . hath sould Eight Chalder of Coles to A man of warr . . . . It is therefore, Ordered That the said Gilbert Ellet shall not, dureing the time of one whole yeare, worke or serve . . . any Brother . . . in any keele or boat. **1656** *Ibid* 109: And whereas also the usual faire for each keele carryinge Eight Chalder of coles to the shipes was heretofore but seaven shillinges. **1679** *Ibid* 139: The said Customehouse officers threaten to seize the keiles that are measured by stoke nales. **1704** Mer. Adven. 243: Ffor takeing forth of every tonne of wine from a keel or boat. **1706** Hostmen 169: And they conceived for avoideing all fraudes in the admeasure[ment] of Keiles, That the Com-[missioners] . . . be applyed to . . . and that one, Two, or more persons be appointed to Examine and give Acc[ount] of the same and of all Screwed upp and Stoaked Keils, the same being a very great fraud. **1784** Ency. meth. 138: Le keel, de 8 chaldrons. **1820** Second Rep. 20: Keel of coals: Newcastle, 8 Newcastle Chaldrons = 21 ton 4 cwt = 424 cwt. **1829** Brockett 65: 8 Newcastle chaldrons make a keel; *ibid* 171: Keel-of-Coals, 8 Newcastle chaldrons, 21 tons, 4 cwt. *See* HUNDRED

keele, keell. KEEL

keever. KIVER

keil, keile, keill. KEEL

keippe. KIP

kele. KEEL

kempkin. KILDERKIN

kemple — 7 kimple (OED); 8–9 kemple [alter of earlier *kimple*, of Scand origin; akin to ON *kimbull*, bundle, Icel *kimbill*, small bundle, small haystack]. A m-c for straw in Midlothian (*c*1800) containing 40 windlens of 5 to 6 lb each (90.718 to 108.862 kg) (Second Rep. 37).

kenning [*]. A m-c for corn in Durham and Northumberland (*c*1800) containing 2 pk (*c*1.76 dkl) (Second Rep. 21).

kepe. KIP
keuer, kevere. KIVER
keyle, kiell. KEEL
kiever. KIVER
kilderkin — 4 kynerkyn, kynerkyne; 4–6 kilderkyn; 5 kynderkyn
(OED); 5–6 kylderkyn; 5–9 kilderkin; 6 kilderkynne, kinderkind
(OED), kynterkyn (OED); 6–7 kinderkin (OED); ? kempkin
(Shipley), kinkin (Shipley) [ME *kilderkin, kilderkyn* < MDu
kindekijn, kinnekijn; see WNID3]. A m-c for ale, beer, butter,
fish, and soap. It was commonly called a half-barrel.

The ale kilderkin contained 16 gal (*c*7.39 dkl) and was equal
to 2 ale FIRKINS or ½ ale bbl. — **1517** Hall 49: xvi galons' to the
ale kylderkyn. **1587** Stat. 595: Euerie kilderkin for ale xvi. gallons.
*c*1590 Hall 22: The firkin is 8 gallons . . . the kilderkyn, or ½
barill, contenith 16 gallons; *ibid* 23: And so the kilderkynne, firkyn,
and tertione fully packed. **1635** Dalton 148: Ale, the measure
thereof is . . . Kilderkin, 16. gallons. **1665** Assize 9: The Kilderkin
sixteen gallons. **1708** Chamberlayne 210: 8 Gallons a Firkin of
Ale . . . 2 such Firkins make a Kilderkin.

The beer kilderkin contained 18 gal (*c*8.32 dkl) and was equal to
2 beer firkins or ½ beer bbl. — **1517** Hall 50: xviii galons to the
kylderkyn'. **1587** Stat. 595: Euerie kilderkin for beere xviii.
gallons. *c*1590 Hall 22: The firkyn contenyth 9 galons: the kilderkyn . . . contenith 18 gallons: the barill . . . 36 gallons. **1616**
Hopton 160: Kilderkins, or halfe Barrels. **1635** Dalton 148: Beere,
the measure thereof . . . Kilderkin, 18 gallons. **1717** Dict. Rus.
sv: Kilderkin, a kind of Liquid Measure, that contains two Firkins
or eighteen Gallons, and two such Kilderkins make a Barrel.

The kilderkin of butter or soap conformed to the 16 gal capacity
(*c*7.39 dkl) of the ale kilderkin, but equally important was the
weight of the cask: generally 13 lb (5.897 kg) before 1662 and 20 lb
(9.072 kg) afterward. — **1587** Stat. 595: And euerie halfe barrell
emptie to be in weight xiii pounds. *c*1590 Hall 24: The halfe barill
of butter, or kilderkin, caske and all, is 128 poundes waight
haberdepoise; in clean butter, but 115 poundes waight haberdepoise. **1635** Dalton 149: Sope, halfe barrell . . . shall be of the
same content that ale is . . . . Butter also shall be of the same measure that sope is of. **1673** Stat. Charles 159: Every Kilderkin of But-

ter ought to weigh One hundred thirty and two pounds gross at the least, that is to say, One hundred and twelve pounds of Neat Butter, and the Cask Twenty pounds.

The kilderkin of salmon, and occasionally of eels, contained 21 gal (*c*7.95 dkl) or 2 firkins of 10½ gal each, while the kilderkin for most other fish, including eels, conformed to the ale kilderkin capacity of 16 gal (*c*7.39 dkl). — **1392** Henry Derby 96: Et per manus eiusdem Ricardi et Willelmi Harpeden pro iij kynerkynes de salmone salso per ipsos emptis ibidem, xxxvij scot; *ibid* 97: Et per manus eiusdem pro j kynerkyn anguillarum per ipsum empt' ibidem, xj scot. **1393** *Ibid* 158: Clerico coquine per manus Johannis Bounche de Linne pro j kilderkyn di. de storgon, xvj s. viij d. **1443** Brokage II.87: A kylderkyn allecii. **1482** Rot. Parl. 6.221: The kilderkin or ½ barill 21 galons . . . . Also it hath ben used, that every Barell for Elys, shuld hold and conteigne XLII Galons, the half Barell . . . after the same rate. *c*1590 Hall 23: That every . . . half Barell, ordeyned for Samon, shuld conteygne . . . XXI Galons. **1635** Dalton 149: Herring . . . the halfe barrell . . . shall be the same content that ale is. **1665** Sheppard 60: For . . . Herring the Barrel, half Barrel, and Firkin, is to be of the same content that Ale is.

kilderkyn, kilderkynne. KILDERKIN
kimple. KEMPLE
kinderkin, kinderkind, kinkin. KILDERKIN
kip — 6 keippe, kepe, kyppe; 6–9 kip (OED); 7 kipp, kippe [cf MLG *kip*, bundle of hides, MDu *kip, kijp*, pack or bundle, ON *kippi*, bundle]. A m-q for skins: lamb, 30, and goat, 50. — **1507** Gras 1.698: Golde skynes the kyppe. **1525** Percy 355: ij Keippe and a half [of lamb skins] after xxx Skynnes in a Kepe. **1616** Hopton 164: The skins of Goats are numbered by the kippe, which is 50. **1682** Hall 30: Skins-Goates: 50 to a Kipp.

kipp, kippe. KIP
kishon [Manx *kishan*, Ir *cisean*, dim of *cis*, kish, basket, hamper]. A m-c on the Isle of Man (*c*1800) containing 8 qt (*c*8.81 l) or 1 pk (Second Rep. 21).
kiver — 5 kevere (OED); 7 keaver (OED), keuer (OED), kiever (OED); 8 keever (OED); 8–9 kiver [ME *kevere*, alter of *keve, kive*, a keeve, tub, vat, < OE *cӯf; see* WNID3 sv keeve]. A m-c in

Derbyshire (*c*1800) for corn; a shallow wooden vessel or tub that
contained 12 SHEAVES (Second Rep. 21).

knightes ffee. KNIGHT'S FEE

knight's fee — 3–7 L feodum; 5 knyghtes fee, knyghts fee; 6–?
knight's fee; 7 knightes ffee [knight < ME *knight*, boy, youth,
knight, < OE *cniht, cneoht*, boy, youth, attendant, military fol-
lower; fee < ME *fee*, fief, payment, < OF *fé, fié, fief*, of Gmc origin; akin to OHG *fihu*, cattle]. A m-a which probably originated as
an amount of land needed to support a knight and his family for a
period of one year. In this sense, the knight's fee (also called
knight's service or servicium militis) was regarded as a unit of
income for a fighting man just as the HIDE was probably a unit of
income for a working man or serf. But, certainly as early as the
thirteenth century, the knight's fee was expressed as a land division
containing a definite number of BOVATES, VIRGATES, or hides, and,
even though there was little uniformity, the following were the
most common: a knight's fee of 4 hides, each hide containing 120
acres, or 480 acres (*c*194.40 ha) in all; of 4 hides of 16 virgates,
each virgate containing 4 FARTHINGDALES of 10 acres each, or 640
acres (*c*259.20 ha) in all; of 5, 5½, 6, 6½, 8, 10, and 12 hides, no
standard acreage established for the hide; of 12 hides totaling 600
acres (*c*243.00 ha); and of 14, 16, 27, and 48 hides, no standard
acreage established for the hide. — **1201** Cur. Reg. 9.53: Unde
xxvii. hide faciunt feodum j. militis. **1202** *Ibid* 177: xlviii hide
faciunt feodum j militis. **1206** Cur. Reg. 11.120: Unde sex hide
faciunt feodum unius militis; *ibid* 284: In Stodham, unde vj. hide
et dimidia faciunt seruicium unius militis. **1208** Feet 2.124: Unde
V carrucate terre et dimidia faciunt seruicium unius militis; *ibid*
148: Unde sexdecim carrucate terre faciunt seruicium unius militis
in eadem uilla pro omni seruicio. **1220** Cur. Reg. 3.151: Unde
xiiij. carucate terre faciunt feodum j. militis. *c***1250** Rameseia
III.47–48: Modus qualiter relevium liberorum tenentium domini
Abbatis Rameseiæ debet solvi et exigi de feodis militum, et
qualiter feodum integrum componitur ex certis hidis, hidæ ex
certis virgatis, et virgata ex certis acris; scilicet, quod quatuor
hidæ faciunt feodum integrum, quatuor virgatæ hidam; *ibid* 48:
Una hida, quæ est quarta pars feodi . . . . Una virgata terræ, quæ
est quarta pars hidæ; *ibid* 209: Quinque hidæ . . . pro uno feodo;

ibid 210: Sex hidæ . . . pro uno feodo. *c*1283 Battle xiii: Nota quod virgata terræ et wysta idem sunt et unum significant: Virgata seu wysta est sextadecima pars unius feodi militis: Quatuor virgatæ seu wystæ faciunt unam hydam: Quatuor hydæ faciunt unum feodum militis. **1304** Swinfield 221: Alanus de Walynton' tenet .j. hydam et dimidium apud Walynton' et Masinton' per militiam pro quarta parte unius feodi. **1338** Langtoft 600–01: Decem acræ faciunt ferdellum. Quatuor fardella faciunt virgatam unam. Quatuor virgatæ faciunt hidam unam. Quatuor hidæ feodum unum faciunt; *ibid* 601: Fardellum Acræ X. / virgata XL. / hida. CLX. / feodum unum CCCCCCXL. **1494** Fabyan 246: viij. hydes make a knyghtes fee, by the whiche reason, a knyghts fee shuld welde c.lx. acres. **1603** Henllys 135: X plowlands make a knightes ffee being . . . 640 acr. **1665** Sheppard 22: And again, some say, Eight Hides are 800 acres, and make a Knight's Fee. **1755** Willis 360: A Knight's Fee contained 12 Plough-Land or 600 Acres of Land. **1777** Nicol. and Burn 615: Virgate of land; a yard land consisting (as some say) of 24 acres, whereof four virgates make an hide, and five hides make a knight's fee.

knipperkin. NIPPERKIN

knoggin. NOGGIN

knot [ME *knot, knotte* < OE *cnotta;* so called from the knot tied around a skein of yarn after reeling]. A m-q for wool yarn in Essex (*c*1800) consisting of 80 turns around a reel (Second Rep. 21).

knyghtes fee, knyghts fee. KNIGHT'S FEE

koome. COOMB

kostorell. COSTREL

krenneke, krennock. CRANNOCK

kylderkyn, kynderkyn, kynerkyn, kynerkyne, kynterkyn. KILDERKIN

kyppe. KIP

L

lade. LOAD
lagan. LAGEN
lagen — 3–8 L lagena; 5 L lagina; 6–9 lagen (OED); 7–9 lagan
(OED); ? laggon (OED), L legina (Finchale) [L *lagena*, a flask].
A m-c for liquid and dry products generally containing 1 gal
(*c*3.78 l). — **1221** Cur. Reg. 4.74: Et j. dolium de cicera de lx.
lagenis. **1256** Burton 376: Vendere in civitatibus duas lagenas ad
denarium. **1287** Select Cases 2.19: Goldingus de Gepewyz, lagena
falsa, quarta falsa, et quia fregit assisam et vendidit pro xvj.d.
1290 Fleta 118: Item scire debet naturam et originem ponderum
et mensurarum vt veraciter et perfecte sciat quantum bladi teneat
lagena et quantum bussellus. **1299** Liber 367: Lagena cerevisiæ.
1320 Rot. Parl. 1.375: Ad Petitionem hominum de Com' Devon' &
Cornub' conquer' de Mercatoribus vinorum, qui vendunt vina
apud civitatem Exon' pro vi d. vide*licet* lagenam . . . & in partibus
London venditur lagena pro IIII denar'. **1443** Brokage II.40: ii
barellis olei continente 1 barello xvi laginas; *ibid* 139: 1 barello
olei continente xvi lagenas; *ibid* 156: 1 jarre olei continente xii
lagenas. *c*1461 Hall 7: Et viij libre faciunt lagenam . . . et viij
lagene faciunt busshelum Londonie. **1678** Du Cange sv lagena:
Mensuræ species apud Anglos. . . . Fuit etiam Lagena non liquidorum dumtaxat, sed et aridorum mensura. **1745** Fleetwood 81:
I have observ'd before, that Lagena . . . holds 4 quarts.
lagena, laggon, lagina. LAGEN
laid. LOAD
langenekre [*langen*, long, + *ekre*, ACRE]. A m-a for land in Kent
(*c*1400) containing 1½ acres (*c*0.61 ha) (Prior 147).
langhsester [*langh*, long, + SESTER]. A m-c at Glastonbury (*c*1300)
which probably contained 5 to 6 gal (*c*1.89 to *c*2.27 dkl) (Prior 154).
lasse. LAST
last — 1 hlæst (OED); 3 L lestum; 3–6 L lastum; 3–7 L lastus, L

lestus; 3–9 last; 4–6 laste, leste (OED); 4–7 lest; 6 lasse (OED); 7 L lasta [ME *last*, load, < OE *hlæst*, load]. A m-c for dry and liquid products: ashes and barrel fish, 12 bbl (*c*17.76 hl); beer, 12 bbl (*c*19.92 hl); bowstaves, 6 C; butter, 12 bbl (*c*17.76 hl); feathers, 1700 lb (771.103 kg); flax, 6 C bonds; grain, 10 SEAMS or 80 bu (*c*28.19 hl); gunpowder, 24 bbl or 2400 lb (1088.616 kg); herrings, 12,000; iron, 12 bbl (?); hides, 20 DICKERS or 200 in number; oatmeal, 12 bbl (*c*17.76 hl); oats, Cambridgeshire, 10½ seams (*c*29.60 hl), Huntingdonshire, 1½ tons (1524.060 kg); pitch, 12 bbl (*c*17.76 hl); potash, 12 bbl or 2688 lb (1219.248 kg); raisins, 24 bbl or 24 Cwt (1219.248 kg); rapeseeds, Yorkshire, 10 seams (*c*28.19 hl); salmon, 6 PIPES or 504 gal (*c*19.08 hl); salt, 10 WEYS or 420 bu (*c*148.00 hl); seeds, Huntingdonshire, 10½ seams or 84 bu (*c*29.60 hl); soap, 12 bbl (*c*17.76 hl); tar, 12 bbl (*c*14.28 hl); and wool, 12 SACKS or 4368 lb (1981.290 kg). — *c*1243 Select Cases 3.lxxxvi: Et in predicta navi fuerunt vj. lesta correi, ij. dakeres minus. *c*1253 Hall 11: Et [ii] ways de layne sunt un sac, et xii sacs sunt un last. . . . Le last de arang' est de xM., et checun mil est de x cent, et chescun cent de vi [×] xx. . . . Le last de quir est de xx dakers, et checun dakir de x quirs. *c*1272 *Ibid* 10: Et due waye faciunt unum saccum. Et duodecim sacci continent le last. 1290 Fleta 119: Et due waye lane faciunt vnum saccum, et xij. sacca faciunt vnum lestum. . . . Lestus autem allecii consistit ex x. miliaribus et quodlibet miliare consistit ex decies centum, et quodlibet centum ex secies viginti. . . . Item lastus coreorum consistit ex [xx.] dakris, et quodlibet dakrum ex x. coreis. 1390 Henry Derby 47: Pro iiij lastes cum di. de bere, xij barellis pro le last. 1402 Gras 1.554: Pro ii lastis sope. 1439 Southampton 2.9: 2 last' allecii albi; *ibid* 10: 2 last' saponis nigri; *ibid* 12: 1 last' de pyche; *ibid* 22: 7 last' et di. allecii rubii; *ibid* 27: 2 last' de tarr. *c*1461 Hall 17: Also hyds of bestes, fresh, salt and tannyd be sold by the dyker; and x hydes make a dyker; and xx dyker make a last; *ibid* 18: And xij barrell Osmond [iron] is a last in byenge and sellynge; *ibid* 19: Flax, vi [×] c bonds make a last; Bowstavys, vi [×] c make a last. *c*1475 Gras 1.193: Of a last wood asshen. 1507 *Ibid* 696: Corke made in barrelles the laste; *ibid* 697: Dogestonys the laste . . . Elys called chaffte elles the laste; *ibid* 698: Fyche barreled the laste; *ibid* 699: Herynge fulle the laste . . . Herynge shotton' the laste. 1549 *Ibid* 630: Pro uno lasto wheate meale. 1555 York Mer. 155: Item, a last of flax and osemondes, for two shillings and sex pence . . . a last of ashes, for twentye pence . . . a last of tarr or pyke, two shillings . . . a last of rede heringe, for two shillings . . . a last of stockfyshe, for two shillings and sex pence. *c*1590 Hall 21: The last of corne is 80 bushells of corne: 10 quarters makith a last; *ibid* 22: The last of gunpowder is 24 barills, and euery barill contening a hundred waight . . . [of] fyve skores poundes waight, haberdepoyse; *ibid* 23: 26 stonnes of woolle is the sacke of woole and the sacke contenith 364 pound waight: 12 sakes is the last of wool . . . . The but of salmone ought to be 84 gallons fully packed . . . the last is 6 buttes conteninge 504 gallons. . . . The last of woole is 4368 poundes waight of woole haberdepoise. . . . The last of lether consistith 20 dickers of leather; *ibid* 28: The last of sault is 420 bushells: the way of sault is 42 bushells: 10 wayes makith a last. **1616** Hopton 162: Herring . . . Last being 10000, euery thousand being 1200, which is 12000 Herrings in the Last, at 120 to the hundred; *ibid* 164: The Last is 20 Dickers, or 200 hides. . . . A Last of Barrell-fish is twelve Ale Barrels. **1635** Dalton 149: Leather, the content of the dicker, and the last. **1665** Assize 5: The sack of Wool is three hundred twenty eight pounds, and a hundred and twelve pounds to every hundred weight . . . Two weights of Wool make a sack, and 12 sacks make a Last. **1678** Du Cange sv lasta: Lastus, Lestus, Last, Lest, voces Onus, pondus, sarcinam in genere denotantes; sed quæ in specie certis quibusdam mensuris ac ponderibus aptantur. **1682** Hall 29: Barrel fish hath 12 Ale barrels to a Last. **1704** Mer. Adven. 243: Ffor takeing up and bearing a last of redd herring. **1708** Chamberlayne 205: Herrings 120 to the C, 12 Hundred to the Thousand, which make a Barrel; and 12 Barrels a Last. **1717** Dict. Rus. sv dry measure: And ten Quarters a Last, which contains 5120 Pints, and so many Pounds Troy-Weight. **1805** Macpherson I.471: 2 weyes (of wool) 1 sack, 12 sacks 1 last. **1820** Second Rep. 21: Last . . . of ashes, codfish, pitch, tar . . . 12 barrels . . . . of butter and soap, 12 ale barrels . . . . of corn and seed, 10 quarters . . . . of feathers . . . 1,700 lbs . . . . of gunpowder and raisins, 24 barrels . . . . of oatmeal and potash, 12 barrels . . . . Cambridgeshire: of oats, 21 comb = 10½ quarters . . . . Huntingdonshire: of . . . seeds, 10½ quarters = 84 bushels . . . of oats, 1½ ton . . . . Yorkshire, N.R. . . . of rape seed, 10 quarters.

lasta, laste, lastum, lastus. LAST
layde. LOAD
leag, leage. LEAGUE
league — 3 leuce, L leuga; 3–7 L leuca; 4 leuk (York Mem. 1),
   L lewa (Prior), lewge (OED); 4–5 leghe (OED), lywe; 4–6 lege,
   leuge; 5 leeke (OED), leuke (OED), lewke (OED), lieke; 5–6 leege
   (OED); 6 legge (OED), lig (OED); 6–7 leag (OED), leage (OED);
   6–9 league [ME *lege* < LL *leuga, leuca,* of Gaulish origin]. A m-l
   generally of 15,840 ft (4.827 km) or 3 mi of 5280 ft each. However,
   various other lengths were occasionally used: a league of 7500 ft
   (*c*2.29 km) or 1½ mi of 5000 ft each; of 7680 ft (*c*2.34 km) or 12
   linear FARTHINGDALES of 40 PERCHES each, the perch containing
   16 ft; of 7920 ft (*c*2.41 km) or 12 FURLONGS of 40 perches each, the
   perch containing 16½ ft; of 8910 ft (*c*2.72 km) or 13½ furlongs of
   40 perches each, the perch containing 16½ ft; of 9375 ft (*c*2.86 km)
   or 15 furlongs of 125 PACES each, the pace containing 5 ft; and of
   10,000 ft (*c*3.05 km) or 16 furlongs of 125 paces each, the pace containing 5 ft. — **1227** trans in Cal. Char. 1.17: Five leagues (leuce)
   from Croyland; *ibid* 20: Eighteen leagues (leugas) of meadow and
   a fishery and a manse. *c***1289** Bray 10: Ambitus villae de Herleston
   est ij leucae et quarta pars unius leucae et continet quaelibet leuca
   xij quadrentenas [farthingdales] et continet quaelibet quadrentena
   xl perticas et continet quaelibet pertica xvi pedes de pedibus rectis.
   . . . Quinque pedes passum faciunt; passus quoque centum viginti
   quinque stadium [furlong]; si miliare des octo facet stadia;
   duplicatum dat tibi leucam. *c***1300** Hall 7: Unde 5 pedes faciunt
   passum, et 125 passus faciunt stadium . . . et 16 stadia faciunt
   miliare Gallicum, quod vocant Gallici unam leucam. **1302** Rot.
   Parl. 1.152: Quod nulli Mercatores in Civitate predicta vel Subur-
   bio nec infra septem leucas circumquaque discarcare mercandisas
   suas presumant, nec emant vel vendant nisi infra portas nundina-
   rum predictarum. *c***1325** Rameseia I.76: Pedes quinque passum;
   passus centum viginti et quinque unum stadium . . . . Et stadia
   quindecim unam leucam. *c***1350** Swithun 66: Per septem leucas in
   circuitu feriæ illius. *c***1400** Henley 8: Byen sault ke vne coture deyt
   estre de quarante perches de long . . . E la perche le rey est de xvi
   pez et demi . . . ceo fet asauoyr ke xii cotures sunt vne lywe. *c***1425**
   Hall 9: Et sexdecim pedes et dimidia faciunt perticatam Regis. Et
   quadraginta perticate faciunt unum stadium. Et tresdecim stadia

et dimidium faciunt leucam. **1430** Rot. Parl. 4.380: P*ur* l'espace de
XII liekes environ le dit Burgh . . . . De user lour poisure p*ur* XII
leuges environ mesme le Burgh. **1494** Fabyan 63: An Hundreth
Legis . . . whereof euery Lege conteyneth .iii. Englysshe myles.
1688 Bernardi 202: Pes Anglicus . . . $\frac{1}{5840}$ . . . Leucæ mariti-
mæ. **1820** Second Rep. 21: League . . . 3 miles.

leap[1] — 3–6 lep (OED), lepe (OED); 4–5 leep (OED), leepe (OED);
5 leippe (OED); 6–7 leape (OED); 7 L lepa; 7–8 lib; 7–9 leap; 8 lip
(OED) [ME *leep*, basket, < OE *lēap*]. A m-c for grain in Sussex
generally containing $\frac{1}{2}$ bu (*c*1.76 dkl). — **1674** Ray 70: A Leap or
Lib; Suss. Half a bushel. **1678** Du Cange sv lepa: Mensuræ species
apud Anglos. Vox formata a Saxonico Leap, Calathus, corbis.

leap[2] — 3 leep (OED), leepe (OED); 4–6 lepe (OED); 6–7 leape
(OED); 6–9 leap [ME *leep* < OE *hlȳp;* akin to OE *hlēapan*, to run,
leap]. A m-l of 6 ft 9 inches (2.057 m) in Wales. — **1820** Second
Rep. 21: Leap, Wales: formerly 6 feet 9 inches.

leape. LEAP[1]; LEAP[2]

leege, leeke. LEAGUE

leep, leepe. LEAP[1]; LEAP[2]

lege, legge, leghe. LEAGUE

legina. LAGEN

leippe. LEAP[1]

leippie. LIPPY

lep, lepa. LEAP[1]

lepe. LEAP[1]; LEAP[2]

lest, leste, lestum, lestus. LAST

leuca, leuce, leuga, leuge, leuk, leuke, lewa, lewge, lewke. LEAGUE

lib. LEAP[1]

liber, libra. POUND

librat, librata. LIBRATE

librate — 3–7 L librata; 6–? librate; 7 librat (OED) [MedL *librata* <
MedL *libra*, English pound]. A m-a for an amount of land worth
1 pound a year. Its total acreage depended on local soil conditions
and on the value of the pound, and it seems to have varied from
several BOVATES or OXGANGS (often 4) to as much as $\frac{1}{2}$ KNIGHT'S
FEE. — **1200** Cur. Reg. 8.145: Et per finem concordie dedit idem
Willelmus eidem Frarico terram illam pro clamio x. libratarum
terre quas clamavit versus eum. *c*1280 Cal. Char. 1.307: Quinque
libratas terre in esterlinggis. **1665** Sheppard 24: And that *Librata*

terræ, some say, containeth four Oxgangs, and every Oxgang thirteen acres. **1777** Nicol. and Burn 612: Librate of land, is a quantity containing four bovates or oxgangs.

libre. POUND

lieke, lig. LEAGUE

line — 7 L linea; 7–9 line (Oldberg; Fr. Clarke) [F *ligne,* line, < L *linea*]. A m-l equal to $\frac{1}{12}$ inch (2.12 mm). — **1678** Du Cange sv alna: Pes Regius est 12. pollicum; pollex 12. linearum.

linea. LINE

lip. LEAP[1]

lippie. LIPPY

lippy — 7 leippie (OED); 7–9 lippy (OED); 9 lippie [dim of LEAP[1]]. A m-c for grain in Scotland equal to $\frac{1}{4}$ pk (*c*2.20 l). — **1820** Second Rep. 17: Forpet or Forpit . . . Scotland: the fourth part of a peck, otherwise called a lippie; *ibid* 22: Lippie, Scotland: a quarter of a peck = .0932 Winchester bushel. *See* FORPIT

liver, livre. POUND

llath [W *llath,* a rod, staff, yard]. A m-a for land in South Wales (*c*1800) varying between $11\frac{1}{2}$ and 24 sq ft (1.068 to 2.230 sq m) (Second Rep. 22).

llathen [*see* LLATH]. A m-l of 9 ft (2.743 m) for cloth in Wales (*c*1800) (Second Rep. 22).

llestraid [*]. A m-c for grain in Wales (*c*1800) containing 20 gal (*c*8.81 dkl) in Cardiff and 22 or 24 gal (*c*9.69 or *c*10.57 dkl) in Neath and Swansea (Second Rep. 22).

load — 3–6 lode (OED); 4–9 lade (OED); 5 layde (OED), lod (OED); 5–6 lood (OED), loode (OED); 5–9 laid (OED); 6–7 loade; 6–9 load [ME *lod, lode,* load, < OE *lād,* course, way, carrying, support]. A m-c originally referring to the amount of goods loaded on a cart or wain, the exact amount varying in relation to the quality of the goods, the strength of the wheels, the condition of the roads, and the distance traveled.

By the late Middle Ages and early modern period, however, standard loads were generally used for the following items: birch brooms, 60 BUNDLES; bulrushes, 63 bundles; gravel, 27 cu ft (0.764 cu m); hay, 18 Cwt or 2016 lb (914.436 kg); lime, 32 bu (*c*11.28 hl); oak bark, 45 Cwt (2286.090 kg); sand, 36 bu (*c*12.69 hl); Scots coal, 1 Cwt (50.802 kg); wheat, 5 SEAMS (*c*14.09 hl); and wood, 20 Cwt (1016.040 kg) or 50 cu ft (1.416 cu m). —

*c*1590 Hall 27: The load of hay is but 18 hundredes to the loade; and euery hundred 112 poundes waight: 36 trusses makith a loade of haye, and euery trusse is 56 poundes waight haberdepoyse; *ibid* 28: Every loade of wood ought to be 20 hundred waight, which is a tunne. **1635** Dalton 149: Timber well-hewen, and perfectly squared, fifty foot thereof maketh the load. **1665** Assize 13: They do reckon and account eighteen hundred weight of Avoirdupois weight to be the common load of Hay. **1820** Second Rep. 22: Load of bullrushes, 63 bundles . . . of hay, 36 trusses of 56 lb. each . . . of wheat is properly 5 quarters . . . of earth or gravel, 1 cubic yard = 27 cubic feet . . . of lime, 32 bushels . . . of oak bark, 45 cwt . . . of timber, round, 50 cubic feet . . . of sand, 36 bushels . . . of Scotch coals, 1 cwt . . . of birch brooms, 60 bundles.

But these and many other items had (*c*1800) local variations (Second Rep. 22–23). *North* — Durham: lime, 27 bu (*c*9.51 hl). *Northwest* — Cheshire: oatmeal, 240 lb (108.862 kg). Lancashire: barley, 6 bu (*c*2.11 hl); beans, 4½ or 5 bu (*c*1.59 or *c*1.76 hl); peas, 4½ bu (*c*1.59 hl); oats, 7½ or 9 bu (*c*2.64 or *c*3.17 hl); potatoes, generally 2 Cwt (101.604 kg); and wheat, 4½ bu (*c*1.59 hl). Westmorland: potatoes, 4½ heaped bu (*c*2.03 hl). *North Central* — Derbyshire: charcoal, 144 level bu (*c*50.74 hl); lead ore, 9 DISHES (9.909 to 11.322 dkl). *Central* — Oxfordshire: straw, 22½ Cwt (1143.045 kg). *East* — Cambridgeshire: osiers, 80 BUNCHES. Suffolk: carrots and turnips, 40 bu (*c*14.09 hl). *Southeast* — Buckinghamshire: chalk, 16 BUCKETs of 1½ bu each equal to 24 bu (*c*8.46 hl). Essex: chalk, 90 bu (*c*31.71 hl); clay, 40 bu (*c*14.09 hl); osiers, 80 BOLTS; and shingle, 24 bu (*c*8.46 hl). Hertfordshire: chalk, 22 buckets equal to 33 bu (*c*11.63 hl). Middlesex: new hay, 2160 lb (979.754 kg) or 36 TRUSSES of 60 lb each; and old hay, 2016 lb (914.436 kg) or 36 trusses of 56 lb each. *South* — Hampshire: rafter poles, 30 bundles. Surrey: chalk, 30 to 35 bu (*c*10.57 to *e*12.33 hl); hoops, 30 bundles or 1800 in number; and limestone, 40 bu (*c*14.09 hl). Sussex: limestone, 12 bu (*c*4.23 hl); oats, 80 bu (*c*28.19 hl); and wheat, 40 bu (*c*14.09 hl). *See* CARTLOAD; FOTHER; HUNDRED

loade, lod, lode. LOAD
log. LUG
lood, loode. LOAD
lug — 3–6 lugge (OED); 7–9 lug, lugg; ? log (Prior) [ME *lugge*, of

obscure origin]. A m-l generally varying from 15 to 20 ft (4.575 to 6.100 m) with 16½ ft (5.029 m) being the most common. It occasionally was equivalent to the GOAD, PERCH, POLE, and ROD. — **1669** Worlidge 330: A Perch, or Lug is sixteen foot and a half Land-measure, but is usually eighteen foot to measure Coppice-woods withal. **1696** Phillips sv pole: In measuring, it is the same with Pearch or Rod, or as some call it Lugg. **1717** Dict. Rus. sv mile: Every Furlong containing 40 Lugs or Poles; and every Lug or Pole 16 Foot and a half. **1725** Bradley sv mile: Every Furlong forty Lugs or Poles . . . every Pole sixteen Foot and a Half. **1820** Second Rep. 23: Lug or Lugg, Dorsetshire . . . 15 feet and an inch; called also Goad, used instead of a pole of 16½ . . . Hertfordshire: 20 feet . . . Wiltshire: a pole or rod of 15, 16½ or 18 feet.

lugg, lugge. LUG
lywe. LEAGUE

M

M. MIL

maand. MAUND

maen [*]. A wt of 26 lb (12.700 kg) or 4 TOPSTONS for wool (c1800) in South Wales (Second Rep. 24).

mainard — 5 mainard (Gras 2); ? maynarde (Prior) [*]. A wt of 32 lb (14.515 kg) for cheese (c1400) in Hampshire (Gras 2.718).

mais, maise, maize. MEASE

mand, mande. MAUND

mase. MEASE

mast [perh < *mass; see* OED sv mast]. A wt of 2½ lb (1.134 kg) for amber (c1800) (Second Rep. 24).

math — 6–7 mathe (OED); 6–9 math [OE *mǣth,* a mowing]. A m-a in Herefordshire equal to approximately 1 acre (0.405 ha) or to the amount of land that a man could mow in a day. — **1820** Second Rep. 24: Math, Herefordshire: mowing; a day's math is about an acre, or a day's work for a mower.

mathe. MATH

maun. MAUND

maund — 5 mawnde; 5–6 mande; 5–7 maunde, mawnd (OED); 5–9 mand (OED), maund; 7 moane (OED); 8 maand (OED); 9 maun (OED), mawn (OED), mound (OED) [ME *maund,* hand basket, < MF *mande;* akin to OE *mand,* MLG *mande*]. A m-c containing perhaps 2 or 3 pk (c1.76 or c2.64 dkl) for most goods and 2 FATTS or 8 BALES for unbound books. It was a wicker-type basket with handles. — **1420** Gras 1.472: Pro 1 fatt' vi pokis i maunde. **1439** Southampton 2.9: 1 maund calcarium et panni picti . . . 1 maunde de wastyng paper; *ibid* 41: 12 maundys pomarum; *ibid* 49: 1 mawnde panni picti. **1443** Brokage II.81: ii maundes orenges; *ibid* 111: i maunde patellarum ferrearum; *ibid* 116: i mawnde cum diversis haberdasshe et grocer; *ibid* 135: ii maundes skowryng-stonys. **1509** Gras 1.563: i maunde cum xii dossenis pannorum depictorum; *ibid* 571: 1 maunde i fat cum iiii grosses gloves; *ibid* 572: ii fardelli i cista i mande i barel trane . . . ii mandes cum ii mastis ambr[e]. **1603** Hostmen 36: Not to exceed in any one Keell or Lighter above two smale maunds or pannyers full, holdinge two or three pecks apeece. **1710** Harris 1. sv: Maund, was anciently a Measure of Capacity with us, being a kind of great Basket or Hamper containing 8 Bales, or 2 Fatts. **1717** Dict. Rus. sv fat: Fat . . . of unbound Books half a Maund or four Bales.

maunde, mawn, mawnd, mawnde. MAUND

maynarde. MAINARD

mayse, maze. MEASE

meal [ME *mel, mele* < OE *mǣl*, measure, mark, sign, fixed time]. A m-c for milk in Suffolk and Sussex (*c*1850) equal to the quantity taken from a cow at 1 milking (Cooper 60).

meas. MEASE

mease — 5 meyse; 5–6 mayse (OED); 5–9 meise; 6 meaz; 6–8 mese; 6–9 maise, meaze (OED); 7 maze (OED), mes (OED); 7–9 mease (OED), mesh (OED); 9 mais (OED), maize (OED), mase (OED), meas (OED), meash (OED) [ME *meise* < MF *maise*, a receptacle for herrings, < MLG *meise, mēse*, barrel]. A m-q for herrings, varying in number from 520 to 630, equal to ⅟₂₀ LAST. — *c*1400 Hall 41: In uno meyse allecis sunt v [×] c et xx: Item xx meyses faciunt lastall. *c*1550 Welsh 58: 1 maises red herring; *ibid* 201: 24 meaz of shotten herrings. **1597** Skene 1. sv mese: Of herring, conteinis fiue hundreth. **1603** Henllys 139: The meise consisteth of XXXI [×] xx of herringes. **1820** Second Rep. 24: Maise . . . of herrings, 30 score of 21 each = 630.

meash. MEASE

measure [ME *mesure* < OF *mesure* < L *mensura* < *metiri, mensus*, to measure]. A m-c (*c*1800) for several products (Second Rep. 24): apples, Guernsey and Jersey, 3 Winchester bu (1.057 hl); barley, Cheshire, 38 qt (*c*4.18 dkl); coal, Kincardineshire, 48 Scots pt (8.196 dkl); lime, Kincardineshire, 64 Scots pt (1.093 hl); malt, Cheshire, 32 to 36 qt (*c*3.52 to *c*3.96 dkl); oatmeal, Westmorland, 16 qt (*c*1.76 dkl); and potatoes, Guernsey and Jersey, 7 gal (*c*3.08 dkl).

meaz, meaze. MEASE

meel. MELL

meiliaid [*]. A m-c for grain in Llandovery (*c*1800) equal to ¼ bu (*c*8.81 l) (Second Rep. 24).

meise. MEASE

mel, mele. MELL

mell — 5 mel (Fab. Rolls), mell (Prior), miell (Fab. Rolls); ? meel (Prior), mele (Prior) [*see* MEAL]. A m-c for lime and other dry products (*c*1400) generally equal to 2 SEAMS (*c*5.64 hl) (Prior 167).

merk [prob var of *mark*, boundary, limit, border, < ME *marke*, *merke* < OE *mearc*, *merc*]. A m-a for land in Shetland (*c*1800) varying from ½ to 2 acres (*c*0.20 to *c*0.81 ha) (Second Rep. 24).

mes, mese, mesh. MEASE

met — 3–7 L mitta; 3–9 met; 6 mett (Shuttleworths); 7 mette (Best); ? L metra (Prior) [OE *gemet*, a measure]. A m-c for grain and other dry products generally containing 2 bu (*c*7.05 dkl), but variations from ½ bu (*c*1.76 dkl) to more than 2 bu were not uncommon. — *c*1200 Rameseia III.158: Et quatuor communes ringæ, duo busselli, faciunt mittam gruti. . . . Et quinque communes ringæ brasei et præbendæ faciunt mittam; *ibid* 159: Et hoc facto, continet mitta gruti quatuor communes ringas, duos bussellos. **1674** Ray 48: A Met: a Strike or four Pecks . . . in York-sh. two Strike. **1678** Du Cange sv mitta: Mensuræ salariæ et frumentariæ species, a Saxonico mitten, mensura.

metra, mett, mette. MET

meyse. MEASE

miell. MELL

mil — 3 L miliare, L millarium; 3–9 L M., mil; 4 L milliare; 7 L miliarium [L *mille*, thousand]. Equivalent to THOUSAND. — **1202** Feet 3.196: Et sex millariorum et duodecim stikarum anguillarum. *c*1253 Hall 11: Le last de arang' est de xM., et checun mil est de x cent, et chescun cent de vi [×] xx. **1290** Fleta 119: Lestus autem allecii consistit ex x. miliaribus et quodlibet miliare consistit ex decies centum, et quodlibet centum ex secies viginti. **1303** Gras 1.160: M ceparum . . . . M de stagno; *ibid* 161: M de cupro; *ibid* 162: M pellium squirellorum; *ibid* 166: Milliare ceparum. **1304** *Ibid* 168: Pro xM ferri. **1396** *Ibid* 437: MMMM tunholt. *c*1461 Hall 13: Also of this Weyght there goo v [×] xx [+] xii lb. to the C; and x [×] c make a M of ony weyght. . . . xxviij lb. [make a quarter Cwt]; lvj lb. make half a C; v [×] xx [+] xij lb. make a

C . . . and x [×] c make a M; *ibid* 17: Also stocke fyssche ys sold by vi [×] xx and a M fysschys make a last. **1507** Gras 1.695: All blades for shomakrs the M . . . Bodkyns the M . . . Ballys the M. **1524** *Ibid* 196: Pro uno M hoopis. **1549** *Ibid* 627: Pro M waight rosen'. **1678** Du Cange sv miliarium: Mille pondo librarum.

mile — 2–5 L miliarium; 3 L miliarius; 3–7 myle; 4 L mileare, L miliare; 4–6 myl (OED); 5 myill (OED); 5–6 mylle (OED); 7 mille OED), L milliarus; 7–9 mile [ME *myle* < OE *mīl* < L *milia*, miles (< *milia passuum*, thousands of paces), pl of *mille*, mile, < *mille passus*, thousand paces, < *mille*, thousand]. A m-l, standardized under Elizabeth I at 5280 ft (1.609 km) or 1760 yd, equal to 8 FURLONGS of 40 PERCHES each, the perch containing 16½ ft. Prior to standardization several other lengths for the mi were common: 5000 ft (*c*1.52 km) or 1000 paces of 5 ft each; 5000 ft (*c*1.52 km) or 8 furlongs of 125 paces each, the pace containing 5 ft; 6600 ft (*c*2.01 km) or 10 furlongs of 220 ft each; and for the *Old English* mi, 1500 paces, the pace varying in size from one region to another. — *c*1300 Hall 7: Unde 5 pedes faciunt passum, et 125 passus faciunt stadium [furlong]; et 8 stadia faciunt mileare Anglicum. *c*1325 Rameseia I.76: Pedes quinque passum; passus centum viginti et quinque unum stadium. Stadio octo unum miliarium. **1395** York Mem. 1.142: Item, quinque pedes faciunt passum; centum et triginta [*sic*] quinque passus faciunt stadium; octo stadia faciunt miliare Anglie. *c*1400 Hall 5: Stadium passus 125 constat. Miliarium 8 stadia, i.[e.] passus mille continet. *c*1461 *Ibid* 14: And there go viij forelonges to a myle, in Yngland. **1502** Arnold 204: V fote make a pace . . . CXXV pace make a furlong and VIII furlong make an English myle. **1592** Berriman 170: A myle to conteyne eight furlongs and every furlong to conteyne fortie luggs or poles and ev'y lugg or pole to conteyne sixteen foot and half. **1616** Hopton 165: Also an English mile is 8 Furlong, 88 scores, 320 pearches, 1056 paces . . . 1760 yards, 5280 feet, 63360 Inches. **1635** Dalton 150: Note that our English mile containes 280 foot more than the Italian mile . . . of 1000 paces, and five foot to a pace. **1665** Sheppard 25: Forty Pole in length make a Furlong; eight Furlongs or 320 Pole, an English Mile. **1682** Hall 29: A Myle is 8 furlongs, or 320 pearches. **1688** Bernardi 202: Pes Anglicus . . . ⅟₆₆₀ Stadii aut Furlongi, et ⅟₅₂₈₀ Milliaris Anglici. **1708** Chamberlayne 207: 8 Furlong or 320 Perch make an English Mile, which . . . ought to be 1760 Yards, 5280 Foot, that is 280 Foot more than the Italian Mile. **1717** Dict. Rus. sv furlong: Furlong . . . contains 40 Poles . . . in length, being the eighth part of a Mile.

mileare. MILE

miliare, miliarium. MIL; MILE

miliarius. MILE

millarium. MIL

mille. MILE

milliare. MIL

milliarus. MILE

mitta. MET

moane, mound. MAUND

mount [prob *mount*, a high hill (here, of material), < ME *mount*, *munt*, *mont* < OE *munt* and OF *mont*, both < L *mons, montis*]. A wt of 3 M (1524.060 kg) for plaster of Paris (*c*1800) (Second Rep. 24). *See* THOUSAND

mow — 5–7 L muwes; 7 mow [ME *mowe* < OE *mūga, mūha, mŭwa*, mow, heap]. A m-c for grain and other dry products. — **1678** Du Cange sv muwes: Mensuræ species, nisi ab Angl. *Mow*, quod acervum, cumulum sonat, accersas.

muchkin. MUTCHKIN

mug — 6 mugge (OED); 6–9 mug; 7–8 mugg (OED) [cf Sw *mugg*, Nor *mugge, mugga*, an open can or jug]. A m-c for ale in Bedfordshire containing 1 pt (*c*0.55 l). It was generally a cylindrical earthenware vessel, often having a handle. — **1820** Second Rep. 24: Mug, Bedfordshire: of ale, a pint.

mugg, mugge. MUG

musking, mutchin, mutchken. MUTCHKIN

mutchkin — 6 musking (OED), mutskin (OED), mychkin (OED); 6–9 mutchkin; 7 mutchin (OED), mwching (OED); 8 muchkin (OED), mutchken (OED), mutchkine (OED) [ME (Sc) muchekyn; cf Du *mudseken*, a liquid measure]. A m-c for liquids in Scotland containing 4 GILLS (*c*0.43 l) and equal to ¼ Scots pt or ½ CHOPPIN. — **1820** Second Rep. 24: Mutchkin, Scotland: ¼ pint = ½ a chopin = 4 gills.

mutchkine, mutskin. MUTCHKIN

muwes. MOW

mwching, mychkin. MUTCHKIN

myill, myl, myle, mylle. MILE

N

naggin. NOGGIN

nail — 3 neil (OED), neile (OED); 3–7 naile (OED), nayle; 4–5 naill
(OED), naille (OED), nayll (OED), naylle (OED); 4–6 nale (OED);
4–7 nayl (OED); 4–9 nail; 6 neayle (OED); 6–7 neale (OED) [ME
nail < OE *nægl; see* WNID3]. A m-l for cloth, originally a unit of
body measurement referring to the last two joints of the middle
finger, taken equal to $\frac{1}{2}$ FINGER, $\frac{1}{4}$ SPAN, and $\frac{1}{8}$ CUBIT. Based on
the ft of 12 inches, it was made equal to $2\frac{1}{4}$ inches (5.715 cm) or
$\frac{1}{16}$ yd. It was also a wt synonymous with the CLOVE. — *c*1461
Hall 13: Also woll is weyd by this weyght, butt itt is nott rekynnyd
soo, for ytt is bowght odyr by the nayle. . . . vij lb. make a nayle;
ibid 19: For thai use to by or sell most comynly odyr by the Clawe,
the Nayle. *c*1590 *Ibid* 23: 7 poundes waight haberdepoyse is the
halfe stonne or clave of woole, or nayle. . . . 7 pounds daberdepoyse [*sic*] is the claue or nayle of woole. **1696** Jeake 80: Beef, in 1
Nail, 8 Pounds of common use. **1820** Second Rep. 24: Nail of
cloth: $\frac{1}{16}$ yard = $2\frac{1}{4}$ inches.

**naile, naill, naille, nale, nayl, nayle, nayll, naylle, neale, neayle, neil,
neile.** NAIL

niperkin. NIPPERKIN

nipperkin — 7 niperkin (OED); 7–8 knipperkin (OED); 7–9 nipperkin [cf Du *nippertje*, a small measure for liquor, and Du *nippen*, to
sip]. A m-c for liquor (*c*1600) containing no more than $\frac{1}{2}$ pt (*c*0.24
l) (Shipley 455).

nive [perh < MF *niveau, nivel*, alter of *livel*, level]. A m-c for salt
(*c*1550) containing 7 bbl (*c*10.36 hl) (Welsh 178).

noggan. NOGGIN

noggin — 7 nogging (OED); 7–9 noggin; 8 knoggin (OED), noggan
(OED); 8–9 naggin (OED) [cf E *nog*, ale]. A m-c for liquids (*c*1600)
generally containing $\frac{1}{2}$ pt (*c*0.24 l) and sometimes synonymous
with the GILL (Jones 90).

nogging. NOGGIN

nok, noke. NOOK

nook — 3–4 nok (OED); 4–6 noke (OED); 4, 6–7 nouke (OED); 5–7 nooke; 6 noque (OED); 6–7 nook (OED) [ME *nok, noke;* cf Nor dial *nok*, hook, bent figure]. A m-a for land in northern England and Scotland containing 20 acres (*c*8.10 ha) and equal to 2 FAR-THINGDALES of 10 acres each. — **1634** Noy 57: You must note, that two Fardells of Land make a Nooke of Land, and two Nookes make halfe a yard of Land.

nooke, noque, nouke. NOOK

O

oenophorum — 3 L anaphorum (Chron. Abing.), L enoforium (Chron. Abing.), L oenophorum, L onophorium [L *oeno* < Gr *oino* < *oinos*, wine, + L *phorum* < Gr *phoros*, bearer]. A m-c for wine equal to a gal (*c*3.78 l). — *c*1275 Chron. Abing. II.339: Primo die admissionis abbatis Abbendonæ debet in refectorio discumbere; conventui necessariæ in cibis et potibus honorifice invenire; scilicet, onophorium, id est galonem vini, unicuique placentam integram, tria fercula piscium honorabilia, exceptis ferculis de consistorio per tabulas in invicem succedentibus; *ibid* 394: In duobus anniversariis, scilicet, Faricii, Vincentii inveniet in refectorio, unicuique monacho oenophorum, id est, galonem vini, et his fercula piscium honorabilia, excepto generali et aliis ferculis consuetudinariis; *ibid* 400: Quoties conventus oenophorum, id est, galonem, habuerit, refectorarius, excepto communi, obbatam vini habebit, obbaque prioris implebitur.

oince. OUNCE

omber, ombor, ombra. AMBER

once. OUNCE

onophorium. OENOPHORUM

oonce. OUNCE

ordeum. BARLEYCORN

osken, oskin. OXGANG

ounc. OUNCE

ounce — 3–6 unce; 3–7 L uncia; 5 once (OED), ouns (OED), owns (OED), oyns (OED), unch (OED), vunce (OED); 5–9 ounce; 6 oince (OED), oonce (OED), ounc (OED), ownce (OED), ownche (OED) [ME *unce* < MF *unce* < L *uncia*, a twelfth, the twelfth part, ounce, inch]. A unit of wt in the ap, avdp, merc, tow, English t, and Scots t systems.

The ap oz contained 24 s, or 8 dr, or 480 t gr (31.103 g), and was equal to $\frac{1}{12}$ ap lb of 5760 gr (373.242 g). — *c*1600 Hall 36: Scrupuli

is 20 barley cornes . . . 3 scruples contain a drachme . . . 8 drachmes, an ounce. **1688** Bernardi 137: Vel more Pharmacopolarum:
Libra de Troy, 12 Unciæ . . . 96 = 12 × 8 drachmæ ℥: Scripuli
℈. 288 = 96 × 3: grana monetaria rursus 5760 = 288 × 20.
1708 Chamberlayne 205: The Apothecaries reckon 20 Grains Gr.
make a Scruple ℈, 3 scruples 1 Drachm ℥, 8 Drachm 1 Ounce ℥,
12 Ounces 1 Pound ℔. **1728** Chambers 1.360: The Apothecaries
also use the Troy Pound, Ounce, and Grain; but they differ from
the rest, in the intermediate Divisions.—They divide the Ounce
into 8 Drachms; the Drachm into 3 Scruples; and the Scruple into
20 Grains.

The avdp oz contained $437\frac{1}{2}$ gr (28.350 g) and was equal to $\frac{1}{16}$
avdp lb of 7000 gr (453.592 g). It was sometimes erroneously
described as the equivalent of the t oz of 480 gr (31.103 g), thereby
making it equal to $\frac{1}{16}$ lb of 7680 gr (497.664 g). Actually the avdp
oz was $42\frac{1}{2}$ gr (2.754 g) lighter than the t oz. Nonetheless, because
of its greater number of the smaller oz, the avdp lb was 1240 gr
heavier than the t lb. — *c*1400 Hall 37: 16 uncie . . . faciunt
libram. **1474** Cov. Leet 396: & xx sterling makith a Ounce of
haburdepeyse; and xvj Ouncez makith a li. **1635** Dalton 143:
And this hath to the pound xvi ounces. **1682** Hall 29: Aver-du-
pois conteynes: every pound, 16 ounces; every ounce, 8 drgmes
[*sic*]; every dragme, 3 scruples; every scruple, 20 graines. . . . But
the ounce Troy is greater than the ounce Averd.; for 73 ounces
Troy are equall to 80 ounces Aver-du-pois. **1688** Bernardi 135:
Insuper uncia Avoirdupois pro mercibus caducis explicat 8
drachmas aut 3 × 8 = 24 scripulos Avoirdupois . . . et vero $\frac{1}{16}$
libræ suæ unciæ Romanæ prorsus æqualis ideoque $\frac{1}{12}$ libræ
Romanæ. **1717** Dict. Rus. sv: Ounce . . . the Sixteenth part of a
Pound Avoir-du-Pois. **1820** Second Rep. 24: Ounce . . . Avoirdupois, $\frac{1}{16}$ lb. = $^{7000}\!/_{16}$ = $437\frac{1}{2}$ grains troy.

The merc and tow oz contained 450 gr (29.160 g), but the merc
oz equaled $\frac{1}{15}$ merc lb of 6750 gr (437.400 g), while the tow oz
equaled $\frac{1}{12}$ tow lb of 5400 gr (349.920 g). Both oz were determined
as 20 dwt, the dwt being 32 wheat gr ($22\frac{1}{2}$ t gr or barleycorns),
and hence each merc or tow oz equaled 640 wheat gr or 450 t gr or
barleycorns. — *c*1253 Hall 11: En lituaris e confeciuns la liver est
de xii uncis; en tutes autre chosis la li. est de xv uncis. **1290** Fleta
119: Item denarius sterlingus, sicut dictum est, ponderat xxxij. d.

facit vnciam, et quindecim vncie faciunt libram mercatoriam. . . . Sterlingus . . . debet ponderare xxxij. grana frumenti mediocra. Et vnde xx. d. faciunt vnciam et xij. vncie faciunt libram xx. s. in pondere et numero. *c*1400 Hall 7: Le denier d'Engleterre round et sanz tonsure poisera xxxii greins de froument en my le spic. Et xx d. font la unce.

The Scots t oz contained 475$\frac{1}{2}$ gr (30.812 g) or 16 DROPS of 29.72 gr each (1.926 g), and was equal to $\frac{1}{16}$ Scots t lb of 7609 gr (493.063 g). The English t oz contained 480 gr (31.103 g) and was equal to $\frac{1}{12}$ t lb of 5760 gr (373.242 g). Consisting of 20 dwt of 24 gr each, the English t oz was 30 gr (1.944 g) heavier than the merc and tow oz and 42$\frac{1}{2}$ gr (2.754 g) heavier than the avdp oz. It was also the standard for the ap oz of 480 gr (31.103 g), the only difference being that the ap oz was divided into 8 dr (3.888 g) of 60 gr each or 24 s (1.296 g) of 20 gr each, while the t oz was divided into 20 dwt (31.103 g) of 24 gr each. — *c*1590 Hall 22: The coyners in the Towre allowith but 24 grayns to a peny sterlinge waight [= $\frac{1}{20}$ t oz]. 1606 *Ibid* 38: Ffor 24 graines or barleycornes, drie, out of the middest of the eare, doe make a 1 d.[wt] . . . Soe the pounde waight is 12 oz . . . or 5760 graines. 1616 Hopton 159: Euery ounce, 20 peny weight, euery peny weight 24 graines. 1635 Dalton 143: Troy weight . . . hath to the pound xii. ounces. 1665 Sheppard 15: Twenty penny weight make an ounce; 24 grains make a penny weight. 1682 Hall 29: Troy weight conteynes: every pound, 12 ounces; every ounce, 20 penny weight; every penny weight, 24 graines. 1688 Bernardi 134–35: Uncia Anglica de Troy . . . 480 grana argenti triticive; *ibid* 137: Libra Anglica de Troy. 12 Unciæ . . . 12 × 20 = 240 p.w. 1708 Chamberlayne 205: 20 Pennyweight make one Ounce. 1717 Dict. Rus. sv troy-weight: Twenty Penny-weight make one Ounce; and twelve Ounces one Pound. 1805 Macpherson I.471: 20 pennies (of money) 1 ounce, 12 ounces 1 pound of London.

ouns, ownce, ownche, owns. OUNCE

oxeland, oxelande. OXLAND

oxengate. OXGATE

oxgang — 7 oxgange; 7–8 oskin (OED), ox-going (OED); 7–9 osken, oxgang [ox < OE *oxa* + gang < OE *gang;* akin to Du and G *gang,* a going, ON *gangr,* Goth *gaggs,* street, way]. A m-a for land generally synonymous with the BOVATE but occasionally described as the equivalent of either the VIRGATE or the HIDE. Like the acreage of other superficial measures, the total acreage of the oxgang depended on local soil conditions, but oxgangs of 7, 8, 10, 12, 13, 15, 16, 18, 20, 24, 30, and 50 acres (*c*2.83 to *c*20.25 ha) seem to have been the most common. It was sometimes called OXGATE and OXLAND. — **1665** Sheppard 23–24: An Oxgange of Land (in Latine *Bovata terræ*) is not a certain quantity of Land, as Fifteen acres, whereof 8 acres make a Plough Land. But (as some say) six Oxganges of Land seem to be as much as six Oxen will plow . . . . And some would say it alwayes to contain 13 Acres, and that four Oxengates is a pound Land of old extent. **1777** Nicol. and Burn 613: Oxgang of land, as much as one yoke of oxen can plough in a year. **1829** Brockett 222: Osken . . . an oxgang of land . . . varying in quantity in different townships, according to the extent of ground. . . . In our old laws it meant as much as an ox-team could plough in a year.

oxgange. OXGANG

oxgate — 7 oxengate; 9 oxgate (OED) [*ox* + *gate; see* OXGANG]. Equivalent to OXGANG. — **1665** Sheppard 23–24: And some would say it alwayes to contain 13 Acres, and that four Oxengates is a pound Land of old extent.

ox-going. OXGANG

oxland — 7 oxeland (OED), oxelande; 9 oxland [*ox* + *land; see* OXGANG]. Equivalent to OXGANG. — **1603** Henllys 135: viii acres make an Oxelande . . . viii oxelandes make a ploweland being . . . 64 acr. **1820** Second Rep. 24: Ox-Land, Glamorganshire and Pembrokeshire: 8 customary acres.

oyns. OUNCE

P

paame. PALM

paas. PACE

pace — 1–7 L passus; 3–5 pas (OED); 4–5 paas (OED), pass (OED), passe (OED); 4–7 pase; 4–9 pace; 5 pasce (OED); 5–6 pais (OED), paiss (OED); 6 paice (OED) [ME *pace, pas* < OF *pas* < L *passus,* a step, pace]. A m-l generally equal to 2 STEPS or approximately 5 ft (*c*1.52 m). — *c*1100 Hall 3: Passus v pedes habet. *c*1289 Bray 10: Quinque pedes passum faciunt. *c*1300 Hall 7: Unde 5 pedes faciunt passum, et 125 passus faciunt stadium. *c*1325 Rameseia I.76: Passus pedes quinque. **1395** York Mem. 1.142: Item, quinque pedes faciunt passum. *c*1400 Hall 5: Passus v pedes habet. *c*1461 *Ibid* 14: And also V fote make a pase. **1616** Hopton 165: Also an English mile is . . . 1056 paces. **1635** Dalton 150: Five foot doe make a Geometricall Pace. **1665** Sheppard 16: 5 foot a Geometrical pace. **1688** Bernardi 202: Pes Anglicus . . . ⅕ Passus Geometrici aut Agri mensorii. **1708** Chamberlayne 207: 5 Foot make a Geometrical Pace. **1717** Dict. Rus. sv: A Geometrical Pace consists of Five Foot, and a thousand such Paces, make up a Mile.

pack — 3–6 pak; 3–7 packe; 4–5 pakke; 4–9 pack; 5 pakk; 5–6 pake [ME *pak, packe, pakke,* of LG origin; *see* OED]. A m-c and m-q for many products: cloth, generally 10 PIECES; flax, 240 lb (108.862 kg); teasels, generally 9000 heads for kings and 20,000 heads for middlings, except in Yorkshire, 1350 bunches of 10 heads each or 13,500 in all; wool, 240 lb (108.862 kg); and yarn, 4 Cwt or 480 lb (217.724 kg). — **1228** Gras 1.157: 1 pak mailede. **1443** Brokage II.27: Flaxe the pack untrussed . . . . Cum iiii pakkes de pannys; *ibid* 119: 1 pak straytes; *ibid* 158: Cum ii pakkys cerseyse. *c*1461 Hall 16: Also clothe is sold by numbyr, for x hole clothys make a pak. **1466** Gras 1.614: Pro i pakke lewent. *c*1475 *Ibid* 192: Of a pakke of wulle cloth. **1507** *Ibid* 695: Brusshys the packe; *ibid* 698: Flexe the pake containing xx [✕] c lbs.; *ibid* 699: Hather the packe that contains as moche as a packe of wolle; *ibid* 704: Torche waxe the pack. **1509** *Ibid* 562: ii packes canvas continent' iii [✕] m ulnarum; *ibid* 566: i packe cum ii bages ginger continent iii [✕] c libras; *ibid* 590: Pro ii packes cum xii [✕] c goodes cotonrusset. **1555** York Mer. 156: A pake of clothe, sixtene pence; a small trusse, as the parties canne agree, so that it excede not the price of the pake, to be rated after the qualitie thereof. **1562** *Ibid* 168–69: A packe of clothe, xx d. **1665** Sheppard 66: And further, That a Pack of Wooll is a horseload, consisting of 17 stone and two pounds. **1717** Dict. Rus. sv: Pack of Wooll, is 17 Stone and 2 Pounds, or 240 Pound weight. **1820** Second Rep. 25: Pack of yarn, 4 hundred weight, each of 120 lb . . . of teazles, 9000 heads of kings; 20000 of middlings . . . Huntingdonshire: of wool, 240 lb . . . Kent: of flax, 240 lb . . . Yorkshire, N.R. of teazles, 1350 bunches of 10 each = 13500.

packe. PACK

packet — 4 pakett; 6–9 packet, pacquet (OED); 7 paquette (OED); 8–9 paquet (OED) [ME *pakett,* dim of ME *pak; see* PACK]. A m-c and m-q probably equal to a small PACK or BUNDLE. — **1304** Gras 1.168: Pro i pakett' canabi. **1820** Second Rep. 25: Packet of leaf metal, 250 leaves.

pacquet. PACKET

paice. PACE

paier. PAIR

pair — 3–5 peire (OED), peyre (OED); 4–5 pare (OED); 4–6 payr; 4–7 paire, payre; 4–9 pair (OED); 5 payir (OED), peyer (OED), peyr (OED); 5–6 par (OED), payer; 6 paier (OED), parre (OED), pere (OED) [ME *peire, paire* < OF *paire* < L *paria,* neut pl of *par,* equal]. A m-q consisting of 2 of the same item or sets of items. — **1443** Brokage II.293: Et xvii payr shetes. **1500** Relation 126: A payre of hosyn of skarlet . . . . Two payre of hosyn, skarlet, garded with crymsyn velvet; *ibid* 127: A paire of stirropes . . . . A paire of buskyns of blacke velvet . . . . A payre of arminge spores; *ibid* 128: iij. payre of shoes of whyte clothe . . . . iij. paire of yellow clothe . . . . A payre of arminge shoes . . . . A payre of slippers of redd letter; *ibid* 129: A payre of slippers of black lether . . . . A payre of fustyans. **1507** Gras 1.703: Shermans sheres the payer. **1532** Finchale cccclxix: j payr ballans and j balk of yron. **1615**

Collect. Stat. 465: And a dicker of gloues consisteth of ten paire of gloues.

paire. PAIR

pais, paiss. PACE

pak, pake. PACK

pakett. PACKET

pakk, pakke. PACK

palm — 1–4 L palma; 1–7 L palmus; 4–6 pame (OED), paume (OED), pawme (OED); 5 paame (OED); 5–6 paulme (OED); 5–7 palme (OED); 7–9 palm [ME *paume* < MF *paume* < L *palma*]. A m-l, originally a unit of body measurement referring to a hand's breadth, which was equal to ⅓ SPAN or ⅙ cubit. Based on the ft of 12 inches, it was made equal to 3 inches (7.62 cm). — *c*1100 Hall 5: Palma extensa est xii digitorum . . . compressa est iiii digita. *c*1300 *Ibid* 7: Et tres pollices faciunt palmam. *c*1325 Rameseia I.76: Palmus autem quatuor digitos habet. **1395** York Mem. 1.142: Et tres pollices faciunt palmam. *c*1400 Hall 6: Quattuor palmi faciunt pedem. **1665** Assize 6: The foot to contain four palms, and every palm containeth four fingers breadth. **1688** Bernardi 193: Palmus— 3 unciæ aut pollices. **1708** Chamberlayne 209: Foot . . . 4 Palm. **1716** Harris 2. sv measure: Palm . . . 3 Inch. **1717** Dict. Rus. sv hand-breadth: A Measure of three Inches. **1820** Second Rep. 25: Palm, sometimes denotes 3 inches.

palma, palme, palmus, pame. PALM

paquet, paquette. PACKET

par, pare. PAIR

pared [*]. A m-l of 3 yd (2.743 m) for cloth in Montgomeryshire (*c*1800) (Second Rep. 25).

parre. PAIR

partica. PERCH

pas, pasce, pase, pass, passe, passus. PACE

paulme, paume, pawme. PALM

payer, payir, payr, payre. PAIR

peace. PIECE

pearch, pearche. PERCH

pease, peax, peayce. PIECE

pec. PECK

peccaid [perh < E PECK]. A m-c for grain in southern and eastern

Wales (*c*1800) containing 5 to 6 gal (*c*2.20 to *c*2.64 dkl) and some-times synonymous with the HOBED and HOOP (Second Rep. 25).

peccum, peccus. PECK

pece, pecia. PIECE

peck — 4 pec, L peccum; 4–6 pek (Nottingham), pekke (OED); 4–9 peck; 5–6 peke (OED); 5–7 pecke; 7 L peccus, pect (OED) [ME *pek* < OF *pek*, of obscure origin]. A m-c for grain and other dry products, generally containing 2 gal (8.810 l) and equal to ¼ Winchester bu. — **1315** Ireland xxxv: Quilibet crannocus [avenarum] continebit quindecim pecks cumulatos boni et mundi bladi. **1319** *Ibid* xxxv: Quiquidem crannocus [avenarum] continebit sexdecim pecks cumulatos boni, sicci et mundi bladi. **1351** Rot. Parl. 2.240: Soient les Mesures, c'est assaver bussell, di. bussell, et pec. **1384** Rot. Parl. 4.185: Vide*lice*t Busselli, dimidii Busselli, & Peck. **1390** Henry Derby 6: Et j pecco auenarum. **1392** *Ibid* 73: Super officio salsarie per manus eiusdem pro j. pecco farine frumenti per ipsum empto ibidem, iiij scot. pr. **1430** Rot. Parl. 5.432: Vide*lice*t, Bus-selli, Dimidii Busselli, et Peck. *c*1590 Hall 20: 4 peckes makith a bushell of Winchester measure, accordinge to the owld standart: 2 galons makith a pecke. **1603** Hostmen 36–37: Holdinge two or three pecks apeece. **1615** Collect. Stat. 468: That the said water measure within the shipboard shall only containe fiue pecks after the said standard rased and stricken. **1616** Hopton 162: Whereof are made Pints, Quarts, Pottles, Gallons, Peckes, Halfe-bushels, Bushels. **1635** Dalton 144: Eight quarts maketh the peck . . . 4 peckes maketh the Bushell. **1665** Sheppard 15: And 4 Pecks make the Bushell. **1682** Hall 30: 1 Last conteynes . . . 80 Bushels, 320 Peckes, 640 Gallons. **1688** Bernardi 69: Bussellus Anglicanus . . . continens in se Peccos 4. Galones siccos 8. **1708** Chamberlayne 212: 2 . . . Gallons makes a Peck . . . 4 Pecks a Bushel. **1717** Dict. Rus. sv: Peck, an English dry Measure containing two Gallons; the fourth part of a Bushel. **1820** Second Rep. 25: Peck, ¼ bushel = 2 gallons = 4 quarterns . . . of flour and salt, generally reck-oned 14 lbs.

pecke, pect. PECK

peece. PIECE

peerch. PERCH

pees, peese. PIECE

peget [perh akin to ME *pegge*, LG *pegel*, a stake, MLG *pegel*, a watermark, a gauge rod, a measure of wine, OE *pægel*, a wine measure]. A m-c in Wales at Anglesey and Caernarvon (*c*1800) for corn, 2 HOBEDS equal to 8 Winchester bu (2.819 hl), and lime, 4 Winchester bu (1.409 hl) (Second Rep. 26).

peice. PIECE

peire. PAIR

peis, peise. PIECE

pek, peke, pekke. PECK

penningus, penny. PENNYWEIGHT

pennyweight — 5–7 peny; 6–7 penyweight; 6–9 pennyweight; 7 L penningus; 7–9 penny [ME *peny* < OE *penig, penning*, + WEIGHT]. A wt in both the t and tow systems. It was originally the wt of a silver penny which equaled $\frac{1}{240}$ of a tow lb, and, as a unit of currency, was called either a denarius or a sterling. The t dwt contained 24 gr or barleycorns (1.555 g) and was equal to $\frac{1}{20}$ t oz of 480 gr (31.103 g), while the tow dwt contained 32 wheat gr, or $22\frac{1}{2}$ t gr (1.458 g), and was equal to $\frac{1}{20}$ tow oz of 450 gr (29.160 g). — *c*1200 Caernarvon 242: Per discrecionem tocius Regni Anglie fuit mensura Domini Regis compoia videlicet quod denarius Anglican qui vocat Sterlingus rotundus & sine tonsura ponderabit xxx . . . & duo g[ra]na frumenti in medio spici. **1290** Fleta 119: Sterlingus . . . debet ponderare xxxij grana frumenti mediocra. *c*1300 Hall 8: Denarius . . . ponderabit xxxii grana frumenti rubei, in medio spice assumpta. **1474** Cov. Leet 396: xxxii graynes of whete take out of the mydens of the Ere makith a sterling other-wyse called a peny. **1540** Recorde 133: As 24 Barley-corns dry, and taken out of the middest of the Ear, do make a penny weight, 20 of those peny weights make an ounce. *c*1590 Hall 22: The coyners in the Towre allowith but 24 grayns to a peny sterlinge waight. **1606** *Ibid* 38: Ffor 24 graines or barleycornes, drie, out of the middest of the eare, doe make a 1 d.[wt]. **1615** Collect. Stat. 467: And euerie ounce containe twentie sterlings, and euerie sterling be of the weight of two and thirtie cornes of wheat that grew in the middest of the eare of the wheat. **1616** Hopton 159: And this Troy weight containes in euery pound 12 ounces, euery ounce 20 peny weight, euery peny weight 24 graines. **1635** Dalton 144: 32 Wheat cornes taken in the midst of the eare, weigheth 1.d. sterling. **1665** Assize 1: And two and thirty grains of Wheat make the whole sterling peny. **1682** Hall 29: Troy weight conteynes: every pound, 12 ounces; every ounce, 20 penny weight; every penny weight, 24 graines. **1688** Bernardi 134–35: Uncia Anglica de Troy. 8 Drachmæ. $8 \times 3 = 24$ Scripuli. $8 \times 3 \times 20$ [denarii] = 480 grana argenti triticive; *ibid* 165: Denarius Elizabethæ regumque sequentium, Penningus novus Anglorum . . . $\frac{1}{240}$ libræ. **1710** Harris 1. sv weights: The Original of all our English Weights, was a Corn of Wheat . . . 32 of these made one Penny-Weight, or were the Weight of the Penny-Sterling: Twenty of these Pence or Penny-Weight, were to make an Ounce. **1717** Dict. Rus. sv: Pennyweight; this consists of 24 Grains . . . of these 20 make an Ounce Troy. **1728** Chambers 1.360: In Troy Weight, 24 . . . Grains make a Penny-weight Sterling; 20 Penny-weight make an Ounce. **1787** Liber xi: The Statute intituled *Assisa Panis et Cervisiæ*, made in the 51st year of King Henry III. ordained, That an English Penny, called a Sterling, round, and without clipping, should weigh 32 wheat grains in the midst of the ear; and that 20 of those penny-weights should make an ounce. **1790** Jefferson 1.986: According to the subdivision for gold and silver, the ounce is divided into twenty pennyweights, and the pennyweight into twenty-four grains. **1793** Leake 18: A Penny-weight, or the twentieth Part of an Ounce. **1820** Second Rep. 26: Penny-Weight . . . Formerly $\frac{1}{240}$ of a money or tower pound, weighing $22\frac{1}{2}$ grains . . . at present 24 grains, $\frac{1}{240}$ of troy pound.

peny, penyweight. PENNYWEIGHT

percata terre. PERCH OF LAND

perch — 1–7 L pertica; 3–6 perche, 5–9 perch; 6 pearche (OED); 6–8 pearch; 7 peerch (OED); ? partica (Prior) [ME *perche* < OF *perche* < L *pertica*, pole, long staff, measuring rod]. A m-l for land, generally containing $16\frac{1}{2}$ ft or $5\frac{1}{2}$ yd (5.029 m), but perches of 9, $9\frac{1}{3}$, 10, 11, $11\frac{1}{2}$, 12, 15, 16, 18, $18\frac{1}{4}$, $18\frac{3}{4}$, $19\frac{1}{2}$, 20, 21, 22, $22\frac{1}{2}$, 24, 25, and 26 ft (2.743 to 7.925 m) were also used. Perches of $16\frac{1}{2}$ ft and smaller were usually agricultural land measures, while those larger than $16\frac{1}{2}$ ft were used by woodsmen in the forest regions and by town craftsmen engaged in draining, fencing, hedging, and walling operations. — *c*1100 Hall 4: Duo vero passus decem pedam perticam faciunt. . . . Pertica ad manus xv pedes habet. **1214** Cur. Reg. 14.283: Sed ad perticam xxvj. pedum. **1229** Close 1.186–87: Mandatum est Hugoni de Nevill' et sociis suis, justiciariis itinerantibus ad placita foreste, quod secundum pertica continere solet vel xxiv vel xxv pedes manupedum temporibus H. regis avi regis, R. regis avunculi, et J. regis patris domini regis, sic placet domino regi et consilio suo quod pertica magis usitata et continente in longitudine xxiiij vel xxv pedes manupedum in essartis mensurandis. *c*1272 Hall 7: Et tres pedes faciunt ulnam; et quinque ulne et dimidia faciunt perticam. *c*1289 Bray 10: Et continet quaelibet pertica xvi pedes de pedibus rectis. *c*1325 Rameseia I.76: Pertica passus duos, id est pedes decem. *c*1400 Henley 8: E la perche le rey est de xvi pez et demi. *c*1461 Hall 14: Also v yerdes dim. make a perche, in London, to mete land by. **1474** Cov. Leet 397: And out of the seid yard growith a Rodde to mesure land by, the wich Rod conteyneth in lengthe V yardes & halfe. *c*1500 Hall 8: V virge dimidia faciunt perticam. **1502** Arnold 173: In dyuers odur placis . . . they mete ground by pollis gaddis and roddis some be of xviij foote some of xx fote and som xvi fote in lengith. **1537** Benese 4: The woodlande perche is communely .xviii. foote in length. . . . The perche of woodlande is longer than is the perche of fyldelande. **1540** Recorde 207: 5 yardes and a halfe make a Perche. *c*1590 Hall 27: 16 foott $\frac{1}{2}$ in lenght is a poole or a perche. **1603** Henllys 133: For in some place the pole is but ix foot, and in some place xij foote. **1616** Hopton 165: 5 yards and a halfe, a pearch. **1635** Dalton 150: Five yards and an halfe (which is 16 foot and an halfe) maketh a pole, rood, or pearch. **1647** Digges 1: Five Yards, $\frac{1}{2}$. a Pearch. **1665** Assize 6: In many countries [= districts] this Pole or Perch doth vary, as in some places it is 18 foot, and in some other places 21 foot. **1669** Worlidge 330: A Perch, or Lug is sixteen foot and a half Land-measure, but is usually eighteen foot to measure Coppice-woods withal. **1682** Hall 28: A Pearch, or a Rod, or a Pole (by statut) must be 5 yards and an half; or 16 feete and an half. But in some places of England they measure w[ith] a pearch of 12 foote called Tenant right or Court measure. In other places they measure w[ith] a pearch of 18, 20, or 24 foote, called Woodland Measure. **1688** Bernardi 197: Pes est . . . $\frac{1}{16,5}$ Perticæ Anglicæ. **1696** Phillips sv pole: In measuring, it is the same with Pearch or Rod, or as some call it Lugg: By Stat. 35 Eliz. this Measure is a length of 16 Foot and a half, but in some Countries [= districts] it consists of 18 Foot and is called Woodland-Measure; in some Places of 21 Foot termed Church-Measure; and in others of 24 Foot under the Name of Forest-Measure. **1708**

Chamberlayne 207: 16 Foot and a half make a Perch, Pole or Rod, but there are other Customary Perches or Poles, viz. Eighteen Feet for Fens and Woodland, Twenty one for Forest, Lancashire and Irish Measure, and 18¾ Scotch. **1717** Dict. Rus. sv: Perch or Pearch, a Rod or Pole, with which Land is measur'd. . . . 18 Foot is the measuring of Coppice-woods . . . . In Herefordshire, a Perch of Walling is 16 Foot and an half, a Perch of Ditching 21 Foot. **1725** Bradley sv mile: Every Furlong forty Lugs or Poles . . . every Pole sixteen Foot and a Half. **1789** Hawney 213: But in some Places the Custom is to allow 18 Feet to the Rod . . . and in some Places . . . 21 Feet. **1820** Second Rep. 26: Perch, Pole or Rod . . . Berkshire: sometimes 18 feet for rough work . . . Herefordshire: of fencing, 7 yds in length; of walling, 5½ . . . Hertfordshire: sometimes 20 ft . . . Lancashire: 5½, 6, 6½, 7, 7½ or 8 yards . . . Leicestershire: of hedging, 8 yards . . . Oxfordshire: of draining, 6 yds . . . Westmoreland: near Lancashire, 7 yds . . . Scotland: 18¼ feet. *See* GAD; LUG; POLE; ROD

perche. PERCH

perch of land — 2–5 L percata terre (terrae) [*perch of land*, trans of L *percata terre* (*terrae*)]. A m-a for land, of no standard dimensions but usually the square of the linear PERCH common in any region. — **1176** Clerkenwell 10: Et tres percatas terre iuxta vallem; *ibid* 29: Et tres percatas terre vltra vallem. **1208** Feet 2.131: Et tres percatas terre pro dimidia acra que jacent in Sewardescrot. **1291** trans in Cal. Char. 2.400: A charter, whereby Adam son of Hugh de Glentham gave to the said abbot and canons two acres of arable land and two perches of meadow in Glentham on the east side of that town. **1405** trans in Cal. Close 18.457: 2 acres 6 perches of land and 1 rood of meadow held of the prior of Bylsyngton.

pere. PAIR; STONE

pertica. PERCH

pes. FOOT; PIECE

pese, pess, pesse. PIECE

petra. STONE

peyce. PIECE

peyer, peyr, peyre. PAIR

peyss, pice. PIECE

picher, picheria. PITCHER

piece — 3–5 L pecia, pees (OED); 3–7 pece; 4 pise (OED); 4–5 peis

(OED), pice; 5 peese (OED), pes (OED), pese (Fountains), peyce (OED), pyece (OED); 5–6 pess (OED), pesse (OED); 5–8 peace (OED); 5–9 piece; 6 pease (OED), peax (OED), peayce, peise (OED), peyss (OED), pysse (OED); 6–7 peece; 6–8 peice (OED) [ME *pece* < OF *pece* < (assumed) VL *pettia* (MedL *pecia*), of Celt origin]. A m-c, m-l, m-q, and a wt for many products.

The piece occasionally was used for agricultural and metallurgical products: cheese, of uncertain wt; fruit, 4 QUARTERNS (50.802 kg) equal to ⅓ SORT; iron, ⅙ dozen (?) of uncertain wt; lead, generally 176 lb (79.832 kg); rosin, of uncertain wt; steel, ⅟₃₀ GARB of uncertain wt; tin, 1½ to 2½ Cwt (76.203 to 127.005 kg); and wax, of uncertain wt. — *c*1253 Hall 11–12: La duzeynne de fer est de vi pecis. *c*1272 Report 1.414: Garba asseris constat ex triginta peciis. . . . Duodena ferri ex sex peciis. **1290** Fleta 120: Garba vero aceri fit ex xxx. peciis. **1439** Southampton 2.21: Pro 80 peciis casiorum; *ibid* 24: 1 pecia de rosyn; *ibid* 52: Pro 169 peciis stanni pond. 41 M.C.; *ibid* 67: X peciis frute; *ibid* 87: 1 pecia plumbi pond. 5 C.; *ibid* 95: ii peciis fructui; *ibid* 108: 1 pipa continente 100 pecias de formag; *ibid* 153: 1 pecia fructui. **1443** Brokage II.13: iiii peciis rasemorum . . . et pro 1 pecia fygus; *ibid* 19: ii peciis de cera; *ibid* 259: Cum xxx peciis rasemorum ponderantibus xx [×] C. **1534** Finchale ccccxl: xij peayce [of lead] . . . 77 stone. **1615** Collect. Stat. 465: The doze*n* of yron consisteth of 6 peeces. **1820** Second Rep. 27: Piece . . . Derbyshire: of lead, at the cupolas, or smelting houses, 176¼ lb.

The piece was used most often for cloth goods, although in usage the word itself was frequently pre-empted by simply "cloth" (or F *drap*, chef, cheef, chiffe, sheet, or caput) or by the name of the particular fabric. Its length (measured by the yd or ELL) and breadth (usually measured by the QUARTER which equaled ¼ yd) varied with the quality of the fabric, its construction, its monetary value, and its place of origin or manufacture. Hence, even though the standard piece of cloth was 24 yd (*c*21.95 m) in length and 7 quarters (*c*1.60 m) in breadth, there were many exceptions: bagging (a coarse cloth) for hops, Worcestershire, 36 yd (*c*32.92 m) by 31 inches (7.874 dm); broadcloth, the standard piece except in Kent, Reading, and Sussex, 28 to 30 yd (*c*25.60 to *c*27.43 m) in length; broad Yorkshire, 24 to 25 yd (*c*21.95 to *c*22.86 m) by 4 quarters (*c*0.91 m); buckram (a stiff cotton fabric), 15 yd (*c*13.72 m) in length; Cheshire cotton, 22 yd (*c*20.12 m) by 3 quarters (*c*0.69 m); colored cloth, 26 or 28 yd (*c*23.77 or *c*25.60 m) by 5, 6, or 6½ quarters (*c*1.14, *c*1.37, or *c*1.49 m) except in Essex, Norfolk, and Suffolk, 28 to 30 yd (*c*25.60 to *c*27.43 m) by 7 quarters (*c*1.60 m); Coventry white, 29 to 31 yd (*c*26.52 to *c*28.35 m) by 7 quarters (*c*1.60 m); dornick (a heavy damask of silk, wool, or silk and wool), 28 yd (*c*25.60 m) in length; Dorsetshire flannel, 35 yd (*c*32.00 m) by 1 yd (*c*0.91 m); frieze (a coarse woolen cloth with a heavy nap on one side), 35 to 40 yd (*c*32.00 to *c*36.58 m) by 3 quarters (*c*0.69 m); fustian (a stout, twilled cotton fabric with a short nap), generally 13 ells (14.859 m) in length; Hampshire calico (a cotton cloth), 28 yd (*c*25.60 m) by 1 quarter (*c*0.23 m); kersey (a coarse woolen cloth), 16 to 18 yd (*c*14.63 to *c*16.46 m) by 4 quarters (*c*0.91 m) except in Devonshire, 12 to 14 yd (*c*10.97 to *c*12.80 m) by 4 quarters (*c*0.91 m); Lancashire cotton, 22 yd (*c*20.12 m) by 3 quarters (*c*0.69 m); Lancashire washer, 15 to 18 yd (*c*13.72 to *c*16.46 m) in length; lawn (a fine, sheer, plain-woven linen or cotton cloth), 18 yd (*c*16.46 m) in length; Manchester cotton, 22 yd (*c*20.12 m) by 3 quarters (*c*0.69 m); Montgomeryshire flannel, 100 to 132 yd (*c*91.44 to *c*120.70 m) by ⅞ yd (*c*0.80 m); muslin (a fine cotton fabric), 14 ells (16.002 m) in length; narrow Yorkshire, 17 to 18 yd (*c*15.54 to *c*16.46 m) in length; penistone or forest white (a coarse woolen cloth), 12 or 13 yd (*c*10.97 or *c*11.89 m) by 3½ to 6½ quarters (*c*0.80 to *c*1.49 m); ray (a striped cloth), 28 yd (*c*25.60 m) by 5 or 6 quarters (*c*1.14 or *c*1.37 m); Rochdale flannel, generally 48 yd (*c*43.89 m) in length; sailcloth, 33 yd (*c*30.17 m) by 1 quarter (*c*0.23 m); short buckram, 5¼ yd (*c*4.80 m) in length; short Worcester, 14 to 15 yd (*c*12.80 to *c*13.72 m) in length; Shropshire flannel, 100 yd (*c*91.44 m) in length; sindon (a fine cloth usually made of linen), generally 10 ells (11.430 m) in length; straits, 12 or 14 yd (*c*10.97 or *c*12.80 m) by 1 yd (*c*0.91 m); Suffolk say (a fine, twilled cloth made of wool or wool and silk), 27 to 42 yd (*c*24.69 to *c*38.40 m) in length; tartarine (an expensive silk cloth), 10 yd (*c*9.14 m) in length; Taunton (a type of broadcloth), 12 to 14 yd (*c*10.97 to *c*12.80 m) by 7 quarters (*c*1.60 m); web (a coarse cloth), 90 to 120 yd (*c*82.30 to *c*109.73 m) by ¾ to ⅞ yd (*c*0.69 to *c*0.80 m); Wiltshire red, 26 to 28 yd (*c*23.77 to *c*25.60 m) in length; Wiltshire white, 26 to 28 yd (*c*23.77 to *c*25.60 m) in length; and Worcester white, 29 to 31 yd (*c*26.52 to *c*28.35 m) by 7 quarters

(*c*1.60 m). — **1253** Hall 12: Le chef de fustayne est de xiii aunes.
. . . Le chef de cendal est de x aunes. *c*1272 Report 1.414: Cheef de
fustiano constat ex tresdecim ulnis. . . . Caput Sindonis ex decem
ulnis. **1290** Fleta 120: Pecia autem fustiani consistit ex xiij. vlnis.
. . . Pecia sindonis de cursu xiiij. vlnis. **1303** Gras 1.280: Pro pice
acero et panno de worstede. **1308** *Ibid* 361: Adduxit iiii pecias
blanketti. **1350** Rot. Parl. 2.231: Qe la longure de chescun Drap de
Rai serra mesure *par* une corde de sept aunes, quatre soitz mesure
par la liste; & la leure . . . sis quarters de lee mesure *par* l'aune. . . .
Et des Draps de colour, la longure soit mesure *par* le dos *par* une
corde des sis alnes & demi, quatre soitz mesure, & la leeure sis
quarters & demy mesure *par* l'aune. **1373** *Ibid* 318: Les Rayes
soleient tener XXVIII aunez en longure, & V quarters de lieure.
*c*1400 Gras 1.215: De qualibet pecia integra de fustian. **1406** Rot.
Parl. 3.598: Qe le Drap de ray serroit en longure de XXVIII auns,
& en leaure VI quarters. **1407** *Ibid* 618: Q*e* les Draps de Ray soient
en longure XXVIII aulnes mesurez *par* la list. . . . Draps de Ray
. . . en longure de XXVIII aulnes, & en laieure V quarters. **1410**
Ibid 645: & l'ou le Dussein de Drap [Devonshire kersey] duist
teigner XIIII verges. **1433** Rot. Parl. 4.451: Clothes called Streytes,
holdyng XIIII yerdes in lenght, and yeerde brode unwette; or elles
XII yerdes wette. . . . Clothe of colour should conteigne in
lenght XXVIII yerdes, mette by the crest, and in brede VI quarters
di. **1439** Rot. Parl. 5.30: For there as they were wonte to mete
Clothe by yerde and ynche, now they woll mete by yerde and hand-
full, the whiche groweth to encrece of the byere, II yerdes of euery
Clothe of XXIIII yerdes. *c*1461 Hall 15: Fryse schold hold xl.
yerdes and more; *ibid* 16: So that every hole cloth or euery
dossynne be hole in lengthe, xxiiij yerdes; *ibid* 18: A pece fust[yan]
cont[aineth] xxx yerdes. . . . Item all maner of bokerammes hold
xl yerdes, save schort bokram ys butt V yerds I quarter. . . .
Dornyk and Bord' Alysaundyr hold xxviij yerdes . . . I pece lawne
or ump[er]ill, xvj plyte or xviij yerds. **1463** Rot. Parl. 5.501: First,
that every hole Wollen Cloth called brode Cloth . . . after al-
manere rakkyng, streynyng or teyntyng . . . be parfitly and
thoroughly wette, and . . . conteigne in lengh XXIIII yerdes, and
to every yerde an ynche, conteynyng the brede of a mannes thombe
. . . . Streytes . . . be partfitly and thoroughly wette, and . . .
conteigne in lengh XII yerdes . . . and in brede a yerde . . . .

Every Cloth of Kersey, to . . . hold and conteigne in lengh XVIII yerdes . . . and in brede a yerde and the nayle. **1524** Gras 1.196: Pro una pecia de say. **1587** Stat. 83: The length of euerie cloth of raie, by a line of seuen yards, foure times measured by the lyst, and the breadth of euerie raie cloth sixe quarters of measure by the yarde . . . . Of coloured clothes the length shall be measured by the backe by a line of six yardes and an halfe, foure times measured, and the breadth six quarters and an halfe; *ibid* 121: Colored cloth of the length of xxvi. yeardes . . . and of the breadth of vi. quarters and an halfe; *ibid* 299: All manner of clothes called streites concerning in length XIIII. yardes . . . or otherwise xii. yardes watered. *c***1590** Hall 25: Every brod cloth . . . mesured by the crest of the clothe, in lenght 24 yardes . . . and in bredith 2 yardes, or 7 quarters. . . . Straites shall contayne in lenght 14 yardes and in bredith one yard . . . . Collerid clothes made in England, are mesurid by the backe; the lenght is 26 yardes, and the bredith 6 quarters. . . . The wholle coolerid clothe . . . shall contayne in lenght 28 yardes; *ibid* 26: Every Brod Cloth, with the list, shall contayne 7 quarters of a yard . . . in bredith. . . . Every brod clothes, Kentishe, Sussex, Reading . . . shall contayne, in lenght, at the watter throughe weett, bettwixxe 28 and 30 yardes; in bredith 7 quarters. . . . All collerid clothes of Essex and Northfolke, elleswheare . . . in lenght, beinge wett, ought to contayne bettwixe 28 and 30 yardes; in bredith 7 quarters. . . . Every kersey with the list shall contayne in bredith one yard. . . . Devonshires kersis, calid dossens, ought to contayne 12 or 14 yardes in lenght . . . and in bredith one yard and a nayle at the lest. . . . Wster clothe [Worcester white] ellswheare being wett shall contayne, in lenght, betwixt 29 and 31 yardes, and in bredith 7 quarters. . . . Whit clothes, called short Wster, made in the cytty, beinge weett, shall conteyne in lenght bettwixt 14 and 15 yardes; *ibid* 28: A chiffe of Fustyane consisteth 14 ells, that is 17 yardes and ½. . . . The chiffe of Syndon consisteth 10 ells, that is 12 yardes and ½. **1615** Collect. Stat. 465: A chef of Fustian consisteth of 14. elles. . . . A chef of Sindon containeth ten elles. **1665** Sheppard 45: All Whites and Reds in Wilts . . . must be in length between 26 and 28 yards, and 7 quarters in breadth; *ibid* 46: The length of Dowseins, must be between 12 and 13 yards. . . . Manchester, Lancashire, and Cheshire Cottons, must be 22 yards long, and 3 quarters broad; *ibid* 47:

Frizes in Wales and elsewhere . . . are to be 36 yards at most in length, and 3 quarters in breadth. . . . Pennystones and Forrest Whites must be between 12 and 13 yards long, and 6 quarters and a half broad; *ibid* 48: The ordinary Kersey between 16 and 17 yards; *ibid* 49: Frizes and Rugs thicked and dryed, are to weigh 44 pound a piece, and to be in length between 35 and 37 yards; *ibid* 54: But in Yorkshire . . . the narrow to be in length between 17 and 18 yards. **1708** Chamberlayne 208: Taunton and Bridgewater, 7 Quarters, 12 and 13 Yards . . . . Devonshire Kersies and Dozens, 4 Quarters, 12 and 13 Yards . . . . Chequer Kersies, Grays, strip'd and plain, 4 Quarters, 17 and 18 Yards . . . . Penninstons or Forrests, 3 Quarters and ½, 12 and 13 Yards . . . . Washers of Lancashire, 17 and 18 Yards. **1717** Dict. Rus. sv cloth-measure: Taunton, Dunstable, Bridge-water, 7 quarters, 12 and 13 yards . . . . Devonshire-Kersies and Dozens, 4 quarters, 12 and 13 yards . . . . Washers of Lancashire, 17 and 18 yards. **1820** Second Rep. 27: Piece . . . of sailcloth, 33 yards, ¼ wide . . . . Dorsetshire: of flannel, 35 yards, yardwide . . . . Hampshire: of calico, 28 yds, ¼ wide . . . . Shropshire: of flannel, 100 yds . . . . Suffolk, Sudbury: of says, 27, 30 and 42 yds . . . . Worcestershire: of bagging, for hops, 36 yards, about 31 inches wide . . . . Wales: of flannels. Rochdale, about 48 yards or less . . . Montgomeryshire: 100 to 120 or 132 yards or more, ⅞ wide . . . . Webs, a coarse cloth, 90 to 120 yards, ¾ to ⅞ wide. In some places a web means two such pieces, making 190 yds.

piere. STONE

pinct. PINT

pint — 4–6 pynt, pynte; 5 pintte (OED), pyynte (OED); 5–7 pinte; 6 point (OED), poynt (OED), poyntt (OED); 6–9 pint; 7 pinct (OED), L pinta [ME *pynte, pinte* < MF *pinte* < MedL *pincta; see* WNID3]. A m-c: for dry products, ⅛ gal (*c*0.55 l) or 1/64 Winchester bu; for liquids, 4 GILLS equal to ½ qt, ¼ POTTLE, or ⅛ gal and standardized at 28.875 cu inches (0.473 l) for wine and 35.25 cu inches (0.578 l) for ale and beer. The Scots pint, also known as the jug or STOUP, equaled 2 CHOPPINS or 104.2 cu inches (1.707 l). — *c*1400 Hall 36: Una libra facit I pynt. **1474** Cov. Leet 396: ii pyntes maketh a quart; & ij quartes maketh a Pottell; & ii Pottels makith a Gallon; and viij Gallons makith a Buysshell. **1517** Hall 48: viii pyntes to the galon'. *c*1590 *Ibid* 21: 2 pyntes makith a quart. . . . Euery pynt waieth one pounde troye. **1603** Henllys 138: Ffor liquid or wette measures . . . wee use heere the usuall pinte, by which wee proceede to make all other measures of greater accompte. **1635** Dalton 144: 8 pintes maketh the gallon . . . 64 pints maketh the Bushell. **1665** Assize 4: From the said gallons made by the said eight pints. **1678** Du Cange sv galo: Mensura liquidorum apud Anglos, quarum unaquæque octo continet pintas Anglicanas. **1688** Bernardi 150: Pinta denique arida, $\frac{1}{8}$ Galonis, seu congii frumentarii, et $\frac{1}{8} \times 8 = \frac{1}{64}$ Brusselli. **1708** Chamberlayne 210: The ordinary smallest Receptive Measure is called a Pint . . . 2 Pints make a Quart. **1820** Second Rep. 27: Pint, $\frac{1}{8}$ gallon = $\frac{1}{2}$ a quart = $28\frac{8}{10}$ cu. inches, wine measure; $35\frac{1}{4}$ customary ale measure; $33\frac{6}{10}$ Winchester measure. . . . Scotland: 2 choppins, about 105 cu. inches, 3 ale pints E.

pinta, pinte, pintte. PINT

pipa. PIPE

pipe — 4–5 L pipa; 5–6 pype; 5–9 pipe [ME *pipe* < MF *pipe*, a cask for wine, a pipe, < (assumed) VL *pippa*, alter of *pipa*]. A m-c for dry and liquid products, generally synonymous with the BUTT: cider, Guernsey and Jersey, approximately 120 gal (*c*4.54 hl); currants, 15 to 22 Cwt (762.030 to 1117.644 kg); peas, generally 12 bu (*c*4.23 hl); salmon, 84 gal (*c*3.18 hl) equal to $\frac{1}{6}$ salmon LAST; salt, generally 16 bu (*c*5.64 hl); wine, oil, and honey, generally 126 gal (*c*4.77 hl), occasionally 120 and 125 gal (*c*4.73 and *c*4.54 hl), and equal to $\frac{1}{2}$ TUN. — **1324** Gras 1.381: Uno dolio et una pipa vini. **1390** Henry Derby 24: Roberto Gobon pro j tonella et j pipa de Rynen, in toto vj s. **1406** Rot. Parl. 3.596: Oille en groos p*ar* tonell ou par pipe. **1423** Rot. Parl. 4.256: The Pipe xx [×] vi [+] VI galons. **1439** Southampton 2.2: Pro 1 pipa de pes' continente 12 bosshell; *ibid* 4: 2 pipis des pes' continentibus 3 quarteria; *ibid* 32: 4 pipis salis continentibus 8 quarteria. **1440** Palladius 57: Lete close hem in a barel or a pipe. **1443** Brokage II. 58: Cum i pipa bastarde. *c*1461 Hall 15: The pipe cont[aineth] i [×] c [+] xxv galounes. . . . The pype vi [×] xx gallounes. **1517** *Ibid* 49: The pype, vi [×] xx et vi galons'. **1587** Stat. 267: The pipe C.xxvi galons. *c*1590 Hall 21: The pipe contenith a butt which is $\frac{1}{2}$ of a tunne, 126 gallons. **1615** Collect. Stat. 467: Euerie Pipe sixe score and six gallons. **1635** Dalton 148: Wine, Oyle, and Honey: their measure is all one, sc. the . . . Pipe, 126. gallons. **1665** Assize 4:

Every Pipe cxxvi gallons. **1704** Mer. Adven. 243: Ffor every pipe of
wine the said bounds. **1708** Chamberlayne 210: Of these Gallons
. . . a Pipe or Butt holds 126. **1717** Dict. Rus. sv butt: Butt or Pipe
of Wine, contains two Hogsheads, or One hundred twenty six
Gallons; and a Butt of Currans from Fifteen to Twenty-two
Hundred weight. **1725** Bradley sv butt: Butt, or Pipe, a Liquid
Measure, whereof two Hogsheads make a Butt or Pipe, as two
Pipes or Butts make one Tun. **1820** Second Rep. 27: Pipe . . .
Guernsey and Jersey: of cider, 240 pots, about 120 gallons.

pipot [prob a dim of PIPE]. A m-c for liquids (1435) equal to $\frac{1}{2}$ PIPE
(Southampton 1.82).

pise. PIECE

pitchaer, pitchard. PITCHER

pitcher — 3–5 picher; 4 L picheria; 4–6 pycher (OED), pychere
(OED); 5 pychare (OED); 5–6 pychar (OED); 6 pitchaer (OED),
pitchard (OED), pytcher (OED); 6–9 pitcher (OED) [ME *picher* <
OF *pichier* < MedL *bicarius*, goblet, beaker]. A m-c for liquids
generally containing 1 gal (*c*3.78 l). — **1390** Henry Derby 21:
Clerico buterie super vino, per manus Payn pro ij sextariis di.
picheria vini albi per ipsum emptis pro ollis unius dolii. **1392** *Ibid*
160: Et per manus eiusdem pro xx sextariis ij picher vini vasconie.
1393 *Ibid* 256: Item pro xij sextariis j picheria di. vini Vasconie ad
ij s. viij d.

ploughland, ploweland, plowelande. PLOWLAND

plowland — 5 plowlonde (OED); 6 plowelande (OED), plowlande
(OED); 6–9 ploughland, plowland (OED); 7 ploweland [ME
plowlonde < *plow*, *plough*, plow, + *lond*, *londe*, *land*, land].
Equivalent to HIDE. — **1603** Henllys 135: viii oxelandes make a
ploweland being . . . 64 acr. **1755** Willis 358: Some hold an Hide
to contain 4 yard Land, and some an 100, or 120 Acres; some
account it to be all one with a Carucate or Plough-Land.

plowlande, plowlonde. PLOWLAND

poak, poake. POKE

poccet. POCKET

pock, pocke. POKE

pocket — 4 pokete; 4–6 poket (OED); 5–6 pokett; 5–8 pockett; 6
pockette (OED), pokit (OED); 6–9 pocket; 7 poccet (OED) [ME
poket < AF and ONF *pokete*, dim of ONF *poke*, *poque*, bag,
pouch]. A m-c, a coarse bag or sack, for several products: hops,

Kent and Surrey, 1¼ Cwt (63.502 kg); nails, in varying quantities, depending on the size and type of nail; umber, of uncertain wt; and wool, generally ½ pack or 120 lb (54.431 kg). — **1350** trans in Memorials 262: Also, in the Chapel there, in a pokete, 2500 of wyndounail. **1507** Gras 1.700: Mather called crope or umbero the pocke . . . and the pockett. **1524** *Ibid* 195: Pro six pokettis hopps. **1820** Second Rep. 27: Pocket of wool; ½ a pack = 120 lbs . . . of hops: Kent, 1¼ cwt, Surrey, 1¼ cwt, measuring about 5¼ ft in circumference, 7½ long; 4 lb being allowed for the weight of the canvas.

pockett, pockette. POCKET

poik. POKE

point — 3–6 pointe (OED), poynte (OED); 3–9 point (OED); 7 L punctum [ME *point, pointe* < OF *point*, a prick, dot, < L *punctum*, a dot, < *pungere*, to prick]. A m-l equal to ⅟₇₂ inch (0.035 cm) or ⅙ LINE. — **1678** Du Cange sv alna: Pes Regius est 12. pollicum; pollex 12. linearum; linea 12. [*sic*] punctorum.

point. PINT

pointe. POINT

pok, poka. POKE

poke — 3–9 poke; 4–5 L poka; 4–6 pok; 5 poyke (OED); 5–6 poik (OED), pokke (OED); 5–7 pooke (OED); 6 polk (OED); 6–7 poake (OED), pocke; 7 poak (OED); 8–9 pock (OED); 9 pooak (OED), pook (OED), pouk (OED), powk (OED), puock (OED), puok (OED), pwoak (OED), pwok (OED), pwoke (OED) [ME *poke* < ONF *poke, poque*, bag, pouch]. A m-c for a variety of products. It was a large bag or sack whose size varied according to the quality and wt of the product enclosed. In particular it was used to transport raw wool. — **1228** Gras 1.157: 1 poke de alum. **1276** *Ibid* 225: xl sackes et 1 poke de laine marchans. **1304** *Ibid* 172: Et i poka lane. **1396** *Ibid* 443: ii pokys farine. **1420** *Ibid* 469: Pro l fat i poka cum iiii pannis. *c*1461 Hall 16: Also Woll ys sold by numbre and schipped to, as by sacks, sarplers, and pokys. ii sacks make a sarpler, and x sarplers make a laste [*sic*], and the poke ys att no serteyne, butt aftre as ytt weys. *c*1475 Gras 1.193: Of a poke mader. **1507** *Ibid* 699: Hoppys the pocke; *ibid* 700: Mather called crope or umbero the pocke. **1524** *Ibid* 194: Pro septem pokes hopps. **1538** Mer. Adven. 63: Of a pok of woll. **1553** *Ibid* 66: And that thar shall no man lay no more deke above hys poke of the

gretest bod iij stone at the most, and every poke of lesse quantyte
to taike lesser dek accordinge to the greatnes of hys poke. **1562**
York Mer. 169: Six small pokes of Brassel to a tonne, and the
greater as they be rayted forthe of the ship. **1704** Mer. Adven. 243:
Ffor a poke or bail of mather.

poket, pokete, pokett, pokit. POCKET

pokke. POKE

pole — 4 pool (OED); 4–6 poole; 4–9 pole; 5–6 poll; 6 polle (OED),
poule (OED); 6–7 powle (OED) [ME *pole* < OE *pāl*, pole, stake,
< L *palus*, stake]. Equivalent to PERCH. — **1502** Arnold 173: In
dyuers odur placis . . . they mete ground by pollis gaddis and
roddis some be of xviij foote some of xx fote and som xvi fote in
length. *c***1590** Hall 27: 16 foott ½ in lenght is a poole or a perche.
1603 Henllys 133: For in some place the pole is but ix foot, and in
some place xij foote. **1635** Dalton 150: Five yards and an halfe
(which is 16 foot and an halfe) maketh a pole, rood, or pearch.
1665 Assize 6: In many countries [= districts] this Pole or Perch
doth vary, as in some places it is 18 foot, and in some other places
21 foot. **1682** Hall 28: A Pearch, or a Rod, or a Pole (by statut)
must be 5 yards and an half; or 16 feete and an half. **1696** Phillips
sv pole: In measuring, it is the same with Pearch or Rod, or as
some call it Lugg: By Stat. 35 Eliz. this Measure is a length of 16
Foot and a half, but in some Countries [= districts] it consists of
18 Foot and is called Woodland-Measure; in some Places of 21
Foot termed Church-Measure; and in others of 24 Foot under the
Name of Forest-Measure. **1708** Chamberlayne 207: 16 Foot and
a half make a Perch, Pole or Rod, but there are other Customary
Perches or Poles, viz. Eighteen Feet for Fens and Woodland,
Twenty one for Forest, Lancashire and Irish Measure, and 18¾
Scotch. **1717** Dict. Rus. sv: Perch or Pearch, a Rod or Pole, with
which Land is measur'd. **1725** Bradley sv mile: Every Furlong forty
Lugs or Poles . . . every Pole sixteen Foot and a Half. **1820**
Second Rep. 26: Perch, Pole or Rod.

polk. POKE

poll, polle. POLE

pollex. INCH

poncheon, ponchion, ponchyn, poncion. PUNCHEON

pond, ponde. POUND

pondus. WEY

pontion, pontioune. PUNCHEON
pooak, pook, pooke. POKE
pool, poole. POLE
poot. POT
pot — 2–8 pott; 3–9 pot; 4–5 poot (OED); 4–7 potte (OED); 5 poyt (OED), putte (OED) [ME *pot, pott* < OE *pott;* akin to MDu *pot,* MLG *pot, put*]. A m-c for ale, generally equal to a qt (c1.15 l), and butter, 20 lb or 6 lb (2.722 kg) for the pot and 14 lb (6.350 kg) for the butter. — **1439** Southampton 2.82: 1 pott synziberys veridis. **1673** Stat. Charles 159: And the Pot of Butter ought to weigh Twenty pounds, viz. fourteen pounds of good and Merchantable Butter Neat, and the Pot Six pounds. **1820** Second Rep. 28: Pot of ale, generally a quart . . . of butter, 14 lbs.
potel, potell, potella, potelle, potellus. POTTLE
pott, potte. POT
pottel, pottell. POTTLE
pottle — 3 L potellus; 4 L potella; 4–5 potel; 4–7 potell; 5 potelle (OED); 5–7 pottel (OED), pottell; 6–9 pottle [ME *potel* < OF *potel,* dim of *pot*]. A m-c containing 2 qt (c1.89 l), used principally for liquids. — **1287** Select Cases 2.19: Robertus Scot de London, potellus falsus et quarta falsa et alia quarta falsa, et quia vendidit pro xvj. d. **1291** *Ibid* 40: Johannes Lysegong cum vino reneys, potellus bonus, quartus bonus et signatus. **1379** Rot. Parl. 3.64: C'est assavoir, Galon, Potel, & Quart. **1390** Henry Derby 6: Clerico Buterie super vino per manus Johannis Taverner pro ij potellis et j quarta vini Vasconie, xxij d. ob. **1395** York. Mem. 2.10: Et unum strikill ligni, lagena, potella et quarta eris pro vino. c**1400** Hall 36: 4 libre faciunt I potell'. **1474** Cov. Leet 396: ii quartes maketh a Pottell. c**1590** Hall 20: 2 quartes makith a pottell. **1603** Henllys 138: Ffor liquid or wette measures . . . wee use heere . . . ii quarts to a pottle. **1616** Hopton 160: Ale and Beere . . . are measured by Pints, Quarts, Pottles, Gallons . . . and these and such like bee Concaue measures. **1635** Dalton 144: Two quarts, maketh the pottle. **1665** Sheppard 7: Two Quarts make a Pottle; Two Pottles make a Gallon. **1708** Chamberlayne 210: 2 Quarts make a Pottle . . . 2 Pottles make a Gallon. **1717** Dict. Rus. sv: Pottle, (in English liquid and dry Measure) is two Quarts.
pouk. POKE
poule. POLE

pound — 1–4 pund (OED); 3 L liber, F liver; 3–7 L libra; 3–9 pound; 4–5 F livre, punde (OED); 4–6 pond (OED), ponde (OED), pownd; 4–7 pounde; 6 L libre [ME *pound* < OE *pund* < L *pondo*, pound, originally "in weight"; akin to L *pondus*, a weight; parallel to *lb* < MedL *libra*, pound, < L *libra*, Roman pound of twelve ounces]. A wt in the ap, avdp, merc, tow, English t, and Scots t systems. Its abbreviations, l, lb, li, and lib, have all derived from the L *libra*.

The ap lb contained 5760 gr (373.242 g), or 288 s of 20 gr each (1.296 g) or 96 dr of 60 gr each (3.888 g) or 12 t oz of 480 gr each (31.103 g). The number of gr (barleycorns) in the ap lb was the same as in the t lb. — *c*1600 Hall 36: Scrupuli . . . is 20 barley cornes. . . . 3 scruples contain a drachme. . . . 8 drachmes, an ounce . . . . Libræ . . . is a pound. **1688** Bernardi 137: Vel more Pharmacopolarum: Libra de Troy, 12 Unciæ ℥, 96 = 12 × 8 drachmæ ℨ: Scripuli ℈. 288 = 96 × 3: grana monetaria rursus 5760 = 288 × 20. **1708** Chamberlayne 205: 12 ounces 1 Pound ℔. **1728** Chambers 1.360: The Apothecaries also use the Troy Pound, Ounce, and Grain.

The avdp lb contained 7000 gr (453.592 g), or 256 dr of 27.344 gr each (1.772 g) or 16 oz of 437½ gr each (28.350 g), and was used for all products not subject to ap or t wt. There was much confusion in medieval and early modern texts concerning the exact wt of this lb. First, the t oz of 480 gr (31.103 g) was sometimes erroneously ascribed to the avdp scale, and thus the avdp lb was miscalculated as 16 oz of 480 gr apiece or a total of 7680 gr (497.648 g). Second, the ap scale of 20 gr to the s, 3 s to the dr, and 8 dr to the oz (again, 480 gr to the ap oz) was incorrectly used in the conversion, and the avdp lb was once more taken as 16 oz of 480 gr each, totaling 7680 gr. Occasionally the avdp dr was mistaken for the ap dr of 60 gr (3.888 g), and the avdp oz was therefore reckoned as 16 dr of 60 gr each, a total of 960 gr (62.208 g), causing the avdp lb to be 15,360 gr (995.328 g) or 16 oz of 960 gr each. In all three cases, the avdp lb was computed to be heavier than the standard of 7000 gr. — *c*1400 Hall 36: Una libra faciunt I pynt, 7,680 grana. *c*1461 *Ibid* 13: The lb. of thys weyght conteynyth xvi unces of Troy weyght. **1474** Cov. Leet 396: The seid xxxij graynes of whete take out of the myddes of the Ere makith a sterling peny & xx sterling makith a Ounce of haburdepeyse; and xvj Ouncez makith a li.

1496 Seventh Rep. 29: The same tyme ordeined that xvi uncs of Troie maketh the Haberty poie [pound]. **1517** Hall 48: So makyth the whete afore namyd the Habar de Payse once . . . . And xvi of that onces the trewe habar de poix lib. *c*1525 *Ibid* 40: Item xvi onces Habar de Payce ys. a lib. . . . Item xviii onces di. of Troy weyghte makys xvi onces Habar de payse. **1588** *Ibid* 46: The waight now used, every pownd conteineing 16 ounces . . . . The whole ounce is 16 drams. **1603** Henllys 138: And all spice, Iron, Rosen, pitche and other drugges uttered by the mercers are sold by the haber-depoies pound. **1606** Hall 38: This waight of Haberdepois is allowed alsoe by Statute being 16 oz. to the pound waight with the which is wayed all phisick drugges, grocery wares, rozen, wax, pitch, tarr, tallowe, sope, hempe, fflaxe, all metalles and mineralles. **1665** Assize 2: There is also another weight named Avoirdupois weight, whereunto there is 16 ounces for the pound. **1682** Hall 29: Aver-du-pois conteynes: every pound, 16 ounces; every ounce, 8 drgmes [*sic*]; every dragme, 3 scruples; every scruple, 20 graines. **1688** Bernardi 137–38: Libra equidem Avoirdupois qua solent populares mei graviores mercium æstimare quam pretiosiores, $\frac{1}{112}$ Hundredi sui sive centenarii crassi, 16 unciæ, $128 = 16 \times 8$ drachmæ; *ibid* 138: Habet et libra Avoirdupois scripulos suos $384 = 128 \times 3$, gravans nobis 1,2169, sed ratione Wybardica $17\frac{7}{14} = 1,2413$ libræ de Troy. **1708** Chamberlayne 206: But the Avoirdupois Pound is more than the Troy Pound, for 14 Pound Avoirdupois are = to 17 Pound Troy-Weight. **1710** Harris 1. sv weight: And the other is called Averdupois, containing 16 Ounces in the Pound. **1717** Dict. Rus. sv dram: Dram or Drachm, the just Weight of sixty Grains of Wheat; in Avoir-du-pois Weight, the sixteenth part of an ounce; *ibid* sv hundred-weight: But ordinarily a Pound is the least Quantity taken notice of in Aver-du-pois Gross Weight; *ibid* sv pound: A sort of Weight containing 16 Ounces Avoir-du-pois. **1742** Account 1.553: The single Averdupois Bell Pound, against the flat Averdupois Pound Weight, was found . . . to be heavier by Two Troy Grains and a half. **1778** Diderot XXVI.420: L'avoir-du-pois est de seize onces. **1790** Jefferson 1.986: So that the pound troy contains 5760 grains, of which 7000 are requisite to make the pound avoirdupois.

The merc lb contained 6750 t gr (437.400 g), or 15 merc oz of 450 t gr each (29.160 g), and was equal to $\frac{5}{4}$ tow lb of 5400 t gr

(349.920 g). However, the merc lb was actually defined in terms of wheat gr, being 9600 wheat gr or 15 oz of 640 wheat gr each. It was used in England for all goods except electuaries, money, and spices until sometime in the fourteenth century, when it was replaced by the avdp lb. — *c*1253 Hall 11: En letuaris e confeciuns la liver est de xii uncis; en tutes autre chosis la li. est de xv uncis. *c*1272 Report 1.414: Libra vero omnium aliarum rerum consistit ex viginti quinque solidis, uncia vero in electuariis consistit ex viginti denariis, et libra continet xii uncias. In aliis vero rebus libra continet quindecim uncias. **1290** Fleta 119: Item denarius sterlingus, sicut dictum est, ponderat xxxij. grana frumenti, et pondus xx. d. facit vnciam, et quindecim vncie faciunt libram mercatoriam. *c*1300 Hall 8: Uncia debet ponderare viginti denarios. Quindecim uncie faciunt libram Londonie. **1665** Sheppard 13: And all our Weights and Measures have their first Composition from the penny Sterling, which ought to weight Two and thirty wheat corns of a middle sort: Twenty of which pence make an ounce, and 12 such ounces a pound of 20 shillings, but Fifteen ounces make the Merchants pound. **1793** Leake 30: The Merchants Pound, which Fleta says, was fifteen Ounces. **1805** Macpherson I.471: The pound of twelve ounces is used only for money, spices, and electuaries, and the pound of fifteen ounces for all other things.

The tow lb, also called the Saxon or moneyer's lb, contained 5400 t gr (349.920 g), or 12 tow oz of 450 t gr each (29.160 g), and was equal to ⅘ merc lb of 6750 t gr (437.400 g). The tow lb, however, was actually defined in terms of wheat gr, being 7680 wheat gr or 12 oz of 640 wheat gr each. It was used in England generally for electuaries, money, and spices until 1527, when Henry VIII declared it illegal and it was replaced by the t lb. — *c*1253 Hall 11: E fet asauer ke lib. de deners e de especis confectiouns, si cum d'eletuari, si est de le peys de xx sol. . . . En letuaris e confeciuns la liver est de xii uncis. **1290** Fleta 119: Et vnde xx. d. faciunt vnciam et xij. vncie faciunt libram xx. s. in pondere et numero. *c*1300 Hall 8: Denarius qui vocatur sterlingus rotundus sit, et sine tonsura; et ponderabit xxxii grana frumenti rubei, in medio spice assumpta. Et xx denarii faciunt i unciam. Et xii uncie faciunt i libram, videlicet xx s. sterlingorum. *c*1400 *Ibid* 6–7: C'est assavoir, que le denier d'Engleterre round et sanz tonsure poisera xxxii greins de froument en my le spic. Et xx d.

font la unce; et xii unces font la livre. **1474** Cov. Leet 396: *That* xxxij graynes of whete take out of the mydens of the Ere makith a sterling *oth*erwyse called a peny; and xx sterling maketh an Ounce; and xij Ounce maketh a Pounde for siluer, golde, bred & Mesure. **1587** Stat. 540: The pounde Towre shall be no more used, but all manner of golde and sylver shall be wayed by the pounde Troye which maketh XII oz. Troye and which excedith the pounde Towre by III quarters of the ounce. **1615** Collect. Stat. 464: That an English penie, which is called the sterling, round without clipping, shall weigh two & thirty grains of dry wheat in the middest of the eare and twenty d. make an ounce, and 12. ouncis make a lb. **1820** Second Rep. 28: Of silver coins, a pound sterling; the money pound, or Tower pound of the Anglo Saxons, used for some centuries after the Conquest, contained 12 ounces of 450 grains each = 5400 grains.

The English t lb contained 5760 t gr (373.242 g), or 240 dwt of 24 t gr each (1.555 g) or 12 t oz of 480 t gr each (31.103 g). It was introduced into England sometime during the fourteenth century and was used principally for electuaries, gold, precious stones, and silver. It became the standard for these and other items when Henry VIII abolished the tow lb in 1527. The Scots t lb contained 7609 t gr (493.063 g), or 256 DROPS of 29.72 t gr each (1.926 g) or 16 t oz of 475½ t gr each (30.812 g). — *c*1461 Hall 13: And by thys weyght is bought and sold Gold, Sylver, Perlys, and odyr precius stonys, and iuwells and beeds schold be sold by this weyght. *c*1525 *Ibid* 40: xii ownces Troye weyghte ys juste a lib. Troy weyghte, for gold & syluer. **1588** *Ibid* 45: Troy Weight is most used by the ounce for Gold and Silver. . . . The pownd waight is 12 oz. *c*1590 *Ibid* 22: 12 ounces makyth the pound troy. **1606** *Ibid* 37: The Troy waight cont[aineth] 12 oz. to the pound waight; *ibid* 38: Ffor 24 graines or barleycornes, drie, out of the middest of the eare, do make a 1 d. . . . Soe 480 graines, 1 oz. or 20 d. . . . Soe the pounde waight is 12 oz. . . . or 5760 graines. **1616** Hopton 159: This Troy weight containes in euerie pound 12 ounces, euery ounce 20 peny weight, euery peny weight 24 graines. **1635** Dalton 143: Troy weight is by law; and thereby are weighed gold, silver, pearle, pretious stones, silke, electuaries, bread, wheat, and all manner of graine, or corne. . . . This hath to the pound xii. ounces. **1682** Hall 29: Troy weight conteynes: every pound, 12

ounces; every ounce, 20 penny weight; every penny weight, 24
graines. **1688** Bernardi 137: Libra Anglica de Troy. 12 Unciæ . . .
12 × 20 = 240 p.w. sive penningi veteres Regum Edvardorum . . .
qui sunt penningi novi ac decurrentes 720 = 240 × 3; aut 5760 =
240 × 25 grana tritici. **1708** Chamberlayne 205: In Troy-Weight
. . . there are 480 Grains in the Ounce and 5760 Grains in the
Pound. . . . By Troy-Weight we Weigh Bread, Corn, Gold, Silver,
Jewels and Liquors. **1716** Harris 1. sv weight: Troy Weight, is that
by which Gold, Silver, Jewels, Amber, Electuaries, Bread, Corn,
Liquors, &c. are weighed; and from this Weight all Measures of
wet and dry Commodities are taken. **1728** Chambers 1.360: In
Troy Weight, 24 of these Grains make a Penny-weight Sterling; 20
Penny-weight make an Ounce; and 12 Ounces a Pound. **1755** Willis
361: The antient Way of paying Money into the Exchequer was
either Pondere or Numero, by Weight or Tale; hence ad Pensam
signifies such Payment by Weight wherein the Payer was obliged
to make the Pound Sterling to be full 12 Ounces Troy. **1820** Second
Rep. 28: Pound Troy: 12 ounces of 480 grains each = 5760 grains.

pounde. POUND
powk. POKE
powle. POLE
pownd. POUND
poyke. POKE
poynt. PINT
poynte. POINT
poyntt. PINT
poyt. POT
prickle [*; *see* citation]. A m-c for fruit in northern England. It was
a wicker or willow basket of uncertain size. — **1829** Brockett 236:
Prickle, a basket or measure of wicker work among fruiterers.
Formerly made of briers. Hence, perhaps, the name.
puncheon — 5 ponchyn, poncion (OED), punshyn, pwncion (OED);
5–6 punchin; 6 poncheon, ponchion (OED), pontion, pontioune
(OED), puncheoun (OED), punchione, punchon (OED), puncioune (OED), punschioun (OED), punshion (OED), punsion
(OED), punsioun (OED), puntion (OED); 6–7 punshon (OED);
6–8 punchion; 8–9 puncheon [ME *poncion* < MF *ponchon, poin-
çon*, of unknown origin]. A m-c, a large wooden vessel resembling
a cask, used for several commodities: beer, 72 gal (*c*3.33 hl); dried

fruit, of uncertain size; soap, of uncertain size; and wine, 84 gal
(*c*3.18 hl), synonymous with the TERTIAN and double the wine
TIERCE of 42 gal (*c*1.59 hl). — **1443** Brokage II.37: Cum ii punshyns
vini . . . . Cum iiii ponchyns saponis; *ibid* 64: 1 ponchyn saponis
albi. **1547** Cal. Pat. 23.397: In buttes, pypes, hoggesheddes, pontions or barrelles. *c*1550 Welsh 8: 20 poncheons raisions; *ibid* 232:
2 punchins prunes. *c*1590 Hall 21: The tertiane or punchione of a
tunne, which is ⅛ part of a tunne, contenith 84 gallons. **1682** *Ibid*
29: 1 Tunne conteynes . . . 3 Punchions. **1708** Chamberlayne 210:
A Puncheon 84 Gallons. **1710** Harris 1. sv measures: The common
Wine Gallon sealed at Guild-Hall in London . . . is supposed to
contain 231 Cubick Inches; and from thence . . . the Punchion
19404. **1717** Dict. Rus. sv wine-measure: A Punchion 84 Gallons.
1820 Second Rep. 29: Puncheon of beer, in London, 72 gallons . . .
of wine, 84 gallons.

puncheoun, punchin, punchion, punchione, punchon, puncioune.
PUNCHEON

punctum. POINT

pund, punde. POUND

punschioun, punshion, punshon, punshyn, punsion, punsioun, puntion.
PUNCHEON

puock, puok. POKE

putte. POT

pwncion. PUNCHEON

pwoak, pwok, pwoke. POKE

pwys [*]. A wt of 2 lb (0.907 kg) for wool in South Wales (*c*1800)
equal to ⅟₁₃ MAEN (Second Rep. 29).

pychar, pychare, pycher, pychere. PITCHER

pyece. PIECE

pynt, pynte. PINT

pype. PIPE

pysse. PIECE

pytcher. PITCHER

pyynte. PINT

Q

quaer, quaier, quair, quaire, quar, quare, quarr. QUIRE

quart — 3 L quartus; 3–4 L quarta; 4–7 quarte; 4–9 quart; 5 qvarte
(OED), qwhart (OED) [ME *quart* < MF *quarte* < OF *quarte*, fem
n, < *quart*, fourth, < L *quartus*, fourth]. A m-c: for dry products,
2 pt (*c*1.10 l) and equal to ¼ gal, ⅛ pk, and ¹⁄₃₂ bu; for liquids,
2 pt (ale and beer = *c*1.16 l, wine = *c*0.95 l) and equal to ½
POTTLE and ¼ gal. The Scots qt contained 2 Scots pt (3.414 l) or 4
CHOPPINS. — **1287** Select Cases 2.19: Willelmus le Barbur, potellus
falsus et quarta bona, et quia vendidit pro xvj. d. . . . Robertus
Raven de Ely, lagena bona, potellus bonus et quartus bonus. **1351**
Rot. Parl. 2.240: Soient les Mesures, c'est assaver bussell, de*mi*
bussell, & pec, galon, potel, & quarte. **1390** Henry Derby 6: Pro ij
potellis et j quarta vini Vasconie, xxij d. ob. *c*1400 Hall 36: 2 libre
faciunt unum quart', 15,360 grana. **1474** Cov. Leet 396: ij pyntes
maketh a quart; & ii quartes maketh a Pottell; & ij Pottels makith a
Gallon; & viij Gallons makith a Buysshell. *c*1590 Hall 20: 4 quartes
makith a gallon; 2 quartes makith a pottell; *ibid* 21: 2 pyntes
makith a quart. **1603** Henllys 138: Two pintes to a quart, ij quarts
to a pottle, ij pottles to a gallon. **1615** Collect. Stat. 464: First, sixe
lawfull men shall bee sworne truely to gather all the measures of
the towne, that is to wit, bushells, halfe a quarter bushells, gallons,
pottels and quarts, as well of Tauernes as of other places. **1635**
Dalton 144: Eight quarts maketh the peck . . . 32 quarts maketh
the Bushel. **1665** Sheppard 7: Of dry things . . . Two pounds or
pints make a Quart. **1708** Chamberlayne 210: 2 Pints make a
Quart . . . 2 Quarts make a Pottle . . . 2 Pottles make a Gallon.
1820 Second Rep. 29: Quart, two pints, whether of wine measure or
ale measure. . . . Scotland: two Scotch pints.

quarta, quarte. QUART

quarter — 3–7 L quarterium; 3–9 quarter; 4–7 L quarteria; 5
quartre; 6 quartyr [ME *quarter* < OF *quartier* < L *quartarius*,

a fourth part, $<$ *quartus*, fourth]. Equivalent to SEAM. — **1200** Cur. Reg. 8.218: De ordeo xj. sceppas et j. quarterium et xxxj. summas avene, unde tercia pars crevit super tenementum quod recuperavit. **1228** Gras 1.156: Quodlibet quarterium bladi. **1256** Burton 376: Quarterium frumenti venditur pro iii.s. vel xl.d. et hordeum pro xx.d. vel ii.s. et avena pro xvi.d. *c*1272 Hall 7: Et viij lagene faciunt busshelum Londonie, quod est viij pars quarterii. **1283** St. Paul's 160: Per mensuram regis xvj. quarteria. **1298** Falkirk 2: Idem computat in Dlviij quarter. iii bus. frumenti. *c*1300 Hall 8: Et viii buselli bladi faciunt i quarterium. *c*1325 Rameseia III.158: Memorandum, quod octodecim communes ringæ faciunt unam magnam quarteriam. **1390** Rot. Parl. 3.281: Oept Busselx pur le Quarter rasez & nient comblez. **1392** Gras 1.527: Pro ccc quarteriis frumenti. *c*1400 Hall 7: Et viii galons de froument sont le bussell' de Loundres, qest le oeptisme partie du quarter. **1413** Rot. Parl. 4.14: C'est assavoir, viii Busselx pur la Quartre, & qe chescun Bussell contiendra oept Galons. . . . La Quarter de Furment noef Busselx p*ar* une Mesure use deins la dit Cite [London] appelle le Faat. **1433** *Ibid* 450: Oept busshels rasez pur le quarter. **1439** Rot. Parl. 5.31: That where as in a Parlement late at Westmynster holden, it was ordeigned, that no Whete shulde passe out of this land, yf the price of a Quarter of Whete passed or exceded the somme of VI s. VIII d., nor no Barly undur the same fourme. **1443** Brokage II.9: Pro iiii quarteriis frumenti. *c*1461 Hall 12: And viii gallons of wyne make a boschell of whete . . . wiche is the viii parte of a quarter whete. **1474** Cov. Leet 396: And viij Gallons makith a Buysshell, and neyther hepe nor Cantell . . . and viij Buysshelles makith a Quarter. *c*1475 Gras 1.193: Of the quarter of iche corn. **1517** Hall 49: So that iiii busshelles wey ii c[-]weyghte of habar de poix powndes; the quartyr weyghte iiii c[-weyghte]. **1549** Gras 1.708: Pro xix [×] xx quarteriis bracii. **1555** York Mer. 156: Item, a quarter of salt of Yorkes mesure, fyve pence. Item, a quarter of any other grayne of Yorkes measure, fore pence. **1562** *Ibid* 168: All manner of grayne Yorke measure the quarter, vi d.; All manner of grayne Hull measure the quarter, vij d. *c*1590 Hall 21: The quarter or seame is 8 bushells. **1615** Collect. Stat. 465: And that none from henceforth doe buy in the Citie of London . . . no maner corne nor malt, but after eight bushels the quarter. **1616** Hopton 162: Whereof are made . . . Coombes, or halfe

Quarters, Quarters, or seames. **1635** Dalton 144: 512 pints [or] 256 quarts [or] 64 gallons . . . [or] 8 bushels maketh the Quarter. **1641** Best 176: In the high Garner foure quarters of malte. **1657** Tower 547: That all the Kings Purveyors do take eight bushels of corn only to the quarter striked. **1678** Du Cange sv quarteria: Quarteria et Quarterium, Mensuræ frumentariæ species. **1708** Chamberlayne 207: 4 Bushels the Comb or Curnock . . . 2 Curnocks make a Quarter, Seam or Raff. **1717** Dict. Rus. sv drymeasure: Two Curnocks make a Quarter, Seam or Raff, and ten Quarters a Last. **1820** Second Rep. 29: Quarter . . . of salt, 4 cwt . . . Devonshire: of Welsh coal or culm, 16 heaped bushels . . . Derbyshire: of lime at the wharfs, 8 level bushels: at the kilns, 8 heaped bushels . . . Yorkshire: of chopped bark, in some parts, 9 heaped bushels; *ibid* 32: Seam or Seem, sometimes a quarter of corn or malt.

quarteren. QUARTERN

quarteria, quarterium. QUARTER

quartern — 3–7 quartron (OED); 4 quartroun (OED), quartrun (OED), quaterone (OED); 4–5 quarteroun (Southampton 2), quarton (Nottingham); 5 quarteren (OED), quarterone (OED); 5–7 quarteron; 6 quateren (OED); 6–7 quarterne (OED); 6–9 quartern; 7 L quartronus [ME *quarteroun, quartron* < OF *quarteron*, the fourth part of a pound, or of a hundred; *see* QUART, QUARTER]. A wt of 28 lb (12.700 kg) for fruit equal to ¼ PIECE or ⅟₁₂ SORT. It was used occasionally as the equivalent of the quarter lb (0.113 kg), or quarter pt (*see* GILL), or quarter pk (*see* POTTLE), or quarter Cwt (*see* HUNDRED). — **1439** Southampton 2.65: 16 quarterons fructui. **1474** Cov. Leet 396: xx [X] v for the C, the wich kepes weyght & mesure 1 li. the halfe C, xxv li the quartern. **1678** Du Cange sv quartronus: Quarta pars libræ, Gall. *Quarteron.*

quarterne. QUARTERN

quarternium. QUIRE

quarteron, quarterone, quarteroun, quarton. QUARTERN

quartre. QUARTER

quartron, quartronus, quartroun, quartrun. QUARTERN

quartus. QUART

quartyr. QUARTER

quateren, quaterone. QUARTERN

quayer, quayere, quayr, quayre, quear, queare, queer, queere, quere.
QUIRE

quire — 3 cwaer (OED), quaer (OED); 4 L quarternium; 4–5 quayer
(OED); 4–6 quayre (OED); 5 quaier (OED), quayere (OED), qvayr
(OED), qwayer (OED), qwayre (OED); 5–6 quair (OED), quar
(OED), quare (OED), quarr (Finchale), qvare (OED); 5–7 quaire
(OED); 6 quayr (Dur. House), quear (OED), queare (OED), quere
(OED), quyr, quyre; 6–7 queere (OED); 6–7, 9 queer (OED); 7–9
quire [ME *quaer, quair* < OF *quaier, caern* (F *cahier*), a book of
loose sheets, < (assumed) VL *quaternum*, sheets of paper (usually
4) packed together, < L *quaterni*, by fours, < *quater*, four times].
A m-q for paper, consisting of either 24 or 25 sheets and equal to
$\frac{1}{20}$ REAM. It was originally a set of 4 sheets of parchment or paper
folded so as to form 8 leaves, and this was the unit most commonly
used for medieval mss. — **1392** Henry Derby 159: CLERICO
speciarie per manus Wilbram pro ij magnis quarterniis papiri pro
officio thesaurarii per ipsum emptis ibidem, ij s. ij d. . . . Et pro
uno quarternio papiri, vj d. *c***1590** Hall 25: Euery reame hathe 20
quyrs of paper; euery quyre hathe 25 sheettes. **1616** Hopton 164:
A Quire is 25 sheetes. **1635** Dalton 150: A bale of paper, is ten
reame; a reame is twenty quires; a quire is 25 sheetes. **1665** Sheppard 18: A Ream is 20 Quire, a quire is 25 sheets. **1708** Chamberlayne 205: Of Paper 24 or 25 Sheets to the Quire; 20 Quire to a
Ream. **1820** Second Rep. 30: Quire of paper, 24 sheets.

quyr, quyre, qvare. QUIRE
qvarte. QUART
qvayr, qwayer, qwayre. QUIRE
qwhart. QUART

R

ras, rasa. RASER

raser — 6 razier (OED), raziere (OED); 6–7 ras; 6–? raser (OED); 7 L rasa [MF *rasier, rasiere;* cf MF vb *raser* < (assumed) VL *rasare,* to scrape often]. A m-c for grain, containing approximately 2 bu (*c*7.00 dkl) or ¼ SEAM. It was a level measure, as opposed to a CANTEL or COMBLE. — **1678** Du Cange sv rasa 2: Rasa, Mensura frumentaria, in agro Dumbensi Ras: ubi plerumque continet quatuor cupas.

razier, raziere. RASER

realme. REAM

ream — 4–6 rem; 5 reeme (OED); 5–6 reme, rym (OED); 5–7 reame; 6 realme (OED), rim (OED); 6–9 ream; 7 rheme (OED); 7–8 rheam (OED) [ME *rem, reme* < MF *raime* < Ar *rizmah,* a bale or bundle]. A m-q for paper, consisting of 20 QUIRES of 24 or 25 sheets each and equal to ¹⁄₁₀ BALE. — **1392** Henry Derby 154: Et pro j rem papiri. **1411** trans in Cal. Close 20.148: One 'reme' of paper. **1439** Southampton 2.108: 12 remys papiri pro wastyng. **1507** Gras 1.701: Paper called wyte the reme. **1509** *Ibid* 573: xx remys papiri. **1524** *Ibid* 196: Pro xxx reames paper. *c*1590 Hall 25: Euery reame hath 20 quyrs of paper. **1616** Hopton 164: A Bale of Paper is 10 Reame or 200 Quires, a Reame is 20 Quires, or 500 sheetes: a Quire is 25 sheetes. **1635** Dalton 150: A reame is twenty quires. **1665** Sheppard 18: A Bale of Paper is 10 Ream, a Ream is 20 Quire, a quire is 25 sheets. **1708** Chamberlayne 205: Of Paper 24 or 25 Sheets to the Quire; 20 Quire to a Ream; 10 Ream to a Bale. **1820** Second Rep. 30: Ream of paper, 20 quires.

reame. REAM

reda. ROOD

reel [ME *reel* < OE *hrēol*]. A m-l for thread and yarn (*c*1800): Clydesdale, 2½ yd (2.286 m); Essex, wool, 1¼ and 1½ yd (1.143

and 1.372 m); and Hampshire, flax, 2 yd (1.829 m) (Second Rep. 30).

reeme. REAM

rees [prob < E dial vb *ree*, sift, < ME *reien*]. A m-q for herrings, consisting of 15 GLEANS or 375 in number. — **1805** Macpherson I.471: 25 herrings 1 glen, 15 glens 1 rees. **1820** Second Rep. 30: Rees of herrings, 15 gleans = 375.

rem, reme. REAM

reode [*]. A m-c for wine containing 2 TUNS or 500 gal (*c*18.92 hl). — *c*1461 Hall 15: Off the mesure of Lycoure. There is a mesure of wyne whyche is called a reode it cont[aineth] ii tunnys, that is v [×] c galons.

rhaw [*]. A m-c for peat in Wales (*c*1800). It was a pile or heap containing 120 or 140 cu yd (91.747 or 107.038 cu m) (Second Rep. 30).

rheam, rheme. REAM

ridge [ME *rigge* < OE *hrycg;* akin to *rig*, the space between the furrows of a plowed field]. A m-l for land in Wales containing 3 LEAPS or 20¼ ft (6.176 m). Similar to BUTT OF LAND and SELION. — **1665** Sheppard 22: A Selion . . . otherwise called a Ridge of Land. **1688** Holme ii §32: 3 Ridges, Butts, Flats, Stitches or small Butts, Pikes. **1820** Second Rep. 30: Ridge of land, Wales, formerly 20¼ feet, or 3 leaps.

rim. REAM

ring — 3–? ring; 4 L ringa [ME *ring* < OE *hring;* prob referred to a band around the rim of the measure]. A m-c at Ramsey containing ½ bu (*c*1.59 hl) and equal to ⅟₁₈ SEAM of 9 bu. — *c*1325 Rameseia III.158: Memorandum, quod octodecim communes ringæ faciunt unam magnam quarteriam. . . . Et quatuor communes ringæ, duo busselli, faciunt mittam gruti.

ringa. RING

roale. ROLL

rod — 1–6 rodd; 5–7 rodde; 5–9 rod [ME *rod* < OE *rodd;* akin to ON *rudda*, club]. Equivalent to PERCH. — **1474** Cov. Leet 397: And out of the seid yard growith a Rodde to mesure land by, the wich Rod conteyneth in lengthe V yardes & halfe. **1502** Arnold 173: In dyuers odur placis . . . they mete ground by pollis gaddis and roddis some be of xviij foote some of xx fote and som xvi fote in lengith. **1682** Hall 28: A Pearch, or a Rod, or a Pole (by statut) must be 5 yards and an half; or 16 feete and an half. **1696** Phillips sv pole: In measuring, it is the same with Pearch or Rod, or as some call it Lugg: By Stat. 35 Eliz. this Measure is a length of 16 Foot and a half, but in some Countries [= districts] it consists of 18 Foot and is called Woodland-Measure; in some Places of 21 Foot termed Church-Measure; and in others of 24 Foot under the Name of Forest-Measure. **1708** Chamberlayne 207: 16 Foot and a half make a Perch, Pole or Rod. **1717** Dict. Rus. sv perch: Perch or Pearch, a Rod or Pole, with which Land is measur'd. **1789** Hawney 213: But in some Places the Custom is to allow 18 Feet to the Rod . . . and in some Places . . . 21 Feet. **1820** Second Rep. 26: Perch, Pole or Rod.

rod, roda. ROOD
rodd, rodde. ROD; ROOD
rode, roed, roide. ROOD
rol, role. ROLL
roll — 3–7 rolle; 4–9 roll; 5–7 rol (OED), rowle; 6 roull (OED), row (OED), rowlle; 6–7 roole (OED), roule; 6–8 rowl (OED); 6–9 role; 7 roale (OED); 7–8 roul (OED) [ME *rolle* < OF *rolle* < VL *rotulus*, a roll, < L *rotulus*, dim of L *rota*, a wheel]. A m-q for parchment, consisting of 60 skins. Occasionally it was used in place of the PIECE as a measure for cloth. — **1507** Gras 1.699: Harffordes the rowle; *ibid* 700: Mynster' clothe the rowlle. **1509** *Ibid* 578: x rolles cours canvas. *c*1590 Hall 25: The parchement rowle is 5 dossen, conteninge 60 skynns. **1616** Hopton 164: A Rowle of parchment is 5 dozen, or 60 skins. **1635** Dalton 150: A roule of parchment is five dozen, or sixtie skins. **1665** Sheppard 18: A Roll of Parchment is 5 dozen or 60 skins. **1708** Chamberlayne 205: Of Parchment, Twelve Skins make a Dozen; and five Dozen a Roll. **1717** Dict. Rus. sv: Roll of Parchment . . . is the quantity of 60 Skins. **1820** Second Rep. 30: Role of parchment, 72 [*sic*] sheets.

rolle. ROLL
rondelet, rondelett, rondellettum, rondlet, ronelet, ronelete, ronlet, ronlett. RUNDLET
rood — 1–6 rod; 2–7 L roda; 3–6 rode; 4–7 roode; 5 roed (OED), rowd (OED), rude (OED), rwd (OED); 5–6 L reda (Finchale), rud (OED); 6 rodd (OED), rodde (OED), roide (OED), roud (OED), ruid (OED); 6–9 rood [ME *rod, roode* < OE *rōd*, a cross, measure of land, rod, pole]. A m-l containing 660 ft (2 .012 hm) and equal to ⅛ mi of 5280 ft (*see* FURLONG), and a m-a containing

40 sq PERCHES (0.101 ha) and equal to $\frac{1}{4}$ statute acre of 160 sq perches (*see* FARTHINGDALE). — **1198** Feet 3.65: Et pro hoc fine et concordia et quieta clamantia ... predictus Radulfus dedit predicto Willelmo iiij acras terre et iij rodas. **1200** *Ibid* 107: Et iij rodas juxta Culuerdespit. **1201** Feet 2.12: Et dimidiam acram et decem rodes in Mikelholm' et dimidiam acram in Quakefen. **1202** Feet 3.196: Et dimidiam rodam prati juxta domum ipsius Simonis uersus orientem. *c***1289** Bray 8: Julia et Matilda Burgeis x acras i rodam; *ibid* 9: Nicholas Pewere unum mesuagium et xxxviij acras et dimidiam et unam rodam. *c***1400** Henley 68: E devet sauer ke lacre ke est mesuree par la verge de xviii peez fet i acre & vne rode. *c***1475** Nicholson 77: Fourty perchys in lengyth makyth a Rode of Lande; put iiij thereto in brede, and that makyth an Acre. **1537** Benese 4: The quarter of an acre (other wayes called a roode) conteyneth in it xl. perches. **1540** Recorde 208: A Rod of land which some call a roode, some a yarde lande, and some a farthingdale. **1647** Digges 1: So an Acre by Statute ought to containe 160. Pearches ... a Roode, commonly called a quarter, 40. Pearches. **1665** Sheppard 19: Particata terræ ... is a Rood of Land. ... A Rood of Land ... is a certain quantity of Land, the fourth part of an Acre. **1678** Du Cange sv roda: Anglis, Quarta pars acræ, quæ et *Farding deale*, seu *Farundel* dicitur, juxta Cowellum, ex Anglico *Rodd*, Pertica. Continet autem acra, secundum stadii longitudinem 40. rodas, seu perticas; in latitudine tantum quatuor. Perinde etiam Roda terræ 40. perticas in longitudine, unam vero solummodo in latitudine. **1717** Dict. Rus. sv: Rood, a Measure being the fourth part of an Acre, and containing 40 Square Pearches or Poles. **1820** Second Rep. 30: Rood of land, properly $\frac{1}{4}$ acre = 40 perches = 1,210 sq. yards; but the term is often provincially used for rod, or a measure approaching to it.

roode. ROOD

roole. ROLL

rope [ME *rope, rap* < OE *rāp*]. A m-q for onions and garlic. The tops of 15 heads, or $\frac{1}{15}$ C of 225, were braided together, giving the appearance of a rope. — *c***1590** Hall 28: Nottes of the 100 of Onyons and Garleke. The Hundred consisteth of 15 ropes and euery rope 15 heades. **1665** Sheppard 58: A hundred of Garleck consisteth of 15 Ropes, and every rope containeth 15 heads.

roud. ROOD

roul [perh a special use of ROLL]. A m-q for eels (*c*1800), numbering 1500 (Second Rep. 31).

roul, roule, roull. ROLL

roundelettus, roundellettus, roundlet. RUNDLET

row. ROLL

rowd. ROOD

rowl, rowle, rowlle. ROLL

rud, rude, ruid. ROOD

rundelet, rundellus. RUNDLET

rundlet — 3–4 L roundellettus (Liber), L rundellus (Liber); 4–6 rondelet (OED); 5 rondelett, L rondellettum (Southampton 2), ronlett (OED); 5–6 ronelet (Nottingham); 6 ronelete (OED), rundelet, runlett (OED); 6–7 rondlet, roundlet (Shuttleworths), rundlett (OED); 6–9 rundlet; 7 ronlet (OED), L roundelettus; 7–9 runlet [ME *rondelet* < MF *rondelet*, dim of *rondel* < OF *rondel*, *rondelle*, a little tun, < *ronde*, round]. A m-c for wine containing 18 or 18½ gal (*c*6.81 or *c*7.00 dkl) and generally equal to $\frac{1}{14}$ TUN. When used for products other than wine, it was synonymous with the KILDERKIN. — **1420** Gras 1.499: Pro viii rondeletts saponis albi. *c*1550 Welsh 294: 3 rondlets muskedine. *c*1590 Hall 21: The Rundelet, which is $\frac{1}{14}$ part of a tunne, contenith 18 galons ½. **1615** Collect. Stat. 467: Euerie Rundlet to contain eighteen gallons and an halfe. **1665** Sheppard 59: The Barrell 31 Gallons and a half, and the Rundlet 18 Gallons and a half. **1678** Du Cange sv roundelettus: Mensura liquidorum . . . continet decem et octo galones cum dimidio. **1682** Hall 29: 1 Tunne conteynes . . . 14 Rundlets, 252 Gallons. **1696** Jeake 72: 1 Rundlet or Rondlet = 18½ Gallons. **1708** Chamberlayne 210: Of these Gallons, a Runlet of Wine holds 18. **1717** Dict. Rus. sv: Rundlet or Runlet . . . of Wine is to hold 18 Gallons. **1790** Jefferson 1.983: Two firkins, or bushels, make a measure called a rundlet or Kilderkin. **1820** Second Rep. 31: Rundlet or Runlet of wine, 18 gallons.

rundlett, runlet, runlett. RUNDLET

rwd. ROOD

rym. REAM

S

saac, sac, sacc, sacca, saccke, saccum, saccus, sache. SACK

sack — 1 saac (OED), sacc (Prior), sæcc (OED); 3 L sacca, L saccum, sec (OED); 3–4 seck (OED); 3–5 secke (OED); 3–5, 8 sac; 3–6 sakke; 3–7 L saccus, sacke; 4–5 sak, sekke (OED); 4–6 sek (OED); 4–9 sack; 5 cek (OED), saccke (OED), sache (OED), L saculus, sakk; 5–6 sake [ME *sac, sak*, sack, bag, sackcloth, < OE *sacc, sæcc* < L *saccus*, sack, bag, < Gr *sakkos*, sack, bag, of Sem origin]. A m-c for dry products: apples, Kent, 3½ bu (*c*1.23 hl), Worcestershire, 4 bu (*c*1.41 hl); ashes, Hertfordshire, 5 bu (*c*1.76 hl); charcoal, Essex, 8 pk (*c*7.05 dkl); coal, generally 4 heaped bu (*c*1.80 hl); flour, 5 bu weighing 2½ Cwt or 280 lb (127.005 kg); grain, generally 4 heaped bu (*c*1.80 hl); meal, 5 bu totaling 2½ Cwt or 280 lb (127.005 kg); potatoes, 180 to 280 lb (81.646 to 127.005 kg); salt, 5 bu (*c*1.76 hl); wheat, North Wales, 1½ HOBEDS totaling 260 lb (117.933 kg); and wool, generally 364 lb (165.107 kg), or 2 WEYS or 13 TODS or 52 CLOVES or 26 STONE of 14 lb each equal to $\frac{1}{12}$ LAST, but occasionally 350 lb (158.756 kg) or 28 stone of 12½ lb each. — **1200** Cur. Reg. 8.144: Willelmus filius Roberti optulit se iiij. die versus priorissam de Svine de placito x. saccorum lane et de x. marcis argenti que ei debet ut dicit. **1228** Gras 1.156: 1 sacca lani. **1229** Close 1.260: Quod unam lestam coriorum et dimidiam et tres saccos lane. *c***1243** Select Cases 3.lxxxvi: In nauta vero fuerunt iiij [X] xx sacci lane. *c***1253** Hall 11: Et xii sacs sunt un last. *c***1272** *Ibid* 10: Et due waye faciunt unum saccum. Et duodecim sacci continent le last. **1275** Gras 1.225: xl sackes et l poke de laine. **1290** Fleta 119: Et due waye lane faciunt vnum saccum, et xij. sacca faciunt vnum lestum. . . . Et tales xij libre et xxviij petre faciunt vnum saccum lane. *c***1300** Hall 8: Duodecim libre et dimidia faciunt petram Londonie. Saccus lane debet ponderare viginti octo petras. *c***1340** Pegolotti 254: Lana si vende in Londra e per tutta l'isola d'Inghilterra a sacco, di chiovi 52 pesi per 1 sacco, e ogni chiovo pesa libbre 7 d'Inghilterra. **1341** Rot. Parl. 2.133: Primes, ce q'est coilly & leve de les xxM. saks de Leyne autrefoitz grantez a no*tr*e Seign' le Roi en maner d'avoir recompensation de ycele de la Noesisme de l'an secounde, soit recoupe & allowe es Countees ou les Leines sont levees, & les pe*r*sones paiez, & les Commissions de xxM. sacks repelles. **1343** *Ibid* 142: La pere serroit de XIIII li. & XXVI petr' facent un sak. **1351** *Ibid* 240: Le Sak ne poise q*ue* vint & sys pieres, & chescune pere poise xiiii livres. **1389** Rot. Parl. 3.272: Qatorsze livers al Pere, & vint & sis Peres al Sak. **1439** Southampton 2.28: 4 sakk' de hoppys; *ibid* 76: 1 saculo de haber-dasshe; *ibid* 85: Pro 1 saculo amygdolarum; *ibid* 86: 1 saculo grani pro panno. **1443** Brokage II.174: 1 parvo sacco piperis. *c***1461** Hall 13: Also woll is weyd by this weyght [avoirdupois], butt itt is nott rekynnyd soo, for ytt is bowght odyr by the Nayle, or the Stone, or the Todde, or els the Sakk; *ibid* 16: A sakk, sarpler, poke, last [of] Woll; *ibid* 19: That ys to say . . . Sacke content' iii [×] c [+] lxiiij. *c***1475** Gras 1.192: Of a sak wulle. **1478** Ricart 84: Item, that all maner of colyers that bryngeth colys to towne for to sille, smale or grete, that they bryng their sakkes of juste measure . . . so that every sak be tryed and provid to be and holde a carnok, and the ij. sakkes to hold a quarter. **1507** Gras 1.698: Flexe hyckeled the sake. **1587** Stat. 116: So that the sacke of woll wey no more but xxvi. stones, and euerie stone to wey fourteene pound. *c***1590** Hall 31: A Last is 12 Sackes; a Sack, 2 Weyes; a Weye, 6½ Toddes; a Todd, 2 Stone; a Stone, 14 pound; a Cleave, half a stone. **1615** Collect. Stat. 465: And two weights of wooll make a sacke, and twelue sackes make a last. **1616** Hopton 163: The Sack of Coles is 4 bushels. **1635** Dalton 149: Wooll, 14 pound weight goeth to the stone of wooll, 28 pounds goeth to the Tod, and 26 stone goeth to the sacke. **1657** Tower 41: It is enacted, That a Stone of Wooll shall contain but fourteen pounds; and that twenty-six Stone make a Sack. **1665** Sheppard 17: Of Wooll, 12 sacks are said to make a Last. **1678** Du Cange sv saccus: Ponderis lanarii species. Constat autem 28. petris, petra vero 12. libris et dimidia. **1682** Hall 30: Coales must conteyn in every sacke, 4 bushels. **1708** Chamberlayne 207: Wooll is weigh'd by the . . . Sack, 364 Pounds. **1717** Dict. Rus. sv: Sack . . . of Sheeps-woll, 26 Stone, every Stone contain-ing 14 Pounds, but in Scotland 24 Stone, and each Stone 16 Pounds. **1778** Diderot XXVI.422: Les marchands de laine ont aussi leurs especes de poids particulieres; le sac . . . le tod . . .

toutes mesures angloises sans termes françois. **1820** Second Rep.
31: Sack . . . of flour or meal, 280 lbs . . . of salt, 5 bushels . . .
Essex: of charcoal: 8 pecks . . . Hertfordshire: of ashes, 5 bushels
. . . Kent: of apples and potatoes, about 3½ bushels . . . Somersetshire: of potatoes, 240 lb . . . Surrey: of potatoes, 3 bushels of
60 lb. each . . . Worcestershire: of apples, 4 bushels . . . N. Wales:
of wheat, 1½ hobaid, to weigh 260 lb.

sacke, saculus, sæcc. SACK

sæm. SEAM

sak, sake, sakk, sakke. SACK

**sarpelar, sarpeler, sarpelere, sarpeller, sarplair, sarplar, sarplare,
sarplarius.** SARPLER

sarpler — 3 sarpeller; 4 sarpuler (OED); 4–7 sarpler; 4–8 sarplar;
5 sarpelar (OED), sarpeler (OED), sarpelere (OED), sarplair
(OED), sarplere, sarpleth (OED), sarpliar (OED); 5–7 sarplare;
6 sarplier (OED); 7 L sarplarius, serplaith (OED); ? L sarplera
(Prior), serpler (Prior), serpliath (Prior) [ME *sarpler* < MF
sarpilliere]. A m-c for wool. It was a large, coarse canvas bag
generally equal to 2 SACKS, totaling 728 lb (330.213 kg) or ⅙ of a
4368 lb LAST. However, there were variations ranging from ½ sack
to more than 2 sacks. — **1275** Gras 1.227: vi saches de laine en vi
sarpellers apaie. **1350** trans in Cal. Close 8.222: Also that no
sarplar shall contain more than 1½ sacks. **1397** trans in *ibid* 16.38:
Robert de Howom paid custom at Kyngeston for 4 sacks 14 stone
and 1 clove of wool in two sarplers . . . 6 sacks 17 stone in three
sarplers . . . 9 sacks 25 stone 1 clove in five sarplers. *c*1461 Hall 16:
Also Woll ys sold by numbre and schipped to, as by sacks, sarplers,
and pokys. ii sacks make a sarpler, and x [*sic*] sarplers make a
laste; *ibid* 19: That ys to say . . . Sarpler content' ii Sackes. . . .
The Sarplere ys made off Sackes. **1665** Sheppard 64: A Cark of
Wooll is said to be a quantity, whereof 30 make a Sarplar. . . .
A Sarplar . . . is a quantity of Wooll, and seems to be all one with
a Weigh of Wooll. . . . A Sarplar (otherwise called a Pocket) is a
half Sack. **1678** Du Cange sv sarplare: Sarplarius, Ponderis lanarii
species sacco major, dicitur, quod lanis involvendis *sarpilleriis*
statutæ mensuræ utuntur præcipue apud Anglos. **1717** Dict. Rus.
sv cark: A certain Quantity of Wooll, the thirtieth part of a
Sarplar.

sarplera, sarplere, sarpleth, sarpliar, sarplier, sarpuler. SARPLER

scain, scan, scane. SKEIN
scape, scappe. SKEP
scayne. SKEIN
sceaftmund. SHAFTMENT
scep, scepe, scepp, sceppa, sceppe. SKEP
schaffa. SHEAF
schafftmon, schaftemonde, schaftmon, schaftmond, schaftmonde,
   schaftmone, schaftmount. SHAFTMENT
schaine. SKEIN
schaldre. CHALDER
scheef, schef, schefe, scheff, scheffe. SHEAF
schepp. SKEP
schide. SHIDE
schiefe. SHEAF
schopin. CHOPPIN
schore. SCORE
schudde, schyd, schydd, schyde, scīd. SHIDE
scoare, scoir, scoore. SCORE
scope [prob < SKEP]. Equivalent in size and application (c1400) to
   CORF (Salzman 1.15).
scor. SCORE
score — 3–6 scor (OED); 3–9 score; 4–5 schore (OED); 4–6 skor
   (OED); 4–7 skore; 5 scoyr (OED), skowre (OED); 5, 7 scoure
   (OED); 6 scoore (OED), scower (OED), skoir (OED); 6–7 scoare
   (OED), scoir (OED) [ME *scor* < ON *skor*, notch, tally]. A m-q
   generally numbering 20 of any item, but there were exceptions:
   barley, beans, and oats, Liverpool, 21 bu (c7.40 hl); coal, Newcastle, 21 CHALDERS (124,656 lb or 56,542.710 kg); grain, Roxburghshire and Selkirkshire, 21 BOLLS (c58.59 hl); lime, Derbyshire,
   20 to 22 heaped bu (c9.01 to c9.91 hl); and sheep, Dumbartonshire,
   21 in number. — 1440 Palladius 48: Ffeet scores nyne in length.
   1562 York Mer. 168: Iron sex skores endes to the tonne. 1616
   Hopton 164: Coney, Kid, Lambe, Budge . . . haue fiue score in the
   hundred. 1635 Dalton 149: Six score herrings shall goe to the
   hundred. 1682 Hall 29: A skore is 20 yards. 1704 Mer. Adven. 244:
   Ffor a score of round letts or great ffish; *ibid* 245: Ffor sorting and
   laying up every score of round wood belonging to a ffreeman or
   fforreigner. 1708 Chamberlayne 213: On Shipboard they allow 21
   Chaldron to the Score. 1717 Dict. Rus. sv timber: Other Skins six

score to the Hundred. **1820** Second Rep. 31: Score . . . Derbyshire: of lime, 20 to 22 heaped bushels . . . Liverpool: of barley, beans and oats, 21 bushels . . . Newcastle: of Chaldrons of coals, 21 . . . Dumbartonshire: of sheep, sometimes 21 . . . Roxburghshire and Selkirkshire: of bolls of grain, sometimes 21.

scoure, scower, scoyr. SCORE

scriple, scripulus. SCRUPLE

scruple — 5 scriple; 6–7 scrupul (OED); 6–8 scrupule (OED); 6–9 scruple; 7 L scripulus, L scrupulus [ME *scriple* < L *scripulum*, *scrupulum*, a small weight, < *scrupulus*, small stone, pebble, dim of *scrupus*]. A wt in the ap system containing 20 gr (1.296 g) and equal to $\frac{1}{3}$ ap dr of 60 gr (3.888 g) or $\frac{1}{24}$ ap oz of 480 gr (31.103 g). It was sometimes mistakenly assigned to the avdp system by early modern writers. — **1440** Palladius 59: A scriple . . . and half a scriple. *c*1600 Hall 36: Scrupuli ℈ is 20 barley cornes. **1606** *Ibid* 38: A scruple is 20 graines. **1616** Hopton 160: You must note that the Auerdupois pound is diuided into Graines, Scruples, Dragmes, and so to Ounces. **1682** Hall 29: Aver-du-pois conteynes . . . every dragme, 3 scruples; every scruple, 20 graines. **1688** Bernardi 137: Vel more Pharmacopolarum: Libra de Troy, 12 Unciæ ℥, 96 = 12 × 8 drachmæ ℈: Scripuli ℈. 288 = 96 × 3. **1708** Chamberlayne 205: The Apothecaries reckon 20 Grains Gr. make a Scruple ℈. **1728** Chambers 1.360: The Ounce into 8 Drachms; the Drachm into 3 Scruples; and the Scruple into 20 Grains. **1778** Diderot XXVI.420: C'est aussi les poids de apoticaires, mais qui se divise autrement; vingt grains sont un scrupule, trois scrupules une dragme et huit dragmes une once. **1790** Jefferson 1.986: The drachm into 3 scruples; The scruple into 20 grains.

scrupul, scrupule, scrupulus. SCRUPLE

seam — 3 sæm (OED); 3–4 L summa; 3–6 seme; 3–9 seem; 4 sem (OED), L summagium; 5 ceme (OED), zeme (OED); 6 seayme (OED), seym (OED), sheme (OED); 6–7 seame; 6–9 seam; 7 seeme, L suma (Select Pleas 1); 9 zame (OED), zeam (OED) [ME *seem*, *sem* < OE *sēam* < (assumed) VL *sauma*, packsaddle, < LL *sagma*]. A m-c and a wt, identical to the QUARTER, for dry products: chopped bark, Yorkshire, 9 heaped bu (*c*4.05 hl); glass, generally 120 lb (54.431 kg) or 24 stone of 5 lb each, but occasionally 100 lb (45.359 kg) or 20 stone of 5 lb each; grain, generally 8 striked or leveled bu (*c*2.82 hl) of 8 gal each and equal to $\frac{1}{4}$ CHALDER, but variations from 7 to 9 bu (*c*2.47 to *c*3.17 hl) were not uncommon; lime, Derbyshire, 8 striked bu (*c*2.82 hl) at the wharves and 8 heaped bu (*c*3.60 hl) at the kilns; salt, 4 Cwt (203.208 kg); and Welsh coal, Devonshire, 16 heaped bu (*c*7.20 hl). — **1200** Cur. Reg. 8.218: De ordeo xj. sceppas et j. quarterium et xxxj. summas avene, unde tercia pars crevit super tenementum quod recuperavit. **1228** Gras 1.156: Quodlibet quarterium bladi . . . . Unum seme ferri. **1290** Fleta 120: Item summa vitri constat ex xx. petris, et quelibet petra ex quinque libris, et sic continentur in summa que dicitur le seem quinquies viginti libre. **1304** Gras 1.169: Pro xlvii summis ordei. *c***1350** Swithun 79: De quolibet summagio bladi. *c***1590** Hall 21: The quarter or seame is 8 bushells. **1603** Henllys 139: Lyme ys sold by the Bushell, and so by the hundred, and not by the seame, or horseloade, as in other places. **1616** Hopton 162: Whereof are made . . . Coombes, or halfe Quarters, Quarters, or seames. **1665** Sheppard 57: The Seem of Glass containeth 24 stone, and euery stone 5 pound, and so the Seeme containeth Six-score pound. **1708** Chamberlayne 207: A Seam of Glass is 24 Stone, 5 Pounds to the Stone, make 120 Pounds. . . . 4 Bushels the Comb or Curnock . . . 2 Curnocks make a Quarter, Seam or Raff. **1717** Dict. Rus. sv dry-measure: Two Curnocks make a Quarter, Seam or Raff, and ten Quarters a Last. **1805** Macpherson I.471: 5 pounds of glass, 1 stone, 24 stones 1 seem. **1820** Second Rep. 32: Seam or Seem, sometimes a quarter of corn or malt.

seame, seayme. SEAM
sec, seck, secke. SACK
seem, seeme. SEAM
seilion, seillon, seilon. SELION
sek, sekke. SACK
seldra. CHALDER
selion — 3 L seilion, L seillon, L seilon; 4–? selion; 5 sellion (OED), seylon (OED); 6 selyon (OED); 7 selione (OED), sillyon (OED) [ME *selion, sellion* < MF *seillon*, a measure of land, < OF *sillon*, ridge, furrow]. A m-a for the strip of land or pathway between two parallel furrows of the open field. Similar to BUTT OF LAND and RIDGE. — **1201** Feet 1.12: Scilicet in orientali parte ville unum seillonem inter terram Walteri filii Willelmi et Walteri filii Adelstan' . . . et duos seillones inter terram Siwathe. **1202** *Ibid* 15: Quatuor seilones terre sue qui jacent inter culturas predicti Jo-

hannis qui uocantur Micheles acras; *ibid* 73: Duos seilones super Swikes et ij seilones super Kirkefurlang'; *ibid* 78: Scilicet unum seillonem ad Aldewellesti et unum seilonem ad Hagethornes et duos seillones ad Baligat'. **1208** *Ibid* 128: Et in escambium cuius tofti et cuius seilionis predicta Basilia dedit et concessit predicto Hugoni . . . et unum seilionem in campo de Goldcroft. **1665** Sheppard 22: A Selion . . . otherwise called a Ridge of Land . . . of no certain quantity, but sometime containeth half an acre, sometimes more and sometimes less.

selione, sellion, selyon. SELION

sem, seme. SEAM

seron — 6–9 seron; 6, 9 serone; 9 ceroon (OED), seroon (OED) [Sp *serón*, a pannier, hamper, crate]. A m-c for dry products: almonds, 2 Cwt (97.976 kg); aniseed, 3 to 4 Cwt (152.406 to 203.208 kg); and castle-soap, 2½ to 3¾ Cwt (127.005 to 190.507 kg). It was a large bale or bundle that was tightly wrapped in animal's hide. — *c***1550** Welsh 62: 1 serone white soap; *ibid* 170: 4 serones divers goods. **1696** Phillips sv: Seron of Almonds, the Quantity of Two Hundred Weight: Of Anis-seeds from 3 to 4 C: Of Castle-Soap from 2½ C to 3¾ C. **1717** Dict. Rus. sv: Seron of Almonds, the quantity of two Hundred-Weight. Of Anis seeds, from 3 to 4 C: Of Castle-soap, from 2½ C. to 3¾ C. *See* HUNDRED

serone, seroon. SERON

serplaith, serpler, serpliath. SARPLER

sesster. SESTER

sester — 1 sestre (Select Doc.); 1–7 L sextarium, L sextarius; 1–9 sester; 3 sestier, L sextertium; 4 cestre (Prior), cistern (Prior), sesster (OED), scxtarye (Prior); 5 cestron, sesteryn, sexter; 6 cester (Prior), sesterne, sestur, systern, systerne; 8 sextar; ? cistra (Prior), sextarie (Prior), L sextercium (Prior), sextur (Prior), L sistarius (Prior), sistern (Prior), sisterne (Prior) [OE *sester; see* OED]. A m-c for dry and liquid products: ale and beer, generally 12 gal (*c*5.54 dkl) but occasionally 13 to 19 gal (*c*6.01 to *c*8.78 dkl); grain, generally 1 SEAM or 8 bu (*c*2.82 hl); lime, 3 to 4 seams (*c*8.46 to *c*11.28 hl); wine, oil, and honey, generally 4 gal (*c*1.51 dkl) but occasionally 5 to 6 gal (*c*1.89 to *c*2.27 dkl). — *c***1050** Select Doc. 79: Unum sextarium mellis triginta duarum unciarum. **1233** Close 1.223: Quod nullus mercator, ducens vina venalia in Angliam vel vina Wasconie . . . vel aliunde, decetero post has nundinas Sancti

Botulfi venire faciat in Angliam aliquod dolium vini, quod minus contineat secundum numerum sextertiorum quam continere consuevit temporibus Henrici regis. **1246** trans in Cal. Char. 1.308: Of the gift of Robert de Maconio, twenty *sestiers* of corn yearly. **1290** Fleta 120: Doleum vini lij. sextaria vini puri debet continere et quodlibet sextarium quatuor ialones. **1390** Henry Derby 15: Clerico buterie super vino, per manus eiusdem pro j sextario iij potellis di. vini Vasconie, altero per ipsum empto ibidem, sextarium ad ij s. viij d. **1421** Cov. Leet 25: That no brewster sell no derre a Cestron ale to noo hukster but for xviij d. **1440** Palladius 58: In half a sexter aged wyne do shake; *ibid* 100: Sex sester old wyne; *ibid* 169: In sesters XII of aisel that soure harde is. *c*1461 Hall 15: The barell cont[aineth] xxxi gallones I quart, there sesteryn cont[aineth] iiij gallouns. **1507** Gras 1.706: He that ys a gawner owght to understonde there ys in a tunne lx systerns and every systerne ys iiii galons be yt wyne or oylle. . . . Any amme of Andwarpe butt xxxvi gallons for ix sesternes ys an ambether. **1521** Cov. Leet 678: And yf the price of Malte be vndur the price of a noboll then the seyd bruers to sell ther ale for xviij d. a sestur; and that thei sell xiiij galondes to the sestur. **1678** Du Cange sv sextarium: Apud Anglos Sextarius vini continet 4. jalones. . . . Variæ fuit capacitatis sextarius, pro variis locis, cum in aridis tum in liquidis. **1745** Fleetwood 52: A Sester or Sextarius was what we now call a Quarter, or a Seam, containing 8 bushels; *ibid* 58: But Sir H. Spelman says, that at Paris, a *Modius Vini* holds 36 Sextarios, and that a Sextar is 8 Pints. **1820** Second Rep. 32: Sester of wheat; before the Conquest was a horse load.

sesterne, sesteryn, sestier, sestre, sestur, sextar, sextarie, sextarium, sextarius, sextarye, sexter, sextercium, sextertium, sextur. SESTER

seylon. SELION

seym. SEAM

shaff, shaffe. SHEAF

shaffment, shafman, shafment, shafmond, shaftemente, shaftman, shaftmen. SHAFTMENT

shaftment — 1 sceaftmund (OED); 4 schaftmonde (OED); 5 chaftmonde (OED), schafftmon (OED), schaftemonde (OED), schaftmon (OED), schaftmond, schaftmone (OED), schaftmount (OED); 5–6 shafmond (OED); 6 shaftemente (OED), shaftman (OED); 6–9 shaftment (OED); 7 shafman (OED), shaftmen

(OED), shaftmet (OED), shaftmont (OED); 7, 9 shafment (OED); 8–9 shathmont (OED); 9 shaffment (OED) [OE *sceaftmund* < *sceaft*, shaft, + *mund*, hand]. A m-l generally regarded as containing 6 inches (*c*15.24 cm) and defined as the distance from the tip of the extended thumb across the breadth of the palm. — **1474** Cov. Leet 399: And his ffagott of wodde of an ob. schal-be iij schaftmond and a halfe a-bout and a yerde of lenthe. And his ffagott of j d. schal-be vij schaftmond a-bout, kepyng the same lenght.

shaftmet, shaftmont, shathmont. SHAFTMENT
shayff. SHEAF
sheaf — 4–5 scheef (OED), schef (OED), shef (Fab. Rolls); 4–6 sheef (OED), shefe (OED); 5 chyfe (OED), sheeffe (OED), sheiff (Fab. Rolls); 5–6 schefe (OED), scheff, scheffe (OED), sheff (OED); 5–7 sheffe; 6 schaffa, schiefe, shaff (OED), shaffe, shayff, sheaffe (OED); 6–7 sheafe (OED); 6–9 sheaf; 7 sheave (OED), sheive (OED); 8 sheaff (OED) [ME *sheef, shef, schef* < OE *scēaf; see* WNID3]. A m-c, m-q, and wt for several products: glass, of uncertain wt; grain, generally $\frac{1}{12}$ to $\frac{1}{24}$ THRAVE, but in Ireland, $\frac{1}{17}$ CRANNOCK of 2 SEAMS or approximately 1 bu (*c*3.52 dkl); and steel, 30 GADS or PIECES of uncertain wt, equal to $\frac{1}{6}$ or $\frac{1}{12}$ BURDEN. — *c*1461 Hall 17: And xxx gaddes make a scheff, and xii scheff make a burdon. **1507** Gras 1.703: Stelle the barelle wyche owght to be iiii [×] xx burden and xxx gaddes makythe sheffe. **1508** Fab. Rolls 353: x shaffe Renysh glase. **1532** Finchale ccccxlvii: 8 shayff brymmys-glasse. **1597** Skene 1. sv schaffa: Ane schiefe of steile. **1787** Liber 363: To hold the produce of 17 sheaves of corn. **1805** Macpherson I.471: 30 pieces of steel 1 sheaf.

sheafe, sheaff, sheaffe, sheave. SHEAF
shede. SHIDE
sheef, sheeffe, shef, shefe, sheff, sheffe, sheiff, sheive. SHEAF
sheldra. CHALDER
sheme. SEAM
shid. SHIDE
shide — 1–3 scīd (OED); 3 sid (OED); 4 chide (OED), szhide (OED); 4–6 schide (OED), schyde (OED); 4–9 shide; 5 chyde (OED), schudde (OED), schyd (OED), schydd (OED); 5–6 shyde, shyyd (OED); 6 shede (OED), shyd (OED); 6–7 shid [ME *shide* < OE *scīd*]. A m-l of 4 ft (1.220 m) for firewood with variations in cir-

cumference of 16 to 38 inches (4.064 to 9.652 dm). In the citations the "carfe," a var of carf, is the cut part at the end of a piece of wood, while the "tall shide," "taleshid," and "tale-shide," var of talshide, refer to a cut shide. — **1559** Fab. Rolls 353: In byllot or shydes. **1587** Stat. 171: And that euerie tall shide, conteine in length foure foot besides the carfe. And euerie tall shide named of one, to conteine in greatnesse within a foot of the middest sixteene inches about. And euerie tall shide named of two ... three and twentie inches about ... three, to conteine ... eight and twentie inches ... foure, to conteine ... three and thirtie inches about ... and five to conteine ... eight and thirtie inches about. *c***1590** Hall 27–28: Euery taleshid conteyn' in lenght 4 foott, besyde the carfe, in lenght eiche alike. The taleshid namid one ought to be 16 ynches about. The taleshid namid 2 ... 23 ynches about. The taleshid namid 3 ... 28 ynches about. The taleshid namid 4 ... 33 ynches about. The taleshid namyd 5 ... 38 ynches. **1616** Hopton 163: All Shids must be foure foot long beside the carfe, and upon them is 1. 2. 3. 4. or 5. markes or notches, and then they must bee in compasse about the middest 16. 23. 28. 33 or 38 inches, according as it hath number of markes. **1665** Assize 18: Item, every Tale-shide must contain in length four foot. **1682** Hall 30: Shids must be 4 foote long, besides the Carfe. They are noted with 1, 2, 3, 4 or 5, and must accordingly be in compasse, about the midst, 16, 23, 28, 33, [38] inches.

shyd, shyde, shyyd, sid. SHIDE

sievf. SIFE

sife — 8–9 sievf; ? L cipha (Prior), sife (Prior) [prob < *sieve* < ME *sive* < OE *sife*]. A m-c, a wicker basket, for dry products in Kent: apples and potatoes, approximately 1 bu (*c*3.52 dkl), and cherries, 48 lb (21.772 kg). — **1820** Second Rep. 32: Sievf, a flat basket for measuring or carrying fruit and vegetables ... Kent: of apples and potatoes, about a bushel ... of cherries, 48 lb.

sillyon. SELION

sistarius, sistern, sisterne. SESTER

skain, skaine, skane. SKEIN

skape. SKEP

skayn, skayne. SKEIN

skeb. SKEP

skef. SKIVE

skein — 5 skayn (OED), skayne (OED); 5–7 skeyne (OED); 6 scan

(OED), scayne (OED), skane (OED); 6–7 skaine (OED); 6–9
skain; 7 scane (OED), schaine (OED); 7–9 skein; 8 scain (OED)
[ME *skayne, skeyne* < MF *escaigne*, of obscure origin]. A m-l for
yarn: Hampshire, 480 yd (43.891 hm), and Suffolk, 1600 or 2400 yd
(146.304 or 219.456 hm). — **1820** Second Rep. 32: Skain or Skein,
Hampshire: of yarn, 480 yards . . . Suffolk: of yarn reeled, 20 leas,
each of 80 or 120 yards.

skeipp. SKEP

skep — 1 sceppe (OED); 3–7 L sceppa; 4 scep (OED), skipp (Prior);
4–6 skeppe (OED); 4, 7 scepp (OED), skippe (OED); 4–7 skepe
(OED); 4–9 skep; 5 scappe (OED), schepp (Fab. Rolls), skype
(OED), skyppe (OED); 5–7 skepp; 6 skeipp (OED); 7–9 skip
(OED); 8 scape (OED), scepe (OED); 9 skape (OED), skeb
(OED); ? L escheppa (Prior), L eschippa (Prior), L eskippa (Prior)
[ME *skep* < OE *sceppe*, skepful, < ON *skeppa*, bushel]. A m-c
for grain and other dry products, varying in size from 1 or 2 bu
(*c*3.52 or *c*7.05 dkl) to approximately 1 or 2 SEAMS (*c*28.19 or *c*56.38
dkl). — **1200** Cur. Reg. 8.218: De ordeo xj. sceppas et j. quarterium et xxxj. summas avene. **1490** Salzman 2.47: No one shall have
nor kepe within hows eny bussell skepp, whych is the iiij[th] parte
of a quarter. **1678** Du Cange sv sceppa: Mensura salis . . . . Alio-
rumque aridorum, puta farinæ. **1777** Nicol. and Burn 613: Skep . . .
a measure of uncertain quantity: In a survey of the forest of Engle-
wood in 1619, it is defined to contain 12 bushels, and every bushel
(Penrith measure) 16 gallons and upwards.

skepe, skepp, skeppe. SKEP

skevy. SKIVE

skeyne. SKEIN

skif. SKIVE

skin [ME *skin* < OE *scinn* < ON *skinn*]. A wt of 3 Cwt (146.964 kg)
for cinnamon (*c*1800), originally the amount bound in animal's
skin (Second Rep. 32). *See* HUNDRED

skip, skipp, skippe. SKEP

skive — 5 skef, skevy, skif (Southampton 1), skive (Southampton 1),
skyve (Southampton 1) [perh < *shive*, a thin piece or fragment; cf
ON *skífa*, a shaving, slice]. A m-q at Southampton for teasels,
consisting of approximately 500 in number. — **1439** Southampton
2.28: 35 skevys tesellarum. **1443** Brokage II.57: Pro vi skevys
tesell'; *ibid* 96: Cum 1 skef tesell. *c*1475 Gras 1.193: Of a skef
tasill'.

skoir, skor, skore, skowre. SCORE

skron [*]. A wt of 2 Cwt (97.976 kg) for almonds and 3 Cwt (152.406 kg) for barilla (c1800) (Second Rep. 32). *See* HUNDRED

skype, skyppe. SKEP

skyve. SKIVE

sleek [prob *sleek* (or *slick*) *measure*, a level or striked measure]. A m-c for apples and pears in Clydesdale (c1800), containing 18 pt or 2½ gal (c1.10 dkl) (Second Rep. 32).

somme. SUM

soortt. SORT

sort — 5 sorte; 5–6 sort; 6 sortte; ? soortt (OED), sortt (OED) [ME *sort* < MF *sorte*, prob < MedL *sors, sortis,* sort, kind, < LL *sors, sortis,* way, manner, < L *sors, sortis,* a lot, share]. A m-c for fruit, generally containing 3 PIECES or 12 QUARTERNS (152.406 kg). Occasionally it was described as the equivalent of 3 FRAILS (40.824 to 102.057 kg). — **1439** Southampton 2.16: 2 sort' fructui; *ibid* 17: 3 sort' et 1 pecia fructui. **1443** Brokage II.100: Cum ix sortes fructui; *ibid* 111: iiii sortes fyges. **1507** Gras 1.697: Fygges the sortte that ys to saye iii frayles for the sortte.

sorte, sortt, sortte. SORT

span — 4–5 spane (OED); 4–7 spanne (OED); 4–9 span; 5 spayn (OED); 8 spand (OED) [ME *spanne* < OE *spann*]. A m-l which originated as a unit of body measurement equal to the distance from the tip of the smallest finger to the tip of the thumb on the outstretched hand. Based on the ft of 12 inches, the span was made equal to 9 inches (2.286 dm). — **1717** Dict. Rus. sv: Span, a Measure from the Thumb's end to the top of the little Finger, containing three Hands-breadth or 9 Inches. **1820** Second Rep. 32: Span, 9 inches.

spand, spane, spanne, spayn. SPAN

spindle [ME *spindel* < OE *spinel;* akin to OHG *spinila,* spindle, MHG *spinel, spinle,* OE *spinnan,* to spin]. A m-l for thread in Clydesdale (c1800) containing 14,400 yd (c1316.74 dkm) or 48 cuts of 120 threads each on a reel 2½ yd in circumference (Second Rep. 32).

sstakke, stac, staca, stacca. STACK

stack — 2 L staca (Prior); 3, 6 stac (OED); 3–7 stak (OED); 4–9 stack; 5 sstakke (OED); 5–6 stake (OED), stakk (OED); 5–7 stacke (OED); 6 stayke (OED); 7 L stacca (Henllys) [ME *stak, stack* < ON *stakkr,* haystack]. A m-c for dry products (c1600 to *c*1800): barley and wheat, Glamorganshire, 3 bu (*c*1.06 hl); coal, Derbyshire, 105 cu ft (2.973 cu m), and Shropshire, 4 cu yd (3.058 cu m) totaling 25 Cwt (1270.050 kg); oats, Glamorganshire, 6 bu (*c*2.11 hl); and wood, Bedfordshire, Middlesex, and Northamptonshire, 4 cu yd (3.058 cu m) (Henllys 138 and Second Rep. 32).

stacke. STACK

stæn. STONE

staff [ME *staf* < OE *stæf*, staff; *see* WNID3]. A m-q for teasels (*c*1800): Essex, 1250 or 50 GLEANS of 25 teasels each, and Gloucestershire, 500 or 25 gleans of 20 teasels each (Second Rep. 32).

stain, staine. STONE

stak, stake, stakk. STACK

stan, stane. STONE

stang — 3 stong (OED); 3–9 stang; 4–5 L stanga; 4–7 stange; 6–7 stangue; 7 stonge (OED); 8 steng (OED); 8–9 stangell [ME *stang, stange, stong* < ON *stöng;* akin to OE *steng*, pole]. A m-a for land in Wales commonly identified with the customary acre of 3240 sq yd (0.271 ha). In certain regions, however, it was much smaller for it was considered the equivalent of ¼ erw, or standard acre, of 4320 sq yd. — **1400** trans in Cal. Close 17.202: Five stangs (*stanga*) of meadow called 'Farthyngstanges'. **1603** Henllys 134: 8 poles in bredth, and xx in length, or 4 in bredth and 40 in length maketh a stange, w[hich] is Just in accompte (thoughe not in measure) w[ith] the statute acre, and the difference is onely in the length of the landpole; *ibid* 134–35: 4 of those stangues make the Penbrokeshire acre. **1820** Second Rep. 32: Stang, or Stangell, S. Wales: ¼ Erw. *See* ACRE

stanga, stange, stangell, stangue. STANG

stayke. STACK

stayne, stean, steane, sten. STONE

steng. STANG

step [ME *step* < OE *stæpe, stepe*]. A m-l (*c*1500) generally equal to ½ PACE or approximately 2½ ft (*c*0.76 m) (Harkness xliii).

stetch [a var of *stitch*, a narrow ridge of land, a ridge between furrows]. A m-l of 8 ft 2 inches (2.489 m) for land in Suffolk (*c*1100) (Prior 150).

stica. STICK

stick — 3 estik, L estika (Swinfield), estike, L sticka, stik, L stika; 3–4 L stica (Battle); 3–6 sticke; 4 styk, styke; 5 stike, styck; 7–9 stick [ME *sticke* < OE *sticca; see* WNID3]. A m-q for eels, numbering 25 and equaling ⅟₁₀ BIND or ⅟₁₀ GWYDE. — **1202** Feet 3.196: Tenendam de predicto abbate et successoribus suis sibi et heredibus suis in perpetuum per liberum seruitium xx solidorum et sex millariorum et duodecim stikarum anguillarum per annum pro omni seruitio saluo forinseco seruitio. *c***1253** Hall 12: E checun estike de xxv anguilles. *c***1272** *Ibid* 10: Bynda vero anguillarum constat ex decem stickes; et quelibet sticke ex viginti et quinque anguillis. **1289** Swinfield 3: j. estik' ang'll. **1290** Fleta 120: Et quelibet sticka ex xxv anguillis. **1303** Report 1.414: Et quelibet stik ex viginti quinque anguillis. **1390** Henry Derby 20: Et per manus Thome Fyssher pro xlviij styks anguillarum ab ipso emptis apud Boston, le styk ad iiij d.; *ibid* 29: Et per manus eiusdem pro j styke di. anguillarum, xiiij d. *c***1461** Hall 17: Also Elys be sold by the stike, that ys xxv elys; and x styckys make a gwyde. *c***1590** *Ibid* 23: A bynd of eeles consistith 10 stikes. **1717** Dict. Rus. sv bind: 10 strikes [*sic*], each 25 Eels. **1805** Macpherson I.471: 25 eels 1 stick, 10 sticks 1 bind. **1820** Second Rep. 32: Stick of eels, 25.

sticka, sticke, stik, stika, stike. STICK

stimpart [of obscure origin; possibly contraction of *saxteenth*, sixteenth, + *-part* (OED)]. A m-c for grain in Ayrshire (*c*1800) equal to ¼ pk (*c*0.27 hl) or ⅟₁₆ bu (Second Rep. 32).

stoan, stoane. STONE

stoke [E *stock*, in the sense of a store or supply of goods]. A m-q for dinnerware, consisting of 60 pieces. — *c***1461** Hall 17: Also there ys a numbyr that ys called a stoke, and yt conteynyth lx; thereby be sold Pruse trenchers, dysshes and platters and dyuers oder.

stolp. STOUP

ston. STONE

stone — 1–3 stan (OED); 3 stæn (OED); 3–4 F pere; 3–5 ston (OED); 3–7 L petra; 4 F piere; 4–5 sten (OED); 4–6 stoon (OED); 4–9 stane (OED), stone; 5 stayne (OED); 5–6 stoone (OED); 5–7 stonne; 6 steane (OED), stoan (OED), stoane (OED); 6–7 stain (OED), staine (OED); 8–9 stean (OED) [ME *stan, ston, stoon* < OE *stān*]. A wt for dry products generally of 14 lb (6.350 kg), but there were several important exceptions, ranging from 5 to 32 lb (2.268 to 14.515 kg): almonds, 8 lb; alum, generally 8 lb but occasionally 13½ lb; beef, London, 8 lb, and Herefordshire, 12 lb; cumin, 8 lb; flax, generally 14 lb but occasionally 16 lb; glass, 5 lb;

hemp, generally 16 lb but occasionally 20 and 32 lb; lead, generally 12 lb but occasionally 15 lb; pepper, sugar, and wax, 8 lb; wool, generally 14 lb but Herefordshire, 12 lb, Gloucestershire, 15 lb, and Wales, 17 lb. It was commonly called a half-quartern. — *c*1253 Hall 11: Checun pere [de plum] est de xii lib. . . . La centeine de cire, sucre, peyuer, cumin, almand, et de alume, si est de xiii peris et di., et checune pere de viii li.; *ibid* 12: La sem de veyr est de xxiiii peris, e checune pere est de V li. *c*1272 *Ibid* 9: Petra [plumbi] constat ex duodecim libris; *ibid* 10: Item centena zucari, cere, piperis, cimini, amigdalorum, et allume continet tresdecim petras et dimidiam; et quelibet petra continet octo libras. **1275** Gras 1.233: xl sackes V peres et demy de laine en xxxix sarpellers et i poke que poisa xvi peres apaie. **1290** Fleta 119: Et quelibet petra ponderat xij. libras in pondere plumbi. . . . Item summa vitri constat ex xx. petris, et quelibet petra ex quinque libris. *c*1300 Hall 8: Duodecim libre et dimidia faciunt petram Londonie. **1304** Gras 1.169: Pro xxii petris canabi. **1341** Rot. Parl. 2.133: C'est assavoir, XIIII livres pur la piere. **1389** Rot. Parl. 3.272: Qatorsze livers al Pere. **1391** Henry Derby 68: Clerico speciarie per manus Johannis Scorell pro xj stone cere. *c*1461 Hall 13: xiiij lb. make a stone. **1474** Cov. Leet 396: xij li. & halfe the halfe quartern, *the* wich was called of olde tyme . . . beyng Stone of London. **1540** Recorde 203: In woolle . . . the 14 pounde is not named halfe quarterne, but a Stone. **1575** Mer. Adven. 57: Every stone of the same flax shall conteign but onelye fowertene pounds, and no more. *c*1590 Hall 23: 14 poundes waightes haberdepoyse is the stonne of woole; *ibid* 25: Item waxe and spyce . . . euery stonne 8 [lb]. **1603** Henllys 138: The Stone of wooll is in those partes of the Countrye [Wales] that haunteth the sheere marketts aforesaid accompted xvij lb. **1606** Hall 38: A halfe quarterne is 14 pounde. **1616** Hopton 164: Of Wooll . . . a stone is 14 pound. **1635** Dalton 149: Beefe and other flesh are 16. ounces averdepois to the pound, and 8 of them pounds to make the stone. . . . Hemp, 20. li. weight maketh the stone. **1665** Assize 5: And every Stone [of lead] must consist of twelve pound Avoirdupois. **1678** Du Cange sv petra: Ponderis species, quod constat 12. libris et dimidia. **1708** Chamberlayne 207: Butchers commonly allow but eight Pounds to the Stone. . . . Iron and Shot are Weighed 14 Pounds to the Stone. **1717** Dict. Rus. sv: Stone, a certain Quantity or Weight of some

Commodities. A Stone of Beef at London, is the quantity of 8 Pounds; in Herefordshire 12 l. A Stone of Glass is 5 l. Of Wax 8 l. **1805** Macpherson I.471: 12½ pounds 1 stone of London. . . . 15 ounces of lead 1 pound, 12 pounds 1 stone. **1820** Second Rep. 32–33: Stone, Formerly in London 12½ lb. 31 Ed. 1; that is ⅛ of 100 lb . . . of alum, 13½ lb . . . of glass, 5 lb . . . of hemp, 20 lb. 21 H. 8. Sometimes 32 lb . . . of hemp, or flax, 16 lb. 24 G. 2 . . . of lead, 15 lbs, each 25 shillings in weight. 31 Ed. 1; that is, each of 6750 grains . . . . In modern times, 12 lb make a stone of lead.

stong, stonge. STANG

stonne. STONE

stook — 5–6 stouk (OED), stouke (OED), stowk (OED); 5–7 stowke (OED); 6 stuk (OED); 6–9 stook; 9 stuck (OED) [ME *stouk, stowke;* akin to MLG *stūke,* pile; *see* WNID3]. A m-c for corn, generally containing 12 SHEAVES and equal to ½ THRAVE. — **1820** Second Rep. 34: Sometimes 12 sheaves make a stook. . . . Devonshire: of thresher's work, 10 sheaves from 7 to 10 inches through at the band.

stoon, stoone. STONE

stoope, stopa, stoppa. STOUP

stored [perh < *store,* in the sense of a supply or provision for future use]. A m-c for corn in North Wales (*c*1800) containing 2 bu (*c*7.05 dkl) (Second Rep. 34).

stouk, stouke. STOOK

stoup — 3 L stoppa (Prior); 4 L stopa; 4–6 stowpe (OED); 6 stolp (OED); 6–7 stoope (OED); 6–7, 9 stoupe (OED); 6–9 stoup (OED), stowp (OED) [ME *stowpe,* prob of Scand origin; cf ON *staup,* cup, MLG *stop,* Du *stoop*]. A m-c for liquids, generally wine and honey, varying in size from 1 pt (*c*0.47 l) to 1 or more gal (*c*3.78 + l). — **1390** Henry Derby 9: Clerico speciarie per manus eiusdem pro j stopa et di. mellis per ipsum emptis ibidem, xix d.; *ibid* 14: Clerico buterie super vino per Yngram Northouer pro vij [×] xx [+] viij stopis vini Rochell ab ipso emptis ibidem, le stopa ad v d. lxj s. viij d. **1391** *Ibid* 39: Et eidem pro cccij stopis vini emptis per manus Johannis Payn, et expensis in hospicio domini ibidem per tempus predictum, le stopa j scot, in toto xij marc; *ibid* 47: Et pro iij barellis vini de Rynesch continentibus ccclxxvj stopas, le stopa xxxiiij d.

stoupe. STOUP

stowk, stowke. STOOK
stowp, stowpe. STOUP
strica, strik, strika. STRIKE
strike — 3 L strica (St. Paul's); 3–4 L estarium (Prior), L esteria (Prior), L estricha (Prior), L estricum (Prior); 4 strikill; 4–6 strik (OED), stryk; 4–7 stryke; 4–9 strike; ? L strika (Prior), L strikum (Gras 2) [ME *strik, strike* < vb *striken,* in the sense of leveling or scraping off with a straight instrument called a strike or streek]. A m-c for grain generally containing 2 bu (c7.05 dkl) and equal to ¼ SEAM. In some of the shires, however, strikes of ½ to 4 bu (c1.76 to c14.10 dkl) were occasionally used. The strike was commonly called a half-coomb. — **1395** York Mem. 2.10: Et unum strikill ligni. **1440** Palladius 21: A strike is for vi [✕] xx oon daies mete. **1540** Nottingham 378: We thengk that the brassen stryk be lefful acordyng to the 5 Kynges Standard, after viij gallans to the stryke. **1616** Hopton 162: All kind of graine is measured by . . . strikes, or halfe coombs. **1682** Hall 30: I Last conteynes: 10 Quarters . . . 40 Strikes, 80 Bushels. **1820** Second Rep. 34: Strike . . . a measure of corn, varying in its contents from ½ to 1, 2, and 4 bushels.
strikill, strikum. STRIKE
stroak [prob < STRIKE]. A m-c for corn in northern England (c1800) containing 2 pk (c1.76 dkl) or ½ bu (Hunter 124).
stryk, stryke. STRIKE
stuck, stuk. STOOK
styck, styk, styke. STICK
sullinga. SULUNG
sulung — 1–? sulung (Select Doc.); 3 L sullinga [OE *sulung* < *sulh,* a plow, an area of land]. A m-a for land in Kent equivalent to a HIDE. — **1204** Cur. Reg. 10.208: Kent.—Jurata inter priorem Roffensem petentem et Hugonem de Bosco tenentem utrum debet forinsecum servitium de tenemento suo de Brunhee de una sullinga vel de dimidia sullinga ponitur in respectum usque in octabas sancti Yllarii pro defectu juratorum.
sum — 5 somme (Brokage II), summe; ? sum [ME *summe, somme* < OF *summe, somme* < L *summa* < *summus,* highest]. A wt of 10,000 lb (4535.900 kg) for nails. — c1461 Hall 17: A summe . . . conteynythe X [✕] M lbs.: and therby be sold paten nayle, sadelers' naylys, cardemakers' nalys, and dyuers odyr.

suma, summa, summagium. SEAM
summe. SUM
swod [prob var of *swad*, pod, shell, prob < OE *swethian*, to bind].
A m-c for fish in Sussex (*c*1850), a basket generally holding the
equivalent of 1 bu (*c*3.52 dkl) (Cooper 81).
systern, systerne. SESTER
szhide. SHIDE

T

taal, taale, tail, taile, taill, taille. TALE

tale — 2–9 tale; 3–5 talle (OED); 3–6 tayle (OED); 4 taal (OED), taale (OED), tayl (OED); 4–5 taille (OED); 4–7 tail (OED); 5 tayll (OED), taylle (OED); 5–6 taill (OED); 5–7 taile; 6 tell (OED), telle (OED); 6–9 teale (OED) [ME *tale*, talk, narrative, list, < OE *talu;* akin to ON *tal, tala*, number, speech, Sw *tal*, Dan *tal*, number]. A m-q for the number or count of fish or other products in a C, M, or LAST. — *c*1461 Hall 18: Also there be odyr merchandyse that go by tale. **1603** Henllys 139: Oysters are allso sold by tale, as by hundred and thousand and not by the bushell, as ys used in London. **1635** Dalton 149: Also Herrings are sold by taile, sc. six score herrings shall goe to the hundred, ten hundred to the thousand, and ten thousand to the Last. **1665** Sheppard 60: Also Herrings are sold by Tale, viz. Six score Herrings go to the 100 [one hundred]; 1000 [ten hundreds] to the Thousand and Ten thousand to the Last. *See* COUNT

talle. TALE

talvett. TOVET

tancard, tancarde, tanckerd. TANKARD

tankard — 4–5, 8 tancard (OED); 4–9 tankard; 5–7 tankerd (OED); 6 tancarde (OED), tanckerd (OED), tankarde (OED), tankert (OED); 7, 9 tanker (OED) [ME *tankard*, of obscure origin; cf MDu *tanckaert*]. A m-c for ale containing 1 qt (*c*1.15 l). It was originally a large, wooden tub, hooped with iron or leather staves, which was used principally for carrying water. — **1820** Second Rep. 34: Tankard of ale, a quart.

tankarde, tanker, tankerd, tankert. TANKARD

tapnet — 6 tapnet, tapnett, topnet (OED) [of obscure origin; possibly a measure whose contents were drawn from a tap (OED)]. A wt of 20 lb (9.072 kg) for figs. — *c*1550 Welsh 128: 1 tapnet figs; *ibid* 191: 124 tapnetts figs.

tapnett. TAPNET
tarcian. TERTIAN
tavort. TOVET
tayl, tayle, tayll, taylle, teale. TALE
tearce, tearse, teers, teirce, teirse. TIERCE
tell, telle. TALE
terce. TIERCE
tercian, terciane, tercien, tercion, tercyan, tercyen. TERTIAN
ters. TIERCE
tersan. TERTIAN
terse. TIERCE
tertian — 4–6 terciane, tercyan (OED), tertiane; 4–7 tercian; 5 tercien
(Southampton 1); 5–9 tertian; 6 tarcian (OED), tercyen (OED),
tersan (OED), tertione; 8 tercion (OED) [ME *tercian* < L *tertianus*, of the third]. A m-c for wine, oil, and honey containing 84
gal (*c*3.18 hl) and equal to ⅓ TUN of 252 gal. It was synonymous
with the PUNCHEON and was double the TIERCE of 42 gal. — **1423**
Rot. Parl. 4.256: Plese it to your wise discretions tendirly to con-
sider, howe that of ald tyme ordined and trewly used Tonnes,
Pipes, Tertians, Hoggeshedes of Wyn of Gascoign . . . . The
Terciane XX [×] IIII [+] IIII galons . . . . The pipe XX [×] VI
[+] VI galons, and so aftir the afferant the Tercian, and the
Hoggeshede of Wyn of Gascoign. **1439** Rot. Parl. 5.30: Chescun
Tercian XX [×] IIII [+] IIII galons; *ibid* 31: Toutz maners Tonels,
Pipes, Tertians & Hoggeshedes, taunt de Vin, come de Oyle &
Mele . . . . Ascune Tonelle, Pipe, Tertiane ou Hoggeshed, de Vin,
Oyle ou Mele. **1540** Recorde 206: Of wine and oyle the Tertian
holdeth 84 Gallons. **1587** Stat. 267: The tercian lxxxiiii. galons.
*c***1590** Hall 21: The tertiane or punchione of a tunne, which is ⅓
part of a tunne, contenith 84 gallons; *ibid* 23: And so the kilderkynne, firkyn, and tertione. **1615** Collect. Stat. 466: The pipe 126
gallons, and so after the rate, the tercian, & the hogshead of
Gascoine wine; *ibid* 467: Euerie Tercian fourescore and foure
gallons. **1665** Sheppard 58–59: The Tercian fourscore and four
Gallons. **1820** Second Rep. 35: Tertian of wine, 84 gallons. *See*
PUNCHEON
tertiane, tertione. TERTIAN
teyrse. TIERCE
thousand — 1–3 thusend (OED); 2–3 thusennd (OED), thusent

(OED); 3 thousunt (OED), thusand (OED), thusund (OED); 3–4 thousend (OED); 3–6 thousande (OED); 4–5 thowsande; 4–7 thowsand; 4–9 thousand; 5 thouzand (OED) (*see* additional var in OED sv thous- and thows-) [ME *thousend, thusend* < OE *thūsend; see* WNID3]. A m-q, the MIL (M), generally 10 times larger than the C of 100, 106, 120, 124, 132, 160, and 225; and a wt, the M, generally 10 times larger than the Cwt of 100, 104, 108, 112, and 120 lb. Hence, for example, if the C for the product or the region numbered 120, the corresponding M numbered 1200; if the Cwt for the product or region weighed 112 lb (50.802 kg), the corresponding M weighed 1120 lb (508.020 kg). — *c*1461 Hall 13: Also of this Weyght there goo v [×] xx [+] xii lb. to the C; and x [×] c make a M of ony weyght. . . . xxviij lb. [make a quarter Cwt]; lvj lb. make half a C; v [×] xx [+] xij lb. make a C . . . and x [×] c make a M. **1549** Gras 1.627: Pro M waight rosen'. **1559** Fab. Rolls 353: In byllot or shydes, with ij thowsand lyeng on Lynts grene, iiij thowsand. **1578** Mer. Adven. 100: Yt is enacted, &c., That whosoever, broother or suster of this Feoloship aforesaid, that shall rate him or herselfe at twoo thowsande skinnes. **1603** Henllys 139: Oysters are allso sold by tale, as by hundred and thousand. **1615** Collect. Stat. 465: But a last of herrings containeth ten thousand, and euery thousand containeth ten hundred, and euery hundred six score. **1616** Hopton 162: Herring are counted by the hundreds, thousands, and Lasts. **1635** Dalton 149: Six score herrings shall goe to the hundred, ten hundred to the thousand, and ten thousand to the Last. **1678** Du Cange sv miliarium: Mille pondo librarum. **1708** Chamberlayne 205: Herrings 120 to the C . . . 12 Hundred to the Thousand.

thousande, thousend, thousunt, thouzand, thowsand, thowsande. THOUSAND

thraf, thrafe, thraive, thraue, thrava. THRAVE

thrave — 2–4 L trava; 4 L thrava (Hatfield); 4–6 threve (Fountains), L trefa (Fountains); 5 thraf (OED), threfe (OED); 5–6 thrafe (OED), thraue (OED), thrawe (OED); 5–9 thrave; 6 thravffe (OED), thrayf (OED), threafe (OED), threff (OED), threif (OED), threiff (OED); 7 thref (OED); 7–9 threave; 8 threive (OED); 9 thraive (OED), thrief (OED), thrieve (OED) [ME *thrave, threve* < OE *threfe,* of Scand origin; cf ON *threfi,* thrave, Dan *trave*]. A m-c for grain and straw for thatching, generally containing 12 or 24 SHEAVES, but there were several exceptions: Derbyshire, corn, 2 KIVERS equal to 24 sheaves in all; Gloucestershire, straw, 24 BOLTINGS or TRUSSES of 24 lb each or 576 lb (261.268 kg) in all; and Yorkshire, straw, 12 BUNDLES. — **1164** Malcolm 264: Et quatuor clauinos farine et decem trauas euene. **1621** Best 184: 40 threaves of mown rye in the lathe. **1820** Second Rep. 35: Thrave of corn, Derbyshire: 2 kivers ... of straw, Gloucestershire: 24 boltings or trusses, of 24 lb. each = 576 lb. .... Threave ... Yorkshire, E.R. 12 bundles, not precisely limited in magnitude.

thravffe, thrawe, thrayf, threafe, threave, thref, threfe, threff, threif, threiff, threive, threve, thrief, thrieve. THRAVE

thusand, thusend, thusennd, thusent, thusund. THOUSAND

thymber. TIMBER

tierce — 4–8 terse; 4–9 tierce; 5 tyerce (OED), tyrse (OED); 5–9 terce; 6 teers (OED), teyrse (Dur. House); 6–7 tearce (OED); 7 tearse (OED), teirce (OED), teirse (OED), ters (OED), tierse [ME *terce, tierce* < MF *tierce* < fem of *ters, tiers*, third, < L *tertius*, third]. A m-c for wine, oil, and honey containing 42 gal (*c*1.59 hl) and equal to ½ TERTIAN, or ⅓ PIPE of 126 gal or ⅙ TUN of 252 gal. — *c*1590 Hall 21: The terce of a pipe or a butt, which is ⅙ part of a tunne, contenith 42 gallons. **1616** Hopton 161: I Tierce ... 42 Gallon. **1665** Sheppard 14: A Terse or Tierse is but the 6th part of a Tun, or third part of a Pipe. **1682** Hall 29: I Tunne conteynes: 2 Pipes or Butts ... 6 Tierces. **1708** Chamberlayne 210: Of these Gallons ... a Tierce of Wine holds 42 Gallons. **1710** Harris 1. sv measures: The common Wine Gallon sealed at Guild-Hall in London ... is supposed to contain 231 Cubick Inches; and from thence, the Tierce will contain 9702 Cub. Inch. **1717** Dict. Rus. sv: Tierce or Terce, a Liquid Measure containing Forty two Gallons. **1778** Diderot XXI.673: Tierce ... 42 Gallon. **1820** Second Rep. 35: Tierce of wine, 42 gallons.

tierse. TIERCE

timber — 3 L timbrium, L tymbra; 3–4 L tymbrium; 3–9 timber; 4 L timbra; 4–5 tymbre; 5–7 tymber; 6 thymber, tymbber (Gras 1) [OF *timbre* < MLG *timber, timmer*, lumber; so called because the fur skins were packed and shipped between two heavy boards]. A m-q numbering 40 for the following fur skins: beaver, calaber (squirrel), cony (rabbit), ermine, ferret, fitch (fitchew), gray (badger), jennet, martin, miniver, mink, otter, and sable. Most other fur skins were measured by the C. — *c*1253 Hall 12: La timber de peus de cunnis et de gris, ou ver, est de xl peus. *c*1272 *Ibid* 10: Tymbra vero de pellibus cuniculorum et grisonum constat ex quadraginta pellibus. **1290** Fleta 120: Lunda autem pellium continet xxxij timbria, et seuellio cuniculorum et de grises continet xl. pelles. **1303** Gras 1.166: Timbra squirellorum. **1323** *Ibid* 210: De quolibet tymbrio de grys. **1392** Henry Derby 92: Et per manus Johannis Dyndon pro j furrura de grys per ipsum empta ibidem de vj tymbre, et de ij tymbre de meniuer, xij nobles. **1406** trans in Cal. Close 19.33: Six 'tymbre' of 'menyver'. *c*1461 Hall 17: And xl fells make a Tymber. **1507** Gras 1.695: Bever wombys the tymber . . . . Armyns the tymber that ys to saye the xl skynes; *ibid* 696: Callabur rawe that ys to saye xl skynes the tymber; *ibid* 698: Gray tawyd the tymber . . . that ys to saye xl skynnes . . . . Gray ontawed [the] thymber; *ibid* 700: Marterns the tymber . . . . Mynkes the tymber; *ibid* 701: Otter the tymber that ys to saye xl skynnes to the tymber; *ibid* 703: Sablles the tymber. **1615** Collect. Stat. 465: A timber of conie skins and grayes consisteth of 40. skins. **1616** Hopton 164: Sables, Martins, Minkes, Jenits, Fitches, & Grayes, haue 4[0] skins in the Timber. **1665** Sheppard 57: A Tymber of Cony-skins and Grayes, consisteth of 40 Skins. **1682** Hall 30: Sables, Martins, Minks, Ferrits, Fitches, and Grayes: 40 Skins in a Timber. **1708** Chamberlayne 205: Of Furrs, Fitches, Grays, Jennets, Martins, Minks, Sables, 40 Skins in a Timber. **1717** Dict. Rus. sv: Timber, of Furrs, i.e. Fitches, Genets, Grays, Marterns, Sables, &c. is forty Skins. **1805** Macpherson I.471: 40 skins of conies or grise 1 timber.

timbra, timbrium. TIMBER

tirrs. TRUSS

toad. TOD

tobit. TOVET

tod — 5 tode (OED); 5–7 todd, todde; 6 toad (OED); 6–7 tood; 7–9 tod [ME *todd, todde;* cf LG *tod, todde,* bundle, small load]. A wt for wool of 28 lb (12.700 kg), equal to $\frac{1}{13}$ SACK or $\frac{1}{26}$ SARPLER. — *c*1461 Hall 13: Woll . . . is most used to be sold by the Stone and by the Todde; *ibid* 19: That ys to say . . . Todde content' xxviij [lb]. . . . The Todd amountythe in Poundes xxviij; *ibid* 20: The Sacke amountythe in . . . Toddes xiij. **1540** Recorde 203: In woolle, 28 pounde is not called a quarterne, but a Todde. *c*1590

Hall 23: 28 poundes waight haberdepoyse is the tood of woole. **1603** Henllys 138: By the todde there is none sold except yt be to an Englishe buyer, that cometh of purpose, and maketh his bargaine by the todde, as a weight best knowne to himself. **1616** Hopton 164: A Todde is 28 pounds, or two stone. **1635** Dalton 149: 28 pounds goeth to the Tod. **1665** Sheppard 63: For Wooll, some say 14 pound goeth to the Stone; 28 pounds to the Todd; *ibid* 64: Each Tod 2 stone, each stone 14 pounds. **1678** Du Cange sv todde: Pondus 28. librarum, Angl. Tod. **1682** Hall 31: A Todd, 2 Stone; a Stone, 14 pound. **1708** Chamberlayne 207: Wooll is Weigh'd by the . . . Tod, i.e. 28 Pounds; *ibid* 208: Tod 28 Pound, to 1 Sack 13 Tods. **1717** Dict. Rus. sv: Tod of Wooll, the quantity of 28 Pounds or 2 Stone. **1820** Second Rep. 35: Tod of wool, 2 stone = 28 lb.

todd, todde, tode. TOD

tofet, toffet, toflet. TOVET

toltrey [*tolt*, toll, + *rey*, king; so called because it was the fixed toll in kind on salt, paid by the men of Malden to the Bishop of London]. A m-c for salt (c1400) containing 2 bu (c7.05 dkl) (Prior 158).

tolvet, tolvett. TOVET

ton — 4–6 tonne; 5 tone (Southampton 1), toun (OED); 5–7 tunne; 5–9 ton; 6 tune; 6–7 toonne; 6–8 tun; 7 tunn (OED); 8 tonn [ME *tonne, toun*, unit of ship capacity or of weight; originally the same word as TUN]. A wt containing 20 Cwt or 2 M of 10 Cwt each. The total wt was 2000, 2160, 2240, or 2400 lb (907.180, 979.760, 1016.040, or 1088.620 kg) depending on whether the corresponding Cwt contained 100, 108, 112, or 120 lb. — **1440** Palladius 118: Or lette a tonne of barly him comprende. *c*1461 Hall 13: v [×] xx [+] xij lb. make a C . . . and x [×] c make a M; and ij M make a Tunne. **1507** Gras 1.699: Iryne the tune. **1524** *Ibid* 197: Pro xx tonne de cave stonne. **1555** York Mer. 155: A tonne of iron, accomptinge sex score endes to the tonne, receyved on the shipe bord. *c*1590 Hall 24: The tunne is 20 hundrid waight, conteninge 2240 poundes waight haberdepoyse; after the ratte 112 poundes to the 100; *ibid* 27: The hundrid of irne is but 5 skore to the hundred and 20 hundrid to the tunne; *ibid* 28: Euery loade of wood ought to be 20 hundred waight, which is a tunne. **1603** Henllys 139: Iron is sold by the stone w[hich] consisteth of xvi haberdepoys, of which stones viij make the C. of Iron, and xx [×] c make a toonne. **1616** Hopton

163: Iron is counted by the pound, hundred, and Tun. **1682** Hall 30: A Tunne of iron. **1704** Mer. Adven. 244: Ffor carrying of every tonn of iron and weighing the same at the weighouse, belonging to a fforreigner. **1708** Chamberlayne 206: 16 Drachms make an Ounce, 16 Ounces a Pound, 28 Pounds a Quarter, 4 Quarters an Hundred, 20 Hundred a Tun. **1728** Chambers 1.360: Tun . . . 2240 Pound. **1778** Diderot XXVI.422: Tonn . . . 2240 Livre. **1784** Ency. meth. 137: Londres. Le *ton, tun* . . . est de 20 *hundreds*, ou de 2240 l. **1789** Hawney 7: Let .43569 of a Ton be reduced to Hundreds, Quarters, and Pounds.

tone. TON

tonel, tonell, tonelle, tonellum, tonellus. TUN

tonn. TON

tonne. TON; TUN

tonnel. TUN

tood. TOD

toonne. TON

tope [of obscure origin; cf G *topf*, a pot]. A m-c of uncertain size used in Durham for dry products. — *c*1530 Dur. House 263: Item 4 topez of pyese.

topnet. TAPNET

topston [*]. A wt of 6½ lb (2.948 kg) for wool in South Wales (*c*1800), equal to ¼ MAEN (Second Rep. 36).

toun. TON

tovet — 7 talvett (OED), tovit, tovitt (OED); 7–8 tofet, toffet (OED); 7–9 tovet; 9 tavort (OED), tobit (OED), toflet (OED); ? tolvet (OED), tolvett (OED), tuffet (Jones) [of obscure origin; *see* OED]. A m-c for grain, generally containing 2 pk or 4 gal (*c*1.76 dkl) and equal to ½ bu. It arose as a local measure of Kent. — **1674** Ray 77: A Tovet or Tofet, half a bushel: Kent. **1696** Jeake 81: 1 Bushel 2 Tovits or Half Bushels, 1 Tovit 2 Pecks. **1853** Cooper 82: Tovet, a measure of two gallons. **1858** Shuttleworths 1094: 2 gallons = a peck; 2 pecks (4 gallons) = a tovet; 2 tovets, 4 pecks, or 8 gallons = a bushel.

tovit, tovitt. TOVET

towne. TUN

trava, trefa. THRAVE

trenda, trendal, trendel, trendell, trendelle, trendil, trendill. TRENDLE

trendle — 1–5 trendel (OED); 4 L trenda; 4–6 trendil (OED); 4–?

trendle; 5 trendill (OED), trendull (OED), trendyl (OED); 5–6
trendell (OED), trendelle (OED), trendyll (OED); 7 trendal (OED)
[ME *trendle* < OE *trendel*, a circle, ring, dish]. A m-c for wax and
other products. It was a round or oval tub of uncertain size. —
1393 trans in Cal. Close 15.173: One trendle (*trenda*) of wax found
at Byrchelton. **1394** trans in *ibid* 218: One trendle (*trenda*) of wax
found at Dyngemersshe.

trendull, trendyl, trendyll. TRENDLE

troiss, tross, trosse. TRUSS

trug [prob a dial var of *trough* < ME *troug* ; *ħrogh* < OE *trog*].
A m-c for grain (*c*1400) equal to $\frac{1}{12}$ SEAM (*c*2.35 dkl) (Thor.
Rogers 1.168).

trus, truse. TRUSS

truss — 3 L trussa; 3–8 trusse; 4–6 trosse (OED), trus (OED); 5 troiss
(OED), truse (OED), turss (OED); 5–7 turs (OED); 7 tirrs (OED),
turse (OED); 7–9 truss; 9 tross (OED) [ME *trusse* < OF *trousse*,
bundle, pack, < *trousser*, to pack]. A m-c for $\frac{1}{36}$ LOAD of hay and
generally weighing 56 lb (25.401 kg). In 1795 it was standardized at
56 lb (25.401 kg) for old hay and 60 lb (27.215 kg) for new hay. —
1202 Feet 2.180: Et in vigilia sancti Ædmundi mittent predictis
infirmis sex rationabiles trussas straminis et in vigilia natale
domini sex trussas et in vigilia pasche sex trussas. *c*1590 Hall 27:
36 trusses makith a loade of haye, and euery trusse is 56 poundes
waight haberdepoyse. **1665** Assize 13: Thirty six Trusses of Hay
shall make the load, every Truss of Hay to weigh the full weight of
fifty six pounds Avoirdupois. **1708** Chamberlayne 38: Hay is sold
by the Truss 56 Pounds, and by the Load 36 Trusses. **1820** Second
Rep. 36: Truss of hay, 56 lb. if old; 60 lb. if new . . . London:
formerly 36 lb.

trussa, trusse. TRUSS

trussell — 3–5 L trussellus; 5 trusselle (OED); 5–9 trussell (OED);
6 tursall (OED); 6–7 tursell (OED) [ME *trussell*, bundle, trussell,
< MF *troussel, trousel*, dim of OF *trousse*, a bundle, TRUSS]. A m-q
for the number of skins or the amount of cloth that formed a con-
venient bundle. — *c*1243 Select Cases 3.lxxxvii: Item ij. trusselli de
pellipatorio, qui custaverunt xv. marcas. **1323** Gras 1.209: De uno
trussello panni cum cordis legatis. *c*1400 *Ibid* 214: De quolibet
trussello de kerseye Walssh russet et mantell' d'Irland.

trusselle, trussellus. TRUSSELL

tuffet. TOVET

tun — 3–4 L tonellum, L tonellus; 4–5 tonel, tonelle (York Mem. 1); 4–8 tonne; 5 tonell, tonnel (Nicholson); 5–7 tunne; 6 towne (Dur. House), tune (OED); 6–9 tun; ? L tunellum (Prior) [ME *tonne*, *tunne*, a tun, < OE *tunne*, a tun, tub, a large vessel]. A m-c for wine, oil, honey, and other liquids, generally containing 252 gal (*c*9.54 hl), but occasionally 208, 240, and 250 gal capacities were used. It was also known as a DOLIUM. — **1330** Rot. Parl. 2.39: C'est assavoir, de chescun Nief portant vintz tonels. **1341** Gras 1.174: Pro xii tonellis vini. *c*1350 *Ibid* 182: De ii tonellis oleo. **1423** Rot. Parl. 4.256: The Tonne of Wyn xx [×] xii [+] XII galons. **1439** Rot. Parl. 5.30: De chescun Tonell . . . de Vin. **1444** *Ibid* 114: And more overe, wher as of old tyme euery Tonne . . . heeld the full gauge after the gauge of Englond . . . . That every Tonne contene XX [×] XII and XII Galons. *c*1461 Hall 15: The tonne cont[aineth] ii [×] c [+] l galouns. . . . Who some euer schall retayle any tunne or pype . . . he schall rakyn the tunne but xii [×] xx gallounes. *c*1517 *Ibid* 49: The tonne, xii [×] xx & xii galons. **1572** Mer. Adven. 97: By hoggeshed or hoggesheds, tonne or tonnes. **1587** Stat. 267: The tunne of wine cc.lii galons. *c*1590 Hall 21: The tunne contenith 252 gallons of liquor. . . . The tonne, xii [×] xx et xii galons. **1599** Mer. Adven. 57: That if anie person or persons . . . shall sell within this toune anie wyne, by hogshead or tunne. **1615** Collect. Stat. 466: Tunne of Wine . . . it containe of English measure 252. gallons. **1635** Dalton 148: Wine, Oyle, and Honey . . . Tunne: 252. gallons. **1665** Sheppard 14: Two Pipes, a Tun, wherein are 252 Gallons. **1682** Hall 29: I Tunne conteynes: 2 Pipes or Butts, 3 Punchions, 4 Hogsheads, 6 Tierces, 8 Barrells, 14 Rundlets, 252 Gallons. **1704** Mer. Adven. 243: Ffor takeing forth of every tonne of wine from a keel or boat. **1708** Chamberlayne 210: A Tun 252 Gallons. **1805** Macpherson I.637: A tun of wine . . . 252 gallons. **1820** Second Rep. 36: Tun of wine, 2 pipes = 252 gallons.

tun. TON
tune. TON; TUN
tunellum. TUN
tunn. TON
tunne. TON; TUN
turs. TRUSS

tursall. TRUSSELL
turse. TRUSS
tursell. TRUSSELL
turss. TRUSS
tyerce. TIERCE
tymbber, tymber, tymbra, tymbre, tymbrium. TIMBER
tyrse. TIERCE

U·V

uirga. VERGE
ulna. ELL; YARD
unce. OUNCE
unch. INCH; OUNCE
unche. INCH
uncia. INCH; OUNCE

vadome, vathym. FATHOM
verge — 3–7 verge, L virga; 4–7 virge; ? L uirga (Prior) [ME *verge* <
MF *verge* < L *virga*, a twig, rod]. Equivalent to YARD and occasionally to PERCH. — **1308** Gras 1.365: Carcavit iiii [✕] c ferri et
xx virgas panni lanosi. **1390** Henry Derby 8: Eidem pro xvij virgis
j quarterio de blanket ab eodem emptis pro eisdem garcionibus
domini, pretium virge, xvj d. . . . Eidem pro j virga et j quarterio
de blu fryse. *c***1400** Henley 68: E pur ceo ke les acres ne sunt mye
touz de une mesure kar en acon pays mesurent il par la verge de
xviii peez e . . . de xx peez e . . . de xxii peez e . . . de xxiiij peez.
*c***1500** Hall 7: iii pedes faciunt virgam; *ibid* 8: V virge dimidia
faciunt perticam. **1688** Bernardi 12: Virga Anglica. 3 Pedes,
12 Palmi, 2 Cubiti, 4 Spithamæ, ⅘ Ulnæ Anglicæ.
vet. FATT
vetheym, vethym. FATHOM
virga. VERGE
virgat, virgata. VIRGATE
virgate — 1–7 L virgata; 3–? virgate; 8–9 virgat [MedL *virgata* < L
virga; see VERGE]. A m-a for land generally synonymous with the
YARDLAND and in Sussex with the WISTA. Like the acreage of other
superficial measures, its total acreage depended on local soil conditions, but virgates of 15, 16, 20, 24, 28, 30, 32, 40, and 60 acres
(*c*6.07 to *c*24.30 ha) were the most common. It was generally
equal to ¼ HIDE and was occasionally the sum of 2 or 3 BOVATES

177

or 4 FARTHINGDALES. — **1200** Cur. Reg. 8.144: De dimidia virgata terre et de xvj. acris terre cum pertinenciis in Waleton'; *ibid* 145: De placito dimidie virgate terre. **1204** Cur. Reg. 10.220: Et ipse Gilbertus venit et reddidit Orenge matri sue x. virgatas terre sicut dotem suam; *ibid* 221: j virgate terre in Wihcthill'. **1212** Cur. Reg. 13.192: De ij. virgatis terre et de dimidia cotlanda cum pertinenciis in Wikefeld. *c*1221 Clerkenwell 136: Dimidiam virgatam terre et duas acras cum mesuagio. **1222** St. Paul's 147: Habet hæc ecclesia unam virgatam terræ liberam ab omni sæculari officio. *c*1283 Battle xiii: Quatuor virgatæ seu wystæ faciunt unam hydam. *c*1300 Bray 8: Henricus de Bray tenet tres virgatas terrae et continent de terra et prato ccvi acras et dimidiam. **1304** Swinfield 221: Heredes Rogeri de la Sale de Hompton' tenent .ij. virgatas terræ per militiam. **1338** Langtoft 600–01: Decem acræ faciunt ferdellum. Quatuor fardella faciunt virgatam unam. Quatuor virgatæ faciunt hidam unam; *ibid* 601: Fardellum Acræ X. / virgata XL. / hida. CLX. *c*1500 Hall 8: viii [×] xx pertice faciunt acram; duodecim acre faciunt bovatam; ii bovate faciunt virgatam. **1603** Henllys 135–36: There is allso a quantytie of land measure called a yard of land, in latin *Virgata terræ*. **1665** Sheppard 22–23: A Yard Land (in Latine *Virgata Terræ*) is a quantity of Land called by this name, but it is no certain Quantity. For in some places it containeth 20 acres; in others 24 acres; in other places 30 acres, according to the estimation of the Country. **1688** Holme 137: Virgate of land is 20, in some places 24 Acres, or in some 30 Acres. **1710** Langtoft 600: The town, according to Domesday Book, consisted of VIII. virgats of Land. . . . Each virgat comprehending fourty acres. **1755** Willis 358: Virgata, or Yard-Land, whereof 4 made an Hide, was in different Counties 15, 20, 30 or 40 Acres. **1777** Nicol. and Burn 615: Virgate of land; a yard land consisting (as some say) of 24 acres, whereof four virgates make an hide.

virge. VERGE

vunce. OUNCE

W

waga. WEY

wagh. WAW

waigh. WEY

wal, wall. WAW

warp [ME *warp* < OE *wearp*, a warp in weaving; akin to OHG *warf*, warp, ON *varp*, a casting, throwing, Sw *varp*, the draft of a net]. A m-q for herrings in Sussex and Kent (*c*1850). It consisted of a cast of 4 (Cooper 85).

wash [< vb *wash; see* WNID3]. A m-c for oysters (*c*1500), probably originally the amount washed at one time. It contained approximately 1 gal (*c*4.40 l) or ⅛ bu (Prior 170).

waugh. WAW

waw — 4 wagh (OED), waugh (OED), wawe (OED); 5 wal (OED); 5–6 wall (OED), waw [MLG and MDu *wage* (Du *waag*); *see* WEY]. A m-q for glass containing 40 BUNCHES of uncertain wt. **— 1507** Gras 1.698: Glasse called Flemyche glass the waw that ys to saye xl bunchys. **1508** Fab. Rolls 359: A Waw of glasse.

wawe. WAW

way, waya, waye, wegh, weigh. WEY

weight [ME *weght, wight* < OE *wiht, gewiht*]. Equivalent to WEY. **— 1615** Collect. Stat. 466: There is a weight aswel of lead as of wool, tallow and cheese, & weigheth fourteene stone.

werkhop [ME *werk*, work, + *hop*, hopper, receptacle]. A m-c for grain (*c*1300) containing approximately 2½ bu (*c*8.81 dkl) and representing one day's work in thrashing (Battle xxiv).

wey — 1–3 L pondus; 3 L waya, L weya; 3–6 waye; 3–9 weye; 5 wegh (OED); 5–8 way; 5–9 weigh, wey; 7 waigh (OED); ? L waga (Prior) [ME *waye, weye* < OE *wǣge, wǣg*, weight, wey; *see* WEIGHT]. A m-c and a wt for dry products. It was originally called L *pondus* (weight), a name superseded in the thirteenth century by its ME translation, *weye*. Its size varied with the product as well as with the

region: barley, corn, and malt, 40 bu (c14.09 hl) or 5 SEAMS or
CHALDERS of 8 bu each; cheese, 180 lb (81.646 kg) or 15 STONE of
12 lb each, 182 lb (82.553 kg) or 14 stone of 13 lb each, 224 lb
(101.604 kg) or 32 CLOVES of 7 lb each or 2 Cwt of 112 lb each,
256 lb (116.119 kg) or 32 cloves of 8 lb each, and 336 lb (152.406 kg)
or 42 cloves of 8 lb each; flax, 182 lb (82.553 kg) or 14 stone of 13
lb each; glass, 60 BUNCHES or CASES of uncertain wt; hemp, Dorsetshire, 32 lb (14.515 kg), and Somersetshire, 30 lb (13.608 kg); lead,
generally 182 lb (82.553 kg) or 14 stone of 13 lb each, but occasionally 175 lb (79.378 kg) or $\frac{1}{12}$ FOTHER of 2100 lb; lime, Devonshire,
48 double Winchester bu (c33.83 hl); salt, generally 42 bu (c14.80
hl); tallow and wool, 182 lb (82.553 kg) or 14 stone of 13 lb each. —
c1253 Hall 11: La waye de plum, layne, sue, et de furmage peyse
xiiii peris. c1270 Report 1.419–20: Petra duodecim Libræ et dimid'
faciunt unam petram . . . xiv petræ faciunt unum pondus, quod
Anglice dicitur weye; ibid 420: Unum pondus casei xv petræ, et
una petra xii lib. c1272 Hall 9: Charrus constat ex xii wayes; ibid
10: Waya enim tam plumbi quam lane . . . ponderat quatuordecim
petras. Et due waye faciunt unum saccum. 1303 Report 1.414:
Weya enim tam plumbi quam lane, lini, sepi, casei, ponderabunt
xiiii petras. 1430 Rot. Parl. 4.381: That the weight of a weigh of
cheese shal containe xxxii. cloues, that is to say, euery cloue vii.
lb. . . . Que le pois d'une weye de formage, puisse tener xxx & II
cloues; c'est assavoir, chescun cloue VII li. c1475 Gras 1.193: Of
a way chese. 1507 Ibid 696: Chesse the waye; ibid 703: Sawllte the
waye. 1540 Recorde 206: A cloue shoulde contayne 7 pounde:
and a wey 32 cloues, that is 224 poundes. c1590 Hall 23: 182
poundes waight haberdepoyse is a waye of woole. . . . The wey of
cheesse is 32 cloves, conteninge 224 poundes waight haberdepoyse; ibid 28: The way of sault is 42 bushells: 10 wayes makith
a last. 1603 Henllys 137–38: Neither ys the Cranoke or Wey
measures used in selling thereof. 1616 Hopton 164: A Last of
wooll is 4368 pounds, or 12 sackes; a sacke is 364 pounds, or 2
weyes. 1635 Dalton 149: A weigh of cheese must containe 32
cloves, and every clove 8. l. of averdepois weight: although the
statute 9. H. 6 . . . seeme to make 7. l. to be a clove. And yet by
the booke of assize, the weigh of Suff. cheese must containe 256.
l. . . . But the weigh of Essex cheese . . . is 300 l. weight, after the
rate of five score and xii. li. to the hundred, which is 336. l. 1665

Sheppard 61–62: But Suffolk Cheese must be 256 pound . . . the Wey of Essex . . . Cheese must be . . . 336, or sixteen score and 16 l. Averdepoys. **1704** Mer. Adven. 244: Ffor bearing of a weigh of salt. **1708** Chamberlayne 207: Wooll is Weigh'd by the . . . Way, 182 Pounds. **1717** Dict. Rus. sv weigh: Cheese or Wooll [*sic*], the Weight of 256 Pounds Aver-du-pois: Of Corn, 40 Bushels: Of Barley or Malt 6 [*sic*] Quarters or 40 Bushels. Of Glass 6[0] Bunches; *ibid* sv wey: The greatest Measure for dry things, containing 5 Chaldron. **1805** Macpherson I.471: 12½ pounds 1 stone of London, 14 stones 1 weye. **1820** Second Rep. 36: Weigh or Wey of cheese, flax, lead, tallow and wool, 14 stone . . . of window glass, 60 cases . . . Devonshire: of lime . . . sometimes 48 double Winchester bushels . . . Dorsetshire: of hemp, 8 heads of 4 lb. twisted and tied, making 32 lb . . . Somersetshire: of hemp, 30 lb. *See* WEIGHT

weya, weye. WEY

windle [ME *windle* < OE *windel*, basket]. A m-c for grain in Lancashire (*c*1800) containing 3 bu (*c*1.08 hl) for corn and 3½ bu (*c*1.23 hl) for barley, beans, and wheat (Second Rep. 36).

wista — 3–4 L wista (Battle), L wysta [MedL *wista*, prob < OE *wist*, food, sustenance]. Equivalent to VIRGATE. — *c*1283 Battle xiii: Quatuor virgatæ seu wystæ faciunt unam hydam.

wysta. WISTA

X·Y·Z

yacker [dial var of ACRE in Durham, Northamptonshire, and Wilt-shire]. Equivalent to ACRE. — **1842** Akerman 59: Yacker . . . An acre. **1849** Dinsdale 150: Yacker . . . an acre. **1851** Sternberg 125: Yacker . . . An acre. Fields, also, of much larger extent than an acre are called by this name, generally in composition with some other word, as Green's Yacker.

yard — 3 yeorde (OED), yherde (OED); 3–5 L ulna; 3–6 yerd (OED), yerde; 4 yeird (OED); 4–7 yarde; 5 yeerde (OED), yerede (OED); 5–7 yeard (OED), yearde (OED); 5–9 yard; 6 yerdde (OED) [ME *yarde, yerde* < OE *gierd, geard*, a rod, stick, a measure, a yard]. A m-l of 36 inches (0.914 m) or 3 ft for land and sometimes by custom 37 inches (0.940 m) for cloth. It generally was equal to ⅘ ELL, and was synonymous with the VERGE. However, the ell (L *ulna*) was occasionally equated with the yd, and the YARDLAND (yard of land, F *verge de terre*, VIRGATE) was sometimes called a "yard" although it retained its own proper dimensions. — *c*1272 Hall 7: Et xij pollices faciunt pedem; et tres pedes faciunt ulnam. *c*1400 *Ibid* 41: Nota quod tres pedes regii faciunt ulnam Regis. *c*1461 *Ibid* 14: And xii ynchis make a fote; and iij fote make a yard. **1474** Cov. Leet 396: And xij Inches makith a foote, and iij fote makith a yarde. **1507** Gras 1.703: Sattyn crymsen cunterfett the yard . . . Sattyn ryght purled with goold the yarde. **1519** Mer. Adven. 57: It is assented, &c., for our imposicyons beyonde see, to pay of every yerde of canves, one halffpeny. **1541** Mag. Carta §25: Two yardes within the lystes. *c*1590 Hall 27: The yard in lenght is 3 foott. **1603** Henllys 137: Yet doeth yt agree in the ynche, foote, and yard. **1615** Collect. Stat. 464: xii ynches make a foot, three feet make a yard. **1616** Hopton 165: 3 foote a yard. **1635** Dalton 150: Three foot make a yard. **1647** Digges 1: Three Foote a Yard.

1665 Sheppard 16: 3 foot a yard. **1682** Hall 28: A Yard is two Cubits, or three feete. **1708** Chamberlayne 207: 2 Cubits a Yard. **1717** Dict. Rus. sv: Yard, a well known long Measure that consists of 3 Foot. **1820** Second Rep. 36: Yard, 3 feet = 36 inches. But by custom, the legal yard for cloth has become 37 inches in many cases.

yarde. YARD

yardland [YARD + *land*]. Equivalent to VIRGATE. — **1603** Henllys 135–36: There is allso a quantytie of land measure called a yard of land, in latin *Virgata terræ*. **1635** Dalton 71: Every plow land or Carve, is foure yard land . . . every yard land, containing 30. Acres. **1708** Chamberlayne 208: 30 Acres ordinary make a Yard-Land. **1717** Dict. Rus. sv yard-land: A certain quantity of Land; which at Wimbleton in Surrey, is only 15 Acres; but in other counties it contains 20, in some 24, in some 30, and in others 40. **1755** Willis 358: Virgata, or Yard-Land, whereof 4 made an Hide, was in different Counties 15, 20, 30 or 40 Acres. **1777** Nicol. and Burn 615: Virgate of land; a yard land consisting (as some say) of 24 acres, whereof four virgates make an hide.

yeard, yearde, yeerde, yeird, yeorde, yerd, yerdde, yerde, yerede, yherde. YARD

ynce, ynch, ynche, ynsh. INCH

yoke of land — 3 L jugum terre (terrae) [yoke of land, trans of L *jugum terre (terrae)*]. A m-a for land in Kent, generally containing 4 VIRGATES. — **1202** Cur. Reg. 9.121: Assisa inter de Cusinton' petentem et Johannem Hanin tenentem de j. jugo terre cum pertinenciis in Seling'. **1220** Cur. Reg. 2.322: Mabilia filia Gaufridi petit versus Willelmum . . . dimidium jugum terre cum pertinentiis in Aynesford'.

zame, zeam, zeme. SEAM

APPENDIX I

TERMINOLOGY IN ENGLISH WEIGHTS AND MEASURES

GENERAL TERMS

unit A unit is a value, quantity, or magnitude by which other values, quantities, or magnitudes are expressed. Generally a unit is fixed by definition and is independent of such physical conditions as temperature. The pound, bushel, and mile are examples of units used to express a fixed weight, capacity, and length, respectively.

standard A standard is a physical representation of a unit. Generally it is not independent of physical conditions: it is a genuine or absolute representation of a unit only under certain conditions. For example, a physical standard for the yard would vary slightly in length if it were not kept in a hermetically sealed compartment with a controlled constant atmospheric temperature.

measure of length A measure of length or linear measure is the distance between two points established according to some standard. The standard may be simple and primary, such as the pace, the palm, the finger, etc.; or it may be based on an arbitrarily defined unit, such as the medieval English inch that was taken as the length of three medium-sized barleycorns placed end to end. Statutes have furthered the use of the defined standard over the simple primary standard: for example, when multiples of the inch were reconciled with the larger units of length such as the yard, ell, fathom, mile, and league.

measure of area A measure of area or superficial measure is commonly the square of the linear unit and is usually defined in terms of square feet, square yards, or square rods (perches). The acre—the principal superficial measure in medieval England —consisted of 40 linear perches in length and 4 in width or 160 square perches. The actual number of square feet in this acre, however, depended on the size of the linear unit. An acre contained 43,560 square feet only when its linear perch equaled 16½ feet.

measure of capacity   A measure of capacity or volume measure is the cube of the linear unit. In medieval England a capacity measure was usually a vessel that contained a certain mass of liquid or dry substance but it did not necessarily have a definite size or shape. Units such as the bundle, bag, box, cage, chest, and sack had varying dimensions depending on the quality, form, and weight of a particular product.

measure of quantity   A measure of quantity is the number or count of a certain product. In medieval England any related dimensions of quantity measures were usually unspecific and depended upon the physical qualities of the product (e.g., a hundred of hoops versus a hundred of eels). But measures of quantity normally consisted of a specified number. A dozen, for example, was 12 of any item. A hundred was 100, 106, 112, 120, 124, 160, or 225 depending on the product. A score was usually 20, while a gross was 12 dozen.

weight   Weight is the force with which the earth attracts a given body, and this force is proportional to the body's mass. Medieval English systems of weight were based either on the barley or on the wheat grain. The pennyweight, containing 24 barleycorns in the troy system or 32 wheat grains in the tower system, was the unit from which the larger weights, such as the scruple, dram, ounce, and pound, were formed. Hence, the troy pound of 5760 grains consisted of 240 pennyweights of 24 grains each or 12 ounces of 480 grains, each ounce containing 20 pennyweights of 24 grains each.

gross weight   Gross weight refers to the weight of both the container and its contents. The best example of this was the butter barrel, which medieval English documents define as a vessel weighing generally 26 pounds and containing 230 pounds of butter. The total or gross weight, thus, was 256 pounds.

Special Terms

assay   An assay was a testing of weights and measures to determine whether they were in conformity with Crown standards. Private citizens, lords of manors, abbots, bailiffs, chancellors of Oxford and Cambridge, bishops and archbishops, mayors, gilds, courts leet, justices of assize and of oyer and terminer, sheriffs, and coroners shared the privilege of performing assays, along with clerks of the market and justices of the peace.

assize   An assize was an enactment that regulated the quality, quantity, weight, measure, and price of articles for sale. An example of this type of assize was the *Assisa Panis et Cervisiæ* of Henry III, issued in 1266. The assize was also the name for a session at which the examination and authentication of local weights and measures took place. Merchants and producers broke the assize when they adulterated their goods, sold defective merchandise, or employed false weights and measures.

aulnage   Aulnage was the measuring of cloth to determine whether its length and breadth violated any of the specifications laid down by statute.

aulnager   An aulnager was an official stationed in a port or town who measured the cloth brought in by merchants and textile manufacturers to determine whether its length and breadth conformed to statutory specifications.

clerk of the market   A clerk of the market was an appointed official who verified and enforced statutory weights and measures. He represented the Crown in what could be considered a prescriptive office for he had no other function and usually operated independently of local judges and justices. The clerk of the market for the king's household (*clericus mercate hospitu regis*) looked after the king's standards and saw to it that weights and measures in every district conformed to them. There were also clerks of the market (*clerc del marche, clericus marescalciæ*) assigned to the most important shires to oversee and supervise the local use of weights and measures. The authority of the clerks was not always clearly defined.

ponderator   A ponderator was a locally appointed weigher of agricultural and nonagricultural goods in a village market or in a town weighing station. His services appear to have encompassed all magnitudes of commerce and trade. He is also known in medieval English documents as a *pensarius, pesarius,* and *poiser.*

seal   A seal was a mark affixed to weights and measures by either the Crown or local municipal officials to prevent frauds. The practice probably originated during the reign of William I.

APPENDIX II

FUNDAMENTAL ENGLISH LAWS ON WEIGHTS

AND MEASURES

Edgar

959–75 (?) The "measure" of Winchester was made the standard for the realm.

William I

1066–87 (?) All weights and measures were required to bear the king's seal as proof of their authenticity.

Richard I

1197 The *Assisa Mensurarum* directed that certain persons be assigned in every city and borough to take custody of the king's standard weights and measures and to supervise their use.

John

1215 Chapter 25 of *Magna Carta* declared that there should be one measure for wine, one measure for ale, and one measure for corn, and it established a uniform breadth for certain kinds of cloth.

Henry III

1225 *Magna Carta* was reissued; the chapter on weights and measures was identical to the one in the earlier charter.

1266 The *Assisa Panis et Cervisiæ* regulated the weights and measures that applied to bread and ale and declared that bread had to be weighed according to the king's standard pound.

1266–? A document originating sometime in the late thirteenth century—the *Compositio Ulnarum et Perticarum*—defined the principal linear and superficial measures.

Edward I

1303   The *Tractatus de Ponderibus et Mensuris* repeated the formula
       for linear and superficial measurement found in the *Compositio
       Ulnarum et Perticarum* and provided standard capacities for the
       wine gallon and the London bushel.
1305   The *Ordinance for Measuring Land* established various linear
       combinations for constructing an acre of 160 square perches.

Edward II

1324   The lengths of the principal linear measures were fixed by
       statute.
1325   The *Ordinance for Bakers, Brewers and Other Victuallers*
       forbade heaped or shallow capacity measures for all goods
       except oats, malt, and meal and emphasized that all standard
       measures had to be stamped with the iron seal of the king.
           The *Ordinance for Measures* dealt with the London bushel in
       wording identical to that in the *Tractatus de Ponderibus et
       Mensuris*.

Edward III

1328   The lengths of ray and colored cloths were standardized and
       their measurement and vendition regulated.
1340   The command of *Magna Carta* for uniform weights and
       measures was repeated.
1351   The *Statute of Cloths* established regulation over the sale of
       all types of cloths. The *Statute of Purveyors* abolished auncel
       weight.
1353   Chapter 10 of the *Statute of the Staple* confirmed the provi-
       sions in the *Statute of Purveyors* concerning weights and meas-
       ures and prohibited illegal manipulation of the balance.
1357   The *Statute of Westminster I* made it mandatory for merchants
       and producers to take their scales and weights to the sheriff of
       their district for testing.
1360   The duties of the justices of the peace in supervising the use of
       Crown standards were outlined by statute.
1373   A statute reconfirmed the regulations over measurement and
       sales of ray and colored cloths.

Richard II

1380   Parliament ordered the king's gaugers to examine carefully the true measures of vessels of wine being shipped to English ports.

1389   In deference to local custom, the county of Lancaster was granted the privilege of using weights and measures that were larger than statutory standards.

1391   The fatt was prohibited in favor of the statutory seam.

1392   The duties of the clerks of the market were defined by statute.

1393   A statute repealed previous cloth regulations and permitted merchants to sell textiles that did not conform to any particular dimensions.

Henry IV

1405   Parliament repealed the statute of 1393 and renewed regulation over the dimensions of cloths.

1407   The cloth regulations of 1405 were again repealed, and the statute of 1393 was restored.

1409   Parliament declared the statute of 1407 null and void and confirmed all the statutes which had hitherto regulated the sizes of cloth.

Henry V

1413   The 1391 prohibition of the fatt was reissued.

1421   A statute regulated the capacities of coal measures for the first time.

Henry VI

1423   The capacities of tuns, pipes, tertians, hogsheads, and barrels were standardized for each of the various goods they were accustomed to contain.

1429   The 1351 abolition of the auncel scale was repeated.

1430   Parliament ordered merchants to sell cheese by the wey of 32 cloves.

1432   A statute added further duties to those of justices of the peace in their role as supervisors of the king's standards.

Edward IV

1464 Parliament decreed that aulnagers measure cloth with a cord that had 37 inches to every yard.

1477 The *Assize of Fuel* standardized the lengths and widths of salable faggots and billets used for firewood.

1482 A statute standardized the capacities of eel and herring barrels.

Henry VII

1491 Parliament ordered that standard weights and measures be constructed and nationally distributed.

1495 Parliament selected one town from each of the 43 shires to act as custodian of the king's standard weights and measures; the chief officers of each town were appointed to enforce conformity to the standards.

1503 Special rules were issued for periodic inspections of weights and of pewter and brass balances.

Henry VIII

1512 The *Act Concerning Pewterers and True Weights and Beams* confirmed the statute of 1503.

1527 Parliament abolished the tower pound.

1531 The capacities of ale and beer vessels were standardized.

1536 Special rules for the proper gauging of the capacities of wine vessels were established.

1541 The *Act for Butchers* ordered all butchers to sell meat by avoirdupois weight.

Edward VI

1553 The *Assize of Fuel* was reissued and several new regulations were added.

Mary

1557 Parliament decreed that all cloth be sealed with the aulnager's and the town's seals as proof of proper length and breadth.

Elizabeth I

1565 An act regulated aulnage in the courts of Lancaster.

1581 An act made the capacity measures for honey conform to those for wine.

1589   Further provisions were made for the proper gauging and verification of the capacities of casks.

Charles I

1640   Parliament redefined the duties of the clerks of the market.

Charles II

1660   The regulations of 1531 concerning capacities of ale and beer barrels were expanded.

1662   An act regulated the weight and packing of butter.

1670   Parliament standardized the dimensions of coal and salt measures.

1681   An act attempted to initiate a thorough-going reform of the regulation of weights and measures.

William III

1694–95   An act standardized the Newcastle chalder.

1700   All aulnage duties on the exportation of cloths were abolished.

1701   An act regulated the dimensions of the Winchester bushel.

Anne

1706   Parliament declared that the standard capacity for the wine gallon was 231 cubic inches.

1708   An act regulated the lengths and breadths of woolen cloths made in the county of York.

1709   Parliament repealed the 1266 assize of bread and instituted updated regulations over bread; this new assize was modified over the years and abolished by 1836.

1713   An act standardized the coal bushel.

George I

1719   Parliament regulated the dimensions of Scots plaids and serges.

George II

1729   An act set forth regulations, in addition to those of 1670, for selling coal by the sack.

1758   Parliament added still more regulations to the dimensions of the coal sack.

George III

1795   An act set up specific procedures which examiners were to follow while inspecting weights and measures.
1803   The ale and beer barrels were again assigned new standard capacities.
1812   An act set up regulations for the proper gauging and construction of butter casks, and it reaffirmed similar legislation dating back to 1662.

BIBLIOGRAPHY

Abba "Glossarium Abba," in M. Inguanez and C. J. Fordyce (eds.), *Glossaria Latina*, V, 9–143. Paris, 1931. (There are separate entries for stadium and dragma.)

Abingdon *Accounts of the Obedientiars of Abingdon Abbey*, ed. R. E. G. Kirk. (Camden Society Publication, New Series, Vol. 51.) Westminster, 1892.

Account 1 "An Account of a Comparison Lately Made by Some Gentlemen of the Royal Society, of the Standard of a Yard, and the Several Weights Lately Made for Their Use, etc." *Philosophical Transactions*, 42 (1742–43), 544–56. (This article is concerned with the yard and ell, and with the troy and avoirdupois weight standards.)

———— **2** "An Account of the Proportions of the English and French Measures and Weights, from the Standards of the Same, Kept at the Royal Society." *Ibid.*, 42 (1742–43), 185–88. (This article dwells on the similarities among the following weights and measures: Paris half-toise and English yard; Paris dimark and English troy pound; Paris foot and English foot.)

Acts *A Collection of Acts and Ordinances of General Use, Made in the Parliament Begun and Held at Westminster the Third Day of November, Anno 1640*, ed. Henry Scobell. London, 1658.

Adams Adams, John Quincy. *Report of the Secretary of State upon Weights and Measures Prepared in Obedience to a Resolution of the House of Representatives of the Fourteenth of December, 1819*. (16th Congress, 2nd Session, H. R. Document No. 109.) Washington, 1821. (This excellent report deals generally with the simplification and standardization of weights and measures in the early nineteenth century. Adams quotes freely from many English statutes, and he includes a short, but effective, history of English measuring units.)

195

Agricola   Agricola, Georgi. *Medici libri quinque de mensuris et ponderibus*. Basil, 1533. (Agricola concentrates almost exclusively on the Greek and Roman systems of weights and measures and pays very little attention to the medieval.)

Airy   Airy, George B. "Account of the Construction of the New National Standard of Length, and of its Principal Copies." *Philosophical Transactions*, 147 (1857), 621–702.

Akerman   Akerman, John Yonge. *A Glossary of Provincial Words and Phrases in Use in Wiltshire*. London, 1842.

Alexander   Alexander, J. H. *Universal Dictionary of Weights and Measures*. Baltimore, 1850. (This is one of the best compilations of weights and measures to appear in the nineteenth century. Not only does Alexander provide detailed descriptions of individual units, but he defines the standards upon which they were based.)

Anc. Char.   *Ancient Charters Royal and Private prior to A.D. 1200: Part I*. (Pipe Roll Society.) London, 1888.

Anc. Laws   *Ancient Laws and Institutes of England*, ed. Commissioners of the Public Records. London, 1840.

Ansileubus   Ansileubus. "Glossarium," in W. M. Lindsay, J. F. Mountford, and J. Whatmough (eds.), *Glossaria Latina*, I, 1–604. Paris, 1926. (There is an entry for libra.)

Arnold   Arnold, Richard. *Chronicle*. London, 1502.

Arnoult   *Collection des décrets de l'Assemblée nationale constituante*, ed. M. Arnoult. Vols. 2 and 6. Dijon, 1792. (Mainly important for French metrology, these volumes contain references to some English weights and measures.)

Assize   *The Assize of Bread with Sundry Good and Needful Ordinances*. London, 1665. (This book contains translations into English of the most important assizes, among which are those for fuel and tile.)

Bailey   Bailey, Nathan. *An Universal Etymological English Dictionary*. London, 1721.

Baker   Baker, Anne Elizabeth. *Glossary of Northamptonshire Words and Phrases*. 2 vols. London, 1854.

Barrington   Barrington, Daines. *Observations on the More Ancient Statutes from Magna Carta to the Twenty-First of James I*. London, 1796.

Battle *Custumals of Battle Abbey in the Reigns of Edward I and Edward II (1283–1312) from MSS in the Public Record Office,* ed. S. R. Scargill-Bird. (Camden Society Publication, New Series, Vol. 41.) Westminster, 1887. (The documents provide information on the wista and other superficial measures.)

Baudouin *Collection complète des lois, décrets, ordonnances, réglemens, avis du Conseil d'Etat, publiée sur les éditions officielles du Louvre; de l'Imprimerie nationale, par Baudouin; et du Bulletin des Lois; de 1788 à 1830 inclusivement,* ed. J. B. Duvergier. 30 vols. Paris, 1834. (Although most of the metrological information contained in these volumes is French, there are references to English weights and measures, especially for the sake of comparison.)

Baxter Baxter, J. H., and Johnson, Charles. *Medieval Latin Word-List from British and Irish Sources.* London, 1962.

Bello *Chronicon Monasterii de Bello.* (Anglia Christiana Society.) London, 1846. (This is a particularly valuable source for superficial measures.)

Benese Benese, Rycharde. *This Boke Sheweth the Maner of Measurynge of All Maner of Lande.* Southwarke, 1537. (Benese defines those measures that pertain to land.)

Bernardi Bernardi, Edvardi. *De mensuris et ponderibus antiquis.* Oxford, 1688. (Bernardi discusses the weights and measures of Greece, Rome, and medieval England in great detail. Some of his computations, however, are incorrect.)

Berriman Berriman, A. E. *Historical Metrology.* London, 1953. (Berriman discusses the various pound weights used in medieval England and the standards for the gallon found at the Exchequer. He also comments on the historical importance of seals used in authenticating local and state standards.)

Berthelot *La grande Encyclopédie: Inventaire raisonné des sciences, des lettres et des arts,* ed. MM. Berthelot and Laurent. Vol. 26. Paris, n.d. (This volume contains one small section on the weights and measures of the Middle Ages.)

Best *Rural Economy in Yorkshire in 1641, Being the Farming and Account Books of Henry Best, of Elmswell, in the East Riding of the County of York.* (Surtees Society Publication, Vol. 33.) Durham, 1857. (The glossary contains descriptions of the leap and maund.)

Black Prince "Palatinate of Chester: 1351–1365." *Register of Edward the Black Prince*, Part 3. London, 1932. (Several documents are concerned with the standardization of Cheshire's weights and measures.)

Blind Blind, August. *Mass-, Münz- und Gewichtswesen*. Leipzig, 1906. (Blind describes rather superficially several medieval English units.)

Boissonnade Boissonnade, P. *Life and Work in Medieval Europe*. New York, 1950. (Boissonnade mentions the hogshead and the pound.)

Bourquelot Bourquelot, M. Felix. *Etudes sur les Foires de Champagne*. Paris, 1865. (Bourquelot devotes one entire chapter to the weights and measures used by merchants at the fairs of Champagne.)

Bradley Bradley, Richard. *Chomel's Dictionaire Aeconomique, or the Family Dictionary*. Translated and revised by R. Bradley. London, 1725.

Bray *The Estate Book of Henry de Bray of Harleston, Co. Northants* (*c. 1289–1340*), ed. Dorothy Willis. (Camden Third Series, Vol. 27.) London, 1916. (There is a table of land measures among the documents.)

Brehaut Brehaut, Ernest. *An Encyclopedist of the Dark Ages: Isidore of Seville*. New York, 1912. (Brehaut includes a translation of Isidore's short treatise on weights and measures.)

Brockett Brockett, John Trotter. *A Glossary of North Country Words in Use; with Their Etymology, and Affinity to Other Languages; and Occasional Notices of Local Customs and Popular Superstitions*. Newcastle Upon Tyne, 1829. (Brockett includes entries for 15 weights and measures, and he discusses the characteristics of heaped, striked, and shallow capacity measures.)

Brokage *The Brokage Book of Southampton: 1443–1444*, ed. Olive Coleman. 2 vols. Southampton, 1960–61. (Volume 2 is valuable for its lists of products.)

Browne Browne, W. A. *The Money, Weights and Measures of the Chief Commercial Nations in the World with the British Equivalents*. London, 1899. (Browne treats the systems of metrology in use before the nineteenth century rather superficially.)

Buckhurst Buckhurst, Helen McM. "An Anglo-Saxon Index," in W. M. Lindsay (ed.), *The Corpus Glossary*, pp. 267–91. Cambridge, 1921. (Buckhurst does not define the weights and measures included in her list but only gives their declensions in Anglo-Saxon.)

Budé Budé, Guillaume. *Annotationes Gulielmi Budæi Parisiensis, secretarii regii, in quatuor et viginti pandectarum libros, ad Io annem deganaium cancellarium Franciæ.* Paris, 1535. (The weights and measures discussed are Greek and Roman.)

Burton "Annales de Burton (A.D. 1004–1263)," in Henry Richards Luard (ed.), *Annales monastici.* (Rerum Britanicarum Medii Aevi Scriptores.) London, 1864. (This manuscript is important for its table of unusual land measures.)

Caernarvon *Registrum Vulgariter Nuncupatum: The Record of Caernarvon.* London, 1838. (This collection of documents contains the famous description of the tower pound so often found in other medieval manuscripts. There is also a version of the *Assisa Panis.*)

Cal. Char. 1 *Calendar of the Charter Rolls Preserved in the Public Record Office.* Henry III: 1216–57. London, 1904. (Most of the volumes of the various Rolls included in my bibliography contain information dealing with infractions of statutory standards and with the punishments imposed for violations. Seldom are there actual tables of individual units.)

———— 2 ————. Henry III–Edward I: 1257–1300. London, 1906.

———— 3 ————. Edward I–Edward II: 1300–26. London, 1908.

———— 4 ————. 15 Edward III–5 Henry V: 1341–1417. London, 1916.

———— 5 ————. 5 Henry VI–8 Henry VIII: 1427–1516. London, 1927.

Cal. Close 1 *Calendar of the Close Rolls Preserved in the Public Record Office.* Edward II: 1302–07. London, 1908.

———— 2 ————. Edward II: 1313–18. London, 1893.

———— 3 ————. Edward II: 1318–23. London, 1895.

———— 4 ————. Edward II: 1323–27. London, 1898.

———— 5 ————. Edward III: 1330–33. London, 1898.

———— 6 ————. Edward III: 1339–41. London, 1901.

———— 7 ————. Edward III: 1343–46. London, 1904.

——— 8 ———. Edward III: 1349–54. London, 1906.
——— 9 ———. Edward III: 1354–60. London, 1908.
——— 10 ———. Edward III: 1360–64. London, 1909.
——— 11 ———. Edward III: 1369–74. London, 1911.
——— 12 ———. Edward III: 1374–77. London, 1911.
——— 13 ———. Richard II: 1377–81. London, 1914.
——— 14 ———. Richard II: 1381–85. London, 1920.
——— 15 ———. Richard II: 1392–96. London, 1925.
——— 16 ———. Richard II: 1396–99. London, 1927.
——— 17 ———. Henry IV: 1399–1402. London, 1927.
——— 18 ———. Henry IV: 1402–05. London, 1929.
——— 19 ———. Henry IV: 1405–09. London, 1931.
——— 20 ———. Henry IV: 1409–13. London, 1932.
——— 21 ———. Henry V: 1413–19. London, 1929.
——— 22 ———. Henry V: 1419–22. London, 1932.
——— 23 ———. Henry VI: 1435–41. London, 1937.
——— 24 ———. Henry VI: 1441–47. London, 1937.
——— 25 ———. Henry VI: 1447–54. London, 1947.
——— 26 ———. Henry VII: 1500–09. London, 1963.
Cal. Fine 1 *Calendar of the Fine Rolls Preserved in the Public Record Office.* Edward I: 1272–1307. London, 1911.
——— 2 ———. Edward II: 1319–27. London, 1921.
——— 3 ———. Edward III: 1337–47. London, 1915.
Cal. Just. *Calendar of the Justiciary Rolls or Proceedings in the Court of the Justiciar of Ireland,* ed. James Mills. 2 vols. London, 1914.
Cal. Lib. 1 *Calendar of the Liberate Rolls Preserved in the Public Record Office.* Henry III: 1226–40. London, 1916.
——— 2 ———. Henry III: 1240–45. London, 1930.
——— 3 ———. Henry III: 1245–51. London, 1937.
——— 4 ———. Henry III: 1251–60. London, 1959.
——— 5 ———. Henry III: 1267–72. London, 1959.
Cal. Pat. 1 *Calendar of the Patent Rolls Preserved in the Public Record Office.* Henry III: 1266–72. London, 1913.
——— 2 ———. Edward I: 1272–81. London, 1901.
——— 3 ———. Edward II: 1307–13. London, 1894.
——— 4 ———. Edward II: 1317–21. London, 1903.
——— 5 ———. Edward III: 1327–30. London, 1891.
——— 6 ———. Edward III: 1338–40. London, 1898.

———— 7 ————. Edward III: 1340–43. London, 1900.

———— 8 ————. Edward III: 1343–45. London, 1902.

———— 9 ————. Edward III: 1345–48. London, 1903.

———— 10 ————. Edward III: 1348–50. London, 1905.

———— 11 ————. Edward III: 1350–54. London, 1907.

———— 12 ————. Edward III: 1354–58. London, 1909.

———— 13 ————. Edward III: 1358–61. London, 1911.

———— 14 ————. Edward III: 1364–67. London, 1912.

———— 15 ————. Henry IV: 1399–1401. London, 1903.

———— 16 ————. Henry VI: 1422–29. Norwich, 1901.

———— 17 ————. Edward IV: 1461–67. London, 1897.

———— 18 ————. Edward IV, Edward V, and Richard III: 1476–85. London, 1901.

———— 19 ————. Edward VI: 1547–48. London, 1924.

———— 20 ————. Edward VI: 1548–49. London, 1924.

———— 21 ————. Edward VI: 1549–51. London, 1925.

———— 22 ————. Edward VI: 1550–53. London, 1926.

———— 23 ————. Edward VI: 1547–53. London, 1926.

———— 24 ————. Philip and Mary: 1553–54. London, 1937.

Cal. Rot. *Calendarium rotulorum patentium in turri Londinensi.* London, 1802.

Carew Carew, Richard. *The Survey of Cornwall.* London, 1602.

Celsus Celsus, Aulus Corn. *Medicina libri octo.* Lipsiae, 1766.

Chadwick Chadwick, Hector Munro. *Studies on Anglo-Saxon Institutions.* New York, 1963. (Chadwick discusses the pound.)

Chamberlayne Chamberlayne, John. *Magna Britannia Notitia: or, The Present State of Great-Britain with Divers Remarks upon the Ancient State Thereof.* London, 1708. (One chapter is devoted to weights and measures. Chamberlayne is rather repetitious and sometimes quotes materials without indicating his sources. However, he provides many useful tables illustrating the dimensions of superficial and capacity measures.)

Chambers 1 Chambers, Ephraim. *Cyclopædia: or, An Universal Dictionary of Arts and Sciences,* Vol. 2. London, 1728.

———— 2 *Chambers's Encyclopædia* (Revised ed.), Vol. 10. London, 1874. (The sections on weights and measures in this edition are inferior to those in the earlier one.)

Chaney Chaney, H. J. *Our Weights and Measures: A Practical Treatise on the Standard Weights and Measures in Use in the*

British Empire with Some Account of the Metric System. London, 1897. (Chaney outlines some of the duties of the clerks of the market in addition to defining very briefly several medieval English weights and measures.)

Chester *Calendar of County Court, City Court and Eyre Rolls of Chester, 1259–1297,* ed. R. Stewart-Brown. (Chetham Society Publication, Vol. 84.) Manchester, 1925.

Chisholm Chisholm, H. W. "On the Science of Weighing and Measuring, and the Standards of Weight and Measure." *Nature,* 8 (1873), 1–192. (Two discussions by Chisholm are of special value: the toise de Perou and the Imperial standard gallon and bushel.)

Chron. Abing. *Chronicon Monasterii de Abingdon,* ed. Rev. Joseph Stevenson. (Rerum Britanicarum Medii Aevi Scriptores.) London, 1858.

Chron. Joh. *Chronica Johannis de Oxenedes,* ed. Sir Henry Ellis. (Rerum Britanicarum Medii Aevi Scriptores.) London, 1859.

Chron. Lon. *Chronicles of London,* ed. Charles Lethbridge. Oxford, 1905.

Clarke Clarke, A. R. "Results of the Comparisons of the Standards of Length of England, Austria, Spain, United States, Cape of Good Hope, and of a Second Russian Standard, Made at the Ordnance Survey Office, Southampton." *Philosophical Transactions,* 163 (1873), 445–69.

Clerkenwell *Cartulary of St. Mary Clerkenwell,* ed. W. O. Hassall. (Camden Third Series, Vol. 71.) London, 1949.

Close 1 *Close Rolls of the Reign of Henry III Preserved in the Public Record Office.* Henry III: 1227–34. London, 1902.

———— 2 ————. Henry III: 1234–37. London, 1908.

———— 3 ————. Henry III: 1237–42. London, 1911.

———— 4 ————. Henry III: 1242–47. London, 1916.

———— 5 ————. Henry III: 1247–51. London, 1922.

———— 6 ————. Henry III: 1251–53. London, 1927.

———— 7 ————. Henry III: 1254–56. London, 1931.

———— 8 ————. Henry III: 1261–64. London, 1936.

———— 9 ————. Henry III: 1268–72. London, 1938.

Collect. Stat. *A Collection in English of the Statutes Now in Force, Continued from the Beginning of Magna Charta, Made in the 9. Yere of the Raigne of King H. 3. until the End of the Parliament*

Holden in the 7. Yere of the Raigne of Our Soveraigne Lord King James. London, 1615. (This collection provides some valuable commentaries on the statutes, and it is especially important as a source of variant spellings.)

Cooper   Cooper, William Durrant. *A Glossary of the Provincialisms in Use in the County of Sussex.* London, 1853. (Cooper's glossary contains some rather detailed accounts of unusual weights and measures such as the draught, leap, meal, swod, tovet, warp, and wint.)

Cotton   Bartholomaei de Cotton. *Historia Anglicana (A.D. 449–1298),* ed. Henry Richards Luard. (Rerum Britanicarum Medii Aevi Scriptores.) London, 1859. (Bartholomew mentions several of Richard I's decrees dealing with weights and measures.)

Coulton   Coulton, G. G. *Medieval Village, Manor and Monastery.* New York, 1960. (Coulton discusses rather briefly the perch, sheaf, thrave, and yardland and lists some of the problems resulting from variations in these measures.)

Cov. Leet   *The Coventry Leet Book: or Mayor's Register, Containing the Records of the City Court Leet or View of Frankpledge: 1420–1555,* ed. Mary Dormer Harris. (Early English Text Society.) London, 1913. (This is one of the most important sources for information on capacity measures.)

Cripps   Cripps-Day, Francis Henry. *The Manor Farm: The Boke of Husbondry and The Booke of Thrift.* London, 1931.

Cumberland   Cumberland, Richard. *An Essay towards the Recovery of the Jewish Measures and Weights, Comprehending Their Monies; by Help of Ancient Standards, Compared with Ours of England.* London, 1686.

Cunningham   Cunningham, William. *The Growth of English Industry and Commerce during the Early and Middle Ages.* Cambridge, 1927. (Cunningham defines briefly 12 weights and measures.)

Cur. Reg. 1   *Introduction to the Curia Regis Rolls, 1199–1230 A.D.;* ed. Cyril Thomas Flower. (Selden Society Publication, Vol. 62.) London, 1944. (This work contains several references to land measures.)

———— **2**   *Curia Regis Rolls of the Reign of Henry III Preserved in the Public Record Office.* 3–4 Henry III. London, 1938.

———— **3**   ————. 4–5 Henry III. London, 1952.

———— 4 ————. 5–6 Henry III. London, 1949.
———— 5 ————. 7–9 Henry III. London, 1955.
———— 6 ————. 11–14 Henry III. London, 1959.
———— 7 ————. 14–17 Henry III. London, 1961.
———— 8 *Curia Regis Rolls of the Reigns of Richard I and John Preserved in the Public Record Office.* Richard I–2 John. London, 1922.
———— 9 ————. 3–5 John. London, 1925.
———— 10 ————. 5–7 John. London, 1926.
———— 11 ————. 7–8 John. London, 1929.
———— 12 ————. 8–10 John. London, 1931.
———— 13 ————. 11–14 John. London, 1932.
———— 14 ————. 15–16 John. London, 1935.

Daire Daire, M. Eugene. *Oeuvres de Turgot.* 2 vols. Paris, 1844. (Turgot's works include discussions of weights and measures, principally French.)

Dalton Dalton, Michael. *The Countrey Justice.* London, 1635. (One entire chapter is devoted to weights and measures. Especially valuable is the discussion of the duties and responsibilities of the justices of the peace in regard to verification and enforcement of Crown standards.)

Delambre 1 Delambre, Jean Baptiste Joseph. *Grandeur et figure de la terre.* Paris, 1912.

———— 2 ————. *Grundlagen des dezimalen metrischen Systems oder Messung des Meridianbogens zwischen den Breiten von Dünkirchen und Barcelona,* ed. Walter Block. Leipzig, 1911.

Dickinson Dickinson, William. *A Glossary of Words and Phrases Pertaining to the Dialect of Cumberland.* London, 1878.

Dict. Rus. *Dictionarium rusticum, urbanicum et botanicum: or, A Dictionary of Husbandry, Gardening, Trade, Commerce, and All Sorts of Country-Affairs.* London, 1717. (This dictionary contains approximately 100 entries for weights and measures. In several instances there are errors in computation and quite possibly a few printing errors.)

Dict. Univ. *Dictionnaire universel Français et Latin.* Paris, 1752.

Diderot *Encyclopédie ou dictionnaire raisonné des sciences, des arts et des métiers, par une société de gens de lettres,* ed. M. Diderot. Vols. 21 and 26. Geneva, 1778. (Information on measures is in Volume 21 and on weights in Volume 26.)

Digges Digges, Leonard. *A Booke Named Tectonicon*. London, 1647. (Digges provides very little information on individual units aside from defining the inch, yard, and perch when setting up specific arithmetical problems for the reader to solve.)

Dinsdale Dinsdale, Frederick T. *A Glossary of Provincial Words Used in Teesdale in the County of Durham*. London, 1849. (Dinsdale has good definitions of noggin and score.)

Domesday *Domesday Tables for the Counties of Surrey, Berkshire, Middlesex, Hertford, Buckingham and Bedford and for the New Forest*, ed. Francis Henry Baring. London, 1909.

Du Cange Du Cange, Charles du Fresne. *Glossarium mediæ et infimæ Latinitatis*. 10 vols. Paris, 1937. (These volumes contain a wealth of information on medieval English weights and measures. Not only are there definitions for some of them, but Du Cange includes ample documentation.)

Dugdale Dugdale, Sir William. "Monasticon Anglicanum," in William Harrison Douglas (ed.), *The Old Historians of the Isle of Man*, pp. 1–77. Isle of Man, 1871. (There is some treatment of superficial measures in the entry for Rushen Abbey on p. 75.)

Durham *The Inventories and Account Rolls of the Benedictine Houses or Cells, of Jarrow and Monk-Wearmouth, in the County of Durham*. (Surtees Society Publication, Vol. 29.) Durham, 1854. (There is information on weights and measures in the glossary.)

Dur. House *The Durham Household Book; or, the Accounts of the Bursar of the Monastery of Durham from Pentecost 1530 to Pentecost 1534*. (Surtees Society Publication, Vol. 18.) London, 1844. (The glossary contains descriptions of some capacity measures and of several types of cloth.)

Eden Eden, Richard (trans.). *Cortes' (Martin) Arte of Nauigation*. 1561.

Edler Edler, Florence. *Glossary of Medieval Terms of Business: Italian Series 1200–1600*. Cambridge, 1934. (Although the weights and measures are Italian, there are references to their English equivalents in several instances.)

Ency. meth. *Encyclopédie méthodique: Commerce*, Vol. 3. Paris, 1784. (There are many tables and charts comparing the metrological units of one country with another.)

Eng. Gilds *English Gilds: The Original Ordinances of More Than*

One Hundred Early English Gilds, ed. Toulmin Smith. (Early English Text Society.) London, 1870. (There are occasional references to weights and measures and to the verification and enforcement of gild standards.)

Exchequer   *Issues of the Exchequer: Being Payments Made Out of His Majesty's Revenue during the Reign of King James I*, ed. Frederick Devon. London, 1836.

Eyre   *Rolls of the Justices in Eyre Being the Rolls of Pleas and Assizes for Lincolnshire 1218–9 and Worcestershire 1221*, ed. Doris Mary Stenton. (Selden Society Publication, Vol. 53.) London, 1934.

Eyton   Eyton, Rev. Robert William. *Domesday Studies: An Analysis and Digest of the Somerset Survey (According to the Exon Codex), and of the Somerset Gheld Inquest of A.D. 1084*. 2 vols. London, 1880. (Eyton discusses the hide as a unit of superficial measurement.)

Fab. Rolls   *The Fabric Rolls of York Minster*. (Surtees Society Publication, Vol. 35.) Durham, 1859. (The glossary contains definitions of several capacity and superficial measures along with documentary materials illustrating their use.)

Fabyan   Fabyan, Robert. *The Newe Chronycles of Englande and of Fraunce*. London, 1516.

Falkirk   *Scotland in 1298: Documents Relating to the Campaign of King Edward the First in that Year, and Especially to the Battle of Falkirk*, ed. Henry Gough. London, 1888.

Fauve   Fauve, Adrien. *Les Origines du système métrique*. Paris, n.d.

Feet 1   *Feet of Fines for the County of Lincoln for the Reign of King John (1199–1216)*, ed. Margaret S. Walker. London, 1954.

———— 2   *Feet of Fines for the County of Norfolk for the Reign of King John (1201–1215) and for the County of Suffolk for the Reign of King John (1199–1214)*, ed. Barbara Dodwell. London, 1958. (This work is important for its excellent descriptions of superficial measures such as the bovate, virgate, and knight's fee. The subject index also contains some valuable information.)

———— 3   *Feet of Fines for the County of Norfolk for the Tenth Year of the Reign of King Richard the First (1198–1199) and for the First Four Years of the Reign of King John (1199–1202)*, ed. Barbara Dodwell. London, 1952.

Finchale   *The Charters of Endowment, Inventories, and Account Rolls,* *of the Priory of Finchale, in the County of Durham.* (Surtees Society Publication, Vol. 6.) London, 1837.

Fleetwood   Fleetwood, Bishop. *Chronicon preciosum: or, An Account of English Gold and Silver Money; the Price of Corn and Other Commodities; and of Stipends, Salaries, Wages, Jointures, Portions, Day-Labour, etc. in England, for Six Hundred Years Last Past.* London, 1745. (Fleetwood discusses 14 separate units of measurement, but his treatment is very superficial and he confuses the troy with the tower pound. He does have some timely quotations from medieval and early modern manuscripts, however.)

Fleta   *Fleta*, ed. H. G. Richardson and G. O. Sayles. (Selden Society Publication.) London, 1955. (*Fleta* is a valuable source for many capacity measures and for information pertaining to the construction of the tower and mercantile pounds.)

Flores   *Flores Historiarum*, ed. Henry Richards Luard. (Rerum Britanicarum Medii Aevi Scriptores.) London, 1890.

Fountains   *Memorials of the Abbey of St. Mary of Fountains*, ed. Joseph Thomas Fowler. (Surtees Society Publication, Vol. 130.) Durham, 1918. (The glossary has definitions for several dry and liquid capacity measures.)

Fr. Clarke   Clarke, Frank Wigglesworth. *Weights, Measures and Money of All Nations.* New York, 1888. (Clarke lists the weights and measures of the nineteenth century individually and by country and he includes the location and United States–English equivalent for each unit.)

Glazebrook   Glazebrook, Sir Richard. "Standards of Measurement: Their History and Development." *Nature*, 128 (1931), Supplement, pp. 17–28. (Glazebrook concentrates on metrological standardization under Elizabeth.)

Gore   Gore, J. Howard. "The Decimal System of Measures of the Seventeenth Century." *American Journal of Science*, 41 (1891), 241–46.

Granger   Granger, Allan. *Our Weights and Measures.* London, 1917.

Gras 1   Gras, Norman Scott Brien. *The Early English Customs Systems.* Cambridge, 1918. (Occasionally a certain capacity measure is defined, but generally only the price for its contents is given.)

———— 2 ————. *The Economic and Social History of an English*

Village (*Crawley, Hampshire*) *A.D. 909–1928.* Cambridge, 1930.
——— 3 ———. *The Evolution of the English Corn Market from the Twelfth to the Eighteenth Century.* Cambridge, 1915. (There is a short description of the seam.)

Guilhiermoz 1   Guilhiermoz, P. "Note sur les poids du moyen age." *Bibliothèque de l'Ecole des Chartres,* 67 (1906), 161–233 and 402–50. (Guilhiermoz discusses the weights used in most European countries, and he includes tables comparing the various pounds, which he also converts into Paris grains and metric grams.)

——— 2 ———. "Remarques diverses sur les poids et mesures du moyen age." *Ibid.,* 80 (1919), 5–100. (The focus is again European-wide.)

Hall   Hall, Hubert, and Nicholas, Frieda J. "Select Tracts and Table Books Relating to English Weights and Measures (1100–1742)." *Camden Third Series,* 41 (1929), 1–53. (This is the most complete single collection dealing specifically with medieval English weights and measures. The documents cover all five major divisions of measurement as well as cloth regulations. The Cottonian manuscripts have been used in addition to other valuable collections. With few exceptions, the editing is well done; important information is contained in the footnotes.)

Hallock   Hallock, William. *Outlines of the Evolution of Weights and Measures and the Metric System.* New York, 1906. (Among the subjects discussed by Hallock are early standards; primary and defined standards; the metrological systems of the Babylonians, Egyptians, Greeks, Romans, and Moslems; Anglo-Saxon influences; and medieval weights and measures. His remarks on the latter are rather brief, and he tends to exaggerate the influence that ancient systems of metrology had on the development of medieval English and French units.)

Harkness   Harkness, William. "The Progress of Science as Exemplified in the Art of Weighing and Measuring." *Smithsonian: Miscellaneous Collection,* 33 (1888), XLIII–LX. (Harkness dwells on English and French measures of length before 1600; the mercantile and avoirdupois pounds; and the poids de marc and the pile de Charlemagne.)

Harris 1   Harris, John. *Lexicon technicum, or, An Universal English Dictionary of Arts and Sciences,* Vol. 2. London, 1710. (Information is included under the entries, "weights" and "measures.")

——— 2 ———. *Lexicon technicum, or, An Universal English Dictionary of Arts and Sciences* (3rd ed.). London, 1716. (This work is much more detailed than the earlier edition and contains some excellent tables comparing English weights and measures with ancient and contemporary systems.)

Hartmann Hartmann, Carl. *Die Waagen und ihre Construction.* Weimar, 1856.

Hassler Hassler, Ferdinand Rudolph. *Report upon the Comparison of Weights and Measures of Length and Capacity, Made at the City of Washington, in 1831, under the Direction of the Treasury Department, in Compliance with a Resolution of the Senate of the United States of the 29th May, 1830.* (22nd Congress, 1st Session, H.R. Document No. 299.) Washington, 1832. (There is some information dealing with the composition of English gallons and bushels.)

Hatfield *Bishop Hatfield's Survey: A Record of the Possessions of the See of Durham, Made by Order of Thomas de Hatfield, Bishop of Durham,* ed. Rev. William Greenwell. (Surtees Society Publication, Vol. 32). Durham, 1857.

Hauy Hauy, René Just Abbe. *Instruction sur les mesures deduites de la grandeur de la terre, uniformes pour toute la republique, et sur les calculs relatifs à leur division decimale.* Paris, 1795.

Hawney Hawney, William. *The Complete Measurer: or, The Whole Art of Measuring.* London, 1789. (This is basically an arithmetic book that contains occasional descriptions of linear and superficial measures to be used for the solution of the various problems.)

Henley *Walter of Henley's Husbandry: Together with an Anonymous Husbandry, Seneschaucie and Robert Grosseteste's Rules,* ed. Elizabeth Lamond. London, 1890. (There is information on the furlong, perch, and league in Walter's work, while in the *Anonymous Husbandry* there is a discussion of the perch, acre, and rood.)

Henllys Owen of Henllys, George. *The Description of Penbrokshire,* ed. Henry Owen. 3 vols. London, 1892. (Owen's book is valuable for Welsh linear, superficial, and capacity measures, and his description of the perch is especially important.)

Henry Derby *Expeditions to Prussia and the Holy Land Made by Henry Earl of Derby (Afterwards King Henry IV) in the Years 1390–1 and 1392–3 Being the Accounts Kept by His Treasurer during Two Years,* ed. Lucy Toulmin Smith. (Camden Society Publication, New Series, Vol. 52.) London, 1894. (This account of expenditures contains some valuable information on capacity measures.)

Hewitt Hewitt, H. J. *Medieval Cheshire: An Economic and Social History of Cheshire in the Reigns of the Three Edwards.* (Chetham Society Publication, Vol. 88.) Manchester, 1929. (Appendix G describes some of the linear, superficial, and capacity measures that were found in Cheshire.)

Hilderbrand Hilderbrand, Clifton. *Metric Literature Clues: A List of References to Books, Pamphlets, Documents and Magazine Articles on Metric Standardization of Weights and Measures.* San Francisco, 1921. (This collection is somewhat dated.)

Hofmann Hofmann, Joh. Jacob. *Lexicon universale historiam sacram et profanam.* Lugduni Batavorum, 1698.

Holme Holme, Randle. *The Academy of Armory, or a Storehouse of Armory and Blazon.* London, 1688.

Hopton Hopton, Arthur. *A Concordancy of Yeares.* London, 1616. (Chapter 43 deals with weights and measures.)

Hostmen *Extracts from the Records of the Company of Hostmen of Newcastle-Upon-Tyne.* (Surtees Society Publication, Vol. 105.) Durham, 1901.

Hultsch Hultsch, Fridericus. *Metrologicorum scriptorum reliquiæ.* 2 vols. Lipsiae, 1864. (Hultsch includes the writings of Isidore of Seville on weights and measures. His book is especially valuable for late Roman and early medieval tracts dealing with linear measures.)

Hunter Hunter, Rev. Joseph. *The Hallamshire Glossary.* London, 1824.

Huntley Huntley, Rev. Richard Webster. *A Glossary of the Cotswold (Gloucestershire) Dialect.* London, 1868. (Huntley discusses the lug.)

Hylles Hylles, Thomas. *The Arte of Vulgar Arithmeticke.* London, 1600.

Ingalls Ingalls, Walter Renton. *Systems of Weights and Measures.* New York, 1945.

Ireland *Historic and Municipal Documents of Ireland, A.D. 1172–1320,* ed. J. T. Gilbert. (Rerum Britanicarum Medii Aevi Scriptores.) London, 1870.

Jeake Jeake, S. *Arithmetic.* London, 1696.

Jefferson 1 Jefferson, Thomas. "Plan for Establishing Uniformity in the Coinage, Weights and Measures of the United States: Communicated to the House of Representatives, July 13, 1790," in Saul K. Padover (ed.), *The Complete Jefferson,* pp. 974–95. New York, 1943. (Jefferson discusses many different linear, superficial, capacity, and quantity measures in addition to several types of weights.)

———— 2 ————. "Standards of Measures, Weights and Coins," in Saul K. Padover (ed.), *Ibid.,* pp. 1004–11.

Johnson Johnson, Samuel. *A Dictionary of the English Language.* 2 vols. London, 1773. (Although there are many entries for weights and measures, there are occasional errors in both their size and composition.)

Jones Jones, Stacy V. *Weights and Measures: An Informal Guide.* Washington, 1963. (Jones makes relatively few references to medieval English weights and measures.)

Jourdan *Recueil général des anciennes Lois françaises, depuis l'an 420 jusqu'à la révolution de 1789,* ed. MM. Jourdan, Decrusy, and Isambert. 30 vols. Paris, 1830. (Information on weights and measures is contained in volumes 1, 3, 9, 11, 13, 14, 18, 20, 22, 24, 25, 26, and 27.)

Judson Judson, Lewis Van Hagen. "Weights and Measures." *Encyclopædia Britannica,* 23 (1964), 479–88.

Kater 1 Kater, Henry. "An Account of the Comparison of Various British Standards of Linear Measure." *Philosophical Transactions,* 111 (1821), 75–94.

———— 2 ————. "An Account of the Construction and Adjustment of the New Standards of Weights and Measures of the United Kingdom of Great Britain and Ireland." *Ibid.,* 116 (1826), 1–52. (Kater lists the standards found in the cities of Edinburgh, London, and Westminster.)

———— 3 ————. "On the Error in Standards of Linear Measure, Arising from the Thickness of the Bar on which They Are Traced." *Ibid.,* 120 (1830), 359–81.

Kennelly Kennelly, Arthur E. *Vestiges of Pre-Metric Weights and*

Measures Persisting in Metric-System Europe. New York, 1928. (Kennelly is interested principally in French weights and measures.)

Kisch Kisch, Bruno. *Scales and Weights: A Historical Outline.* New Haven, 1965. (Kisch concentrates chiefly on the ancient and modern periods. His most important contributions are his excellent descriptions of scales and his index of important weights used in the world today.)

Klimpert Klimpert, Richard. *Lexicon der Münzen, Mässe, Gewichte: Zählarten und Zeitgrössen aller Länder der Erde.* Berlin, 1896. (Klimpert is concerned primarily with French and German metrology.)

Labbe Labbe, Philippe. *Bibliotheca bibliothecarum curis secundis auctior.* Rothomagi, 1672.

Langtoft Langtoft, Peter. *Chronicle,* ed. Thomas Hearne. London, 1810. (The glossary contains descriptions of the larger superficial measures such as the farthingdale, virgate, and hide.)

Lavoisier 1 Lavoisier, Antoine Laurent. *Oeuvres,* ed. René Fric. 2 vols. Paris, 1955. (Lavoisier was one of the pioneers in the construction of the metric system, which put an end to the complexity and confusion of French weights and measures. These two volumes contain some of his writings on early modern measuring units.)

────── **2** ──────. *Statistique agricole et projets de réformes,* ed. Edouard Grimaux. Paris, 1888.

Laws *The Laws of the Earliest English Kings,* ed. F. L. Attenborough. Cambridge, 1922.

Leake Leake, Stephen Martin. *An Historical Account of English Money from the Conquest to the Present Time.* London, 1793. (Leake discusses the troy and tower systems of weight.)

Leet *Continuation of the Court Leet Records of the Manor of Manchester: A.D. 1586–1602,* ed. John Harland. (Chetham Society Publication, Vol. 65.) Manchester, 1865.

Leet Juris. *Leet Jurisdiction in the City of Norwich during the XIIIth and XIVth Centuries,* ed. William Hudson. (Selden Society Publication, Vol. 5.) London, 1892. (Some of the cases deal with infractions of metrological regulations and with the various fines and amercements levied as penalties.)

Leigh Leigh, Egerton. *A Glossary of Words Used in the Dialect of*

Cheshire. London, 1877. (Leigh includes separate entries for 9 weights and measures.)

Letter 1 "Letter from the Secretary of the Interior Transmitting in Response to a Resolution of the House of Representatives, Reports Concerning the Adoption of the Metric System of Weights and Measures." *Metric System Pamphlets,* 1 (1878), No. 7.

————— 2 "Letter from the Secretary of the Treasury Transmitting to the House of Representatives Certain Reports in Reference to the Adoption of the Metric System." *Ibid.,* No. 2.

————— 3 "Letter from the Secretary of War Transmitting Reports of Chiefs of Bureaus upon the Adoption of the Metrical System, in Response to a Resolution of the House of Representatives." *Ibid.,* No. 6.

Liber *Liber quotidianus contraolulatoris garderobæ: Anno regni regis Edwardi primi: A.D. MCCXCIX and MCCC.* London, 1787. (There are several descriptions of heaped, striked, and shallow capacity measures together with a discussion of the crannock.)

Lipson Lipson, E. *The Economic History of England,* Vol. 1. London, 1949. (Lipson discusses the supervision of weights and measures by state and local officials.)

McCaw McCaw, G. T. "Linear Units Old and New." *Empire Survey Review,* 5 (1939–40), 236–59. (McCaw discusses the primitive measures of length, the foot and cubit, the Greek foot, the "natural" or Olympic foot, and the Gallic leuca.)

Macpherson Macpherson, David. *Annals of Commerce, Manufactures, Fisheries, and Navigation with Brief Notices of the Arts and Sciences Connected with Them.* 4 vols. London, 1805. (Volume I has some excellent tables of medieval English measuring units.)

Mag. Carta *The Great Charter Called I[n] Latyn Magna Carta with Divers Olde Statutes.* London, 1541.

Malcolm *Regesta regum Scottorum: The Acts of Malcolm IV King of Scots 1153–1165,* ed. G. W. S. Barrow. Edinburgh, 1960.

Manydown *The Manor of Manydown Hampshire,* ed. G. W. Kitchin. London, 1895. (There is a brief discussion of superficial measurement in the introduction.)

Margan "Annales de Margan (A.D. 1066–1232)," in Henry Richards Luard (ed.), *Annales monastici.* (Rerum Britanicarum Medii Aevi Scriptores.) London, 1864.

Marianae Marianae, Joannis. *De rege et regis institutione.* Types Wechelianis, apud Laeredes, 1611.

Marshall Marshall, William H. *The Rural Economy of Yorkshire.* London, 1788.

Matthaei 1 Matthaei Parisiensis. *Chronica Majora,* ed. Henry Richards Luard. (Rerum Britanicarum Medii Aevi Scriptores.) London, 1874. (Matthew refers to Richard I's attempt to standardize weights and measures in 1189 in a section entitled *De persecutione Judœorum.*)

———— 2 ————. *Historia Anglorum,* ed. Sir Frederic Madden. (Rerum Britanicarum Medii Aevi Scriptores.) London, 1865–69.

Memorials *Memorials of London and London Life in the XIIIth, XIVth and XVth Centuries,* ed. Henry Thomas Riley. London, 1868. (There are several descriptions of capacity measures in addition to a number of inventories. The footnotes occasionally give information on the types of scales used by merchants.)

Mem. Roll *The Memoranda Roll for the Michaelmas Term of the First Year of the Reign of King John (1199–1200),* ed. H. G. Richardson. (Pipe Roll Society.) London, 1943.

Mer. Adven. *Extracts from the Records of the Merchant Adventurers of Newcastle-Upon-Tyne.* (Surtees Society Publication, Vol. 93.) Durham, 1895. (There is a detailed discussion of the chalder and the keel.)

Met. Univ. "Metrology Universalized; or, A Proposal to Really Equalize and Universalize the Hitherto Unequalized and Arbitrary Weights and Measures of Great Britain and America." *Metric System Pamphlets,* 1 (1828), No. 8. (This article deals primarily with English linear measurement.)

Miller Miller, Sir John Riggs. "Equalization of Weights and Measures." *The Parliamentary History of England from the Earliest Period to the Year 1803,* 28 (1789–91), 639–50. Printed in London, 1816.

Mon. Jur. *Monumenta Juridica: The Black Book of the Admiralty,* ed. Sir Travers Twiss. (Rerum Britanicarum Medii Aevi Scriptores.) London, 1871 and 1873.

Morton Morton, John C. *A Cyclopedia of Agriculture Practical and Scientific.* London, 1855.

Mun. acad. *Munimenta academica, or Documents Illustrative of*

Academical Life and Studies at Oxford, ed. Rev. Henry Anstey. (Rerum Britanicarum Medii Aevi Scriptores.) London, 1868. (The duties of the Chancellor of Oxford University in regard to the maintenance of Crown standards are described in several documents.)

Mun. gild. *Munimenta gildhallæ Londoniensis: Liber Albus, Liber Custumarum et Liber Horn,* ed. Henry Thomas Riley. (Rerum Britanicarum Medii Aevi Scriptores.) London, 1859–62. (The *Liber Albus* and the *Liber Custumarum* are the most important for information on weights and measures.)

Nicholson Nicholson, Edward. *Men and Measures: A History of Weights and Measures: Ancient and Modern.* London, 1912. (There are tables of some medieval English, Irish, Scots, and Welsh weights and measures as well as some valuable discussions dealing with the ancient systems of metrology. Unfortunately, Nicholson exaggerates the influence which many of the ancient systems had on English metrological development. In addition, he seldom indicates the sources of his data.)

Nicol. and Burn Nicolson, Joseph, and Burn, Richard. *The History and Antiquities of the Counties of Westmorland and Cumberland,* Vol. 2. London, 1777. (The glossary has definitions for several superficial measures.)

Nottingham *Records of the Borough of Nottingham: Being a Series of Extracts from the Archives of the Corporation of Nottingham.* 2 vols. London, 1883.

Noy Noy, R. *Complete Lawyer.* London, 1634.

Oldberg Oldberg, Oscar. *A Manual of Weights and Measures.* Chicago, n.d.

Owen Owen, George A. *A Treatise on Weighing Machines.* London, 1922.

Oxford *Medieval Archives of the University of Oxford,* ed. Rev. H. E. Salter. Oxford, 1921. (There are several descriptions of the seals used by the Chancellor of Oxford University in authenticating weights and measures under his jurisdiction.)

Palladius Palladius. *On Husbondrie,* ed. Rev. Barton Lodge. (Early English Text Society.) London, 1873.

Pegolotti Pegolotti, Francesco Balducci. *La Pratica della mercatura,* ed. Allan Evans. Cambridge, 1936. (Pegolotti describes the clove, hundred, and stone in addition to many non-English units.)

Percy *Northumberland Household Book (The Regulations and Establishment of the Household of Henry Algernon Percy, the Fifth Earl of Northumberland) 1512–25.* London, 1770.

Perkin Perkin, F. Mollwo. *The Metric and British Systems of Weights, Measures and Coinage.* New York, 1907.

Perry Perry, John. *The Story of Standards.* New York, 1955.

Petrie 1 Petrie, Sir William M. Flinders. *Measures and Weights.* London, 1934.

———— **2** ————. "The Old English Mile." *Proceedings of the Royal Society of Edinburgh,* 12 (1882–84), 254–66.

———— **3** ————. "Weights and Measures." *Encyclopædia Britannica,* 23 (1964), 488H–K. (Petrie concentrates only on the ancient metrological systems.)

Phillips Phillips, Edward. *The New World of English Words: or, A General Dictionary.* London, 1696.

Pipe *The Great Rolls of the Pipe for the Seventeenth Year of the Reign of King Henry the Second: A.D. 1170–1.* (Pipe Roll Society.) London, 1893.

Prior Prior, W. H. "Notes on the Weights and Measures of Medieval England." *Bulletin du Cange: Archivvm Latinitatis medii ævi,* 1 (1924), 77–170. (Prior defines briefly over 100 weights and measures. He makes occasional errors in computation, but, on the whole, his work is well done.)

Rameseia *Cartularium Monasterii de Rameseia,* ed. William Henry Hart and Rev. Ponsonby A. Lyons. (Rerum Britanicarum Medii Aevi Scriptores.) London, 1884–93.

Ray Ray, John. *A Collection of English Words not Generally Used.* London, 1674.

Recorde Recorde, Robert. *The Ground of Artes, Teachyng the Worke and Practice of Arithmetike.* London, 1540.

Records *Records of the Coinage of Scotland from the Earliest Period to the Union,* ed. R. W. Cochran-Patrick. 2 vols. Edinburgh, 1876. (There are several remarks on the avoirdupois and troy pounds.)

Relation *A Relation, or Rather a True Account, of the Island of England; with Sundry Particulars of the Customs of These People, and of the Royal Revenues under King Henry the Seventh, about* *the Year 1500*, ed. Charlotte Augusta Sneyd. (Camden Society Publication, Vol. 37.) London, 1847. (This collection contains several lists of products and the capacity measures by which they were sold.)

Remembrance *The Third Book of Remembrance of Southampton: 1514–1602*, ed. A. L. Merson. Southampton, 1955.

Report 1 "Report from the Committee Appointed to Inquire into the Original Standards of Weights and Measures in This Kingdom, and to Consider the Laws Relating Thereto." *Reports from Committees of the House of Commons*, 2 (1737–65), 411–51. (This report contains some excellent discussions of medieval English weights and measures. Ample documentation, especially from *Fleta*, and concise summaries of metrological laws make this an important source.)

────── 2 "Report from the Committee Appointed (upon the 1st Day of December, 1758) to Inquire into the Original Standards of Weights and Measures in This Kingdom; and to Consider the Laws Relating Thereto." *Ibid.*, 455–63.

────── 3 "Report from the Select Committee of the House of Lords Appointed to Consider the Petition of the Directors of the Chamber of Commerce and Manufactures, Established by Royal Charter in the City of Glascow Taking Notice of the Bill Entitled 'An Act for Ascertaining and Establishing Uniformity of Weights and Measures etc.' " *Reports from Committees*, 7 (1824), 1–35.

────── 4 "Report from the Select Committee on the Weights and Measures Act; Together with the Minutes of Evidence." *Ibid.*, 18 (1835), 1–60.

────── 5 "Report of the Committee Appointed to Superintend the Construction of the New Parliamentary Standards of Length and Weight." *Ibid.*, 19 (1854), 1–23.

Ricard Ricard, Samuel. *Traité général du Commerce.* 2 vols. Amsterdam, 1781.

Ricart *The Maire of Bristowe Is Kalendar by Robert Ricart, Town Clerk of Bristol 18 Edward IV*, ed. Lucy Toulmin Smith. (Camden Society Publication, New Series, Vol. 5.) Westminster, 1872. (There is a description of the crannock in this calendar.)

Ridgeway Ridgeway, William. *The Origin of Metallic Currency and Weight Standards.* Cambridge, 1892.

Robinson Robinson, Francis Kildale. *A Glossary of Yorkshire Words and Phrases Collected in Whitby and the Neighbourhood.* London, 1855.

Rogers Rogers, W. A. "On the Present State of the Question of Standards of Length." *Proceedings of the American Academy of Arts and Sciences,* 15 (1879–80), 273–312.

Rolls *Three Rolls of the King's Court in the Reign of King Richard the First: A.D. 1194–1195.* (Pipe Roll Society.) London, 1891.

Rot. Parl. 1 *Rotuli parliamentorum ut et petitiones, et placita in parliamento tempore Edwardi R. I,* ed. Rev. John Strachey *et al.* Vol. 1 (1278–1325). London, 1832. (The *Rotuli parliamentorum* are especially valuable for information on capacity measures and for descriptions of cloth measurements.)

———— **2** *Rotuli parliamentorum ut et petitiones, et placita in parliamento tempore Edwardi R. III,* ed. Rev. John Strachey *et al.* Vol. 2 (1326–77). London, 1832.

———— **3** *Rotuli parliamentorum ut et petitiones, et placita in parliamento tempore Ricardi R. II,* ed. Rev. John Strachey *et al.* Vol. 3 (1377–1411). London, 1832.

———— **4** *Rotuli parliamentorum ut et petitiones, et placita in parliamento tempore Henrici R. V,* ed. Rev. John Strachey *et al.* Vol. 4 (1413–37). London, 1832.

———— **5** *Rotuli parliamentorum ut et petitiones, et placita in parliamento ab anno decimo octavo R. Henrici sexti ad finem ejusdem regni,* ed. Rev. John Strachey *et al.* Vol. 5 (1439–68). London, 1832.

———— **6** *Rotuli parliamentorum ut et petitiones, et placita in parliamento ab anno duodecimo R. Edwardi IV ad finem ejusdem regni,* ed. Rev. John Strachey *et al.* Vol. 6 (1472–1503). London, 1832.

Rot. parl. Ang. *Rotuli parliamentorum Anglie hactenus inediti MCCLXXIX–MCCCLXXIII,* ed. H. G. Richardson and George Sayles. (Camden Third Series, Vol. 51.) London, 1935.

St. Gile's *Memorials of St. Gile's, Durham, Being Grassmen's Accounts and Other Parish Records, Together with Documents Relating to the Hospital of Kepier and St. Mary Magdalene.* (Surtees Society Publication, Vol. 95.) Durham, 1896. (This volume contains information on the standard weights for bread.)

St. Paul's *The Domesday of St. Paul's of the Year MCCXXII; or, Registrum de visitatione maneriorum per Robertum Decanum*, ed. William Hale. (Camden Society Publication, Vol. 69.) Westminster, 1858. (This is a particularly important source for capacity measures and for large superficial measures such as the hide and virgate.)

Salzman 1 Salzman, L. F. *English Industries of the Middle Ages*. Oxford, 1923. (Salzman discusses the various capacity measures that were used for coal, iron, fish, and malted beverages.)

———— 2 ————. *English Trade in the Middle Ages*. Oxford, 1931. (One chapter is devoted to English weights and measures. Most of Salzman's remarks are really too brief to be effective, and his most important contribution is his section on Roman and Arabic methods of computation.)

Samson *The Kalendar of Abbot Samson of Bury St. Edmunds and Related Documents*, ed. R. H. C. Davis. (Camden Third Series, Vol. 84.) London, 1954. (This book contains information on socage land and socage dues in addition to several descriptions of unusual capacity measures found at St. Edmund's.)

Sandys Sandys, Sir John Edwin. *A Companion to Latin Studies* (3rd ed.) Cambridge, 1921. (Sandys discusses Roman metrology rather briefly.)

Scot. Lawes *Scotland: The Lawes and Actes of Parliament*. Edinburgh, 1597.

Second Rep. "Second Report of the Commissioners Appointed by His Majesty to Consider the Subject of Weights and Measures." *Reports from Commissioners*, 7 (1820), 1–40. (This report is extremely valuable for it includes a 40-page listing of the state and local units of measurement that were common in the late 1700's and early 1800's.)

Seebohm Seebohm, Frederic. *Customary Acres and Their Historical Importance*. London, 1914.

Select Cases 1 *Select Cases before the King's Council in the Star Chamber Commonly Called the Court of Star Chamber*, ed. I. S. Leadam. (Selden Society Publication, Vol. 26.) London, 1911. (This book contains information on the wey, firkin, butter barrel, and virgate.)

———— 2 *Select Cases Concerning the Law Merchant: A.D. 1270–1638*, ed. Charles Gross. (Selden Society Publication, Vol. 23

[Local Courts].) London, 1908. (There are several descriptions of infractions of weights and measures legislation together with a glossary which defines such capacity measures as the trey and ring.)

———— 3 *Select Cases Concerning the Law Merchant: A.D. 1239–1633*, ed. Hubert Hall. (Selden Society Publication, Vol. 46 [Central Courts].) London, 1930.

———— 4 *Select Cases in the Council of Henry VII*, ed. C. G. Bayne and William Huse Dunham, Jr. (Selden Society Publication, Vol. 75.) London, 1958.

Select Col. *A Select Collection of Early English Tracts on Commerce from the Originals of Mun, Roberts, North and Others*, ed. John Ramsay McCulloch. Cambridge, 1952.

Select Com. "The Select Committee Appointed to Consider the Several Reports Which Have Been Laid Before This House, Relating to Weights and Measures." *Reports from Committees*, 4 (1821), 1–7.

Select Doc. *Select English Historical Documents of the Ninth and Tenth Centuries*, ed. F. E. Harmer. Cambridge, 1914. (There are relatively few documents dealing specifically with weights and measures.)

Select Pleas 1 *Select Pleas in Manorial and Other Seignorial Courts*, ed. F. W. Maitland. (Selden Society Publication, Vol. 28.) London, 1889.

———— 2 *Select Pleas of the Crown*, ed. F. W. Maitland. (Selden Society Publication, Vol. 27.) London, 1888.

Seventh Rep. "Seventh Annual Report of the Warden of the Standards on the Proceedings and Business of the Standard Weights and Measures Department of the Board of Trade for 1872–73." *Reports from Commissioners*, 38 (1873), 1–105. (This long report deals primarily with the laws relating to the inspection and verification of weights and measures. There are some excellent metrological tables in addition to several photographs of common capacity measures.)

Sheppard Sheppard, W. *Of the Office of the Clerk of the Market, of Weights and Measures, and of the Laws of Provision for Man and Beast*. London, 1665. (Sheppard's account of the responsibilities and duties of the clerk of the market is detailed and based on the statutes and ordinances and on his own personal observations.

His tables of weights and measures are not always accurate, however, and there are too many repetitions, which are occasionally contradictory.)

Shipley   Shipley, Joseph T. *Dictionary of Early English.* New York, 1955. (Shipley defines some unusual units such as the fust, fardel, and seron.)

Shuttleworths   *The House and Farm Accounts of the Shuttleworths of Gawthorpe Hall, in the County of Lancaster, at Smithils and Gawthorpe, from September 1582 to October 1621,* ed. John Harland. (Chetham Society Publication, Vols. 43 and 46.) London, 1858. (Both volumes contain glossaries with descriptions of the weights and measures found on this estate.)

Skene 1   Skene, Sir John. *De verborum Significatione.* London, 1597.

——— **2** ———. *Regiam majestatem, the Auld Lawes and Constitutions of Scotland Faithfullie Collected.* London, 1609.

Southampton 1   *The Local Port Book of Southampton for 1435–36,* ed. Brian Foster. Southampton, 1963. (This and the port book for 1439–40 provide numerous examples of the types of capacity and quantity measures which were used for certain products. Occasionally there are descriptions of the measures themselves.)

——— **2**   *The Local Port Book of Southampton for 1439–40,* ed. Henry S. Cobb. Southampton, 1961.

Stat.   *The Whole Volume of Statutes at Large, which at Anie Time Heeretofore Have Beene Extant in Print.* London, 1587. (This is one of the earliest collections of the statutes. It checks out well against later editions and is notable primarily because of its unusual spellings.)

Stat. Charles   *A Collection of the Statutes Made in the Reigns of King Charles the I and King Charles the II,* ed. Tho. Manby. London, 1687.

Stat. Irel.   *The Statutes of Ireland, Beginning the Third Yere of K. Edward the Second, and Continuing untill the End of the Parliament, Begunne in the Eleventh Yeare of the Reign of Our Most Gratious Soveraigne Lord King James.* Dublin, 1621.

Sternberg   Sternberg, Thomas. *The Dialect and Folk-Lore of Northamptonshire.* London, 1851. (Sternberg has entries for 8 measures.)

Swinfield   *A Roll of the Household Expenses of Richard de Swinfield, Bishop of Hereford during Part of the Years 1289 and 1290,* ed.

Rev. John Webb. (Camden Society Publication, Vol. 59.) London, 1854. (The glossary contains descriptions of several weights and measures.)

Swithun *A Consuetudinary of the Fourteenth Century for the Refectory of the House of S. Swithun in Winchester,* ed. George William Kitchin. London, 1886.

Third Rep. "Third Report of Standards Commission, February 1, 1870." *Metric System Pamphlets,* 1 (1878), No. 2. (This short article discusses the troy and tower pounds.)

Thor. Rogers 1 Rogers, James E. Thorold. *A History of Agriculture and Prices in England,* Vol. 1. Oxford, 1866. (Rogers describes 34 weights and measures and examines the standards upon which they were based. His descriptions, however, are not detailed.)

────── 2 ──────. *Six Centuries of Work and Wages.* New York, 1884. (Rogers discusses Arabic numbers, the hide, and the gallon.)

Tower *An Exact Abridgement of the Records in the Tower of London,* ed. Sir Robert Cotton. London, 1657. (This collection contains few references to weights and measures, but occasionally there are summaries of the principal statutes and ordinances that dealt with them.)

Tracts *Old and Scarce Tracts on Money,* ed. J. R. McCulloch. London, 1933.

Tusser Tusser, Thomas. *Fiue Hundreth Pointes of Good Husbandrie.* (English Dialect Society.) London, 1878.

Warburton Warburton, Rev. W. *Edward III.* London, 1924. (There are short definitions of the sack and pack of wool.)

Wedgwood Wedgwood, Hensleigh. *A Dictionary of English Etymology.* London, 1878. (Wedgwood gives etymological derivations for 53 units.)

Weights "Weights, Measures and Coins." *House of Commons Accounts and Papers,* 58 (1864), 1–35.

Weinbaum Weinbaum, Martin. "London unter Eduard I und II." *Vierteljahrschrift für Sozial und Wirtschaftsgeschichte,* Suppl. 29 (1933). (There is information on the *Assisa Panis* and the clove.)

Welsh *The Welsh Port Books (1550–1603),* ed. Edward Arthur Lewis. (Cymmrodorion Record Series, Vol. 12.) London, 1927. (Similar in format to the Southampton Port Books.)

Wil. Airy Airy, Wilfrid. "On the Origin of the British Measures of Capacity, Weight and Length." *Minutes of Proceedings of the Institution of Civil Engineers*, 175 (1909), 164–76. (Airy discusses the origins of the pint, foot, and avoirdupois pound. The appendix includes some drawings of Roman and Egyptian measures together with several extracts from the laws of William I concerning standardization.)

Willis Willis, Browne. *The History and Antiquities of the Town, Hundred, and Deanry of Buckingham*. London, 1755. (Willis discusses the larger superficial measures such as the virgate, bovate, plowland, and hide.)

Wills *Wills and Inventories from the Registers of the Commissary of Bury St. Edmund's and the Archdeacon of Sudbury*, ed. Samuel Tymms. (Camden Society Publication, Vol. 49.) London, 1850.

Winchester *Documents Relating to the Foundation of the Chapter of Winchester: A.D. 1541–1547*, ed. George Williams Kitchin and Francis Thomas Madge. London, 1889.

W. Miller Miller, W. H. "On the Construction of the New Imperial Standard Pound, and its Copies of Platinum; and on the Comparison of the Imperial Standard Pound with the Kilogramme des Archives." *Philosophical Transactions*, 146 (1856), 753–946. (Miller's article contains information on the tower, troy, mercantile, and avoirdupois pounds.)

Worlidge Worlidge, John. *Systema agriculturæ; the Mystery of Husbandry Discovered*. London, 1669.

Wurtele Wurtele, Arthur. *Tables for Reducing English, Old French and Metrical Measures*. Montreal, 1861.

Yates Yates, James. "Narrative of the Origin and Formation of the International Association for Obtaining a Uniform Decimal System of Measures, Weights and Coins." *Metric System Pamphlets*, 1 (1856), No. 11.

Year Bk. *Year Books of Edward IV: 10 Edward IV and 49 Henry VI*, ed. N. Neilson. (Selden Society Publication, Vol. 47.) London, 1931. (This volume contains occasional references to infractions of metrological regulations and to punishments imposed for violations of statutory provisions.)

York Mem. 1 *York Memorandum Book: Part I (1376–1419)*. (Surtees Society Publication, Vol. 120.) Durham, 1912. (There are numerous references to weights and measures in addition to a table defining many linear and superficial units. Several documents are concerned with the proper sealing of weights and measures and with the scope of the mayor's jurisdiction in supervising regular assays.)

———— 2 *York Memorandum Book: Part II* (*1388–1493*). (Surtees Society Publication, Vol. 125.) Durham, 1915. (The glossary has definitions for the selion and the butt of land.)

York Mer. *The York Mercers and Merchant Adventurers: 1356–1917.* (Surtees Society Publication, Vol. 129.) Durham, 1918. (There are several documents that discuss the purchase of new weights and measures to replace the old and defective standards. The glossary contains information on the keel, fatt, and last.)